BASIC THEORIES
of
PHYSICS

Heat and Quanta

by

PETER GABRIEL BERGMANN

Professor of Physics
Syracuse University

For Richard Grossman

Peter G. Bergmann

DOVER PUBLICATIONS, INC.
NEW YORK • NEW YORK

Published in the United Kingdom by Constable and Company Limited, 10 Orange Street, London W. C. 2.

This new Dover edition, first published in 1962, is an unabridged and corrected republication of the work first published by Prentice-Hall, Inc., in 1951.

Manufactured in the United States of America

Dover Publications, Inc.

180 Varick Street

New York 14, N. Y.

Preface

Together with a companion volume, *Basic Theories of Physics: Mechanics and Electrodynamics*, which appeared in 1949, this book is intended to introduce graduate students of physics to the fundamental ideas on which they can build up the detailed technical knowledge required of the modern practicing physicist. Accordingly, the same attitude toward the meaning of theoretical physics and its teaching has governed the writing of both books.

The earlier book was devoted to the description of the classical macroscopic theories. The present book deals with the invasion of theoretical physics by the atom: Part I is devoted to the classical theory of heat, from a consistently statistical point of view; Part II introduces the student to quantum mechanics. Personally, I believe that an explanation of quantum mechanics along roughly historical lines is still very much in order. Actually, all predictions in present quantum mechanics concerning observable facts and measurements are still made in terms of classical concepts, and as long as the theory has not developed beyond this point, we all must understand fully to what extent the classical theories have broken down and had to be replaced by quantum physical approaches. To start, for example, with the Bohr atom or with the facts of electronic diffraction would save a great deal of time, but would require a rather axiomatic and, from the point of view of the physicist, dogmatic approach. We must consciously develop in the student the desire to question, the demand to be shown. And I believe that a discussion of the rough historical lines along which quantum mechanics developed will bring out step by step the necessity for abandoning classical theories. That is why I have given the theory of heat so much space.

Of all the classical theories of physics, the theory of heat is undoubtedly the most difficult and, perhaps because of its intellectual challenge, to many of us the most fascinating. Unfortunately, a really adequate treatment is apt to be one that requires a year's hard work. I have, therefore, concentrated on laying the foundation of statistical mechanics, and I have derived thermodynamics (which historically is older than atomistic theories of heat) as the collection of laws governing canonical ensembles. This approach justifies itself because it provides the needed logical link with the foundations of Newtonian mechanics, and, further, because quantum theory derives its birth from the classical law of equipartition and not, for instance, from the Third Law of thermodynamics. Even though I have omitted many of the ramifications, such as the application of thermodynamics to chemical reactions and phase transitions, the determination of entropy from statistical models, and other applications that remain of the greatest value in physics and in the neighboring sciences, there remains substantially a semester's work to be done in heat before the student can approach the introductory part of his study of quantum mechanics.

Because many teachers and students will not accept this delay, I have interpolated at the beginning of Part II a brief summary of just those concepts required for an appreciation of the equipartition law and its bearing on specific heats.

The treatment of quantum theories includes both the older theories of Planck, Bohr, Sommerfeld, and de Broglie, and the presently accepted theories of wave mechanics and abstract operators. At this time, quantum mechanics has grown into such a vast network of procedures and physical theories that it is quite impossible to teach all that is valuable in less than three terms, and a thorough coverage probably requires four terms. I have restricted myself to a discussion of the most basic theories and concepts that can be managed in one term. Essentially, what I have tried to do is to provide the logical and psychological link between classical and rigorously quantum-mechanical theories, up to the point where the student is able to study quantum mechanics in its own right in a special course devoted exclusively to that subject.

In order to remain within that framework, I have had to forego my desire to treat many admittedly fundamental notions of quantum mechanics. Among the topics treated are wave mechanics and the solution of the basic problems (inverse square law and harmonic oscillator), perturbation methods, degenerate problems, and semi-classical radiation theory; and transition to the abstract formulation of the theory in terms of operators acting on state vectors in a Hilbert space. But I have found it inadvisable to include quantum statistics (Fermi and Bose statistics), relativistic electron theory and spin, and quantization of fields. It is, of course, possible to present one or the other of these topics concisely at the end of an introductory course if time is left, but I do not believe that students who have just been introduced to a completely new set of concepts, to a new manner of thinking about physical situations, would benefit from such a presentation. The assimilation of these new theories requires familiarity with, not merely knowledge of, the foundations of quantum mechanics. It appears to me that this familiarity in the great majority of students requires a lapse of some months between their first introduction to quantum mechanics and the presentation of the theories applying to identical particles, or Dirac's theory of the spinning electron.

Again, I have placed little emphasis on drill in mathematical techniques throughout the book, but have devoted my principal effort to a clear presentation of the fundamentals. All the examples treated are either intrinsically of great physical importance or, I hope, particularly suitable for illustrating a difficult point of the general theory. In general, the majority of students taking an introductory course in theoretical physics will specialize in some experimental branch of physics. For them it is not of prime importance to be able to carry out theoretical computations, but it is important for them to be able to follow the train of ideas in theoretical papers bearing on their own problems.

No doubt, physics and physical theories will continue to grow and to change in our lifetime. I hope that this book will help to prepare its readers not only to accept but also to contribute actively to these new departures.

Again I have to thank my colleagues as well as my students at Syracuse University and at Polytechnic Institute of Brooklyn, whose stimulating criticisms have contributed to the organization and presentation of my material. Professor Melber Phillips of Brooklyn College read the whole manuscript and made a number of welcome suggestions. The Editorial Department of Prentice-Hall has managed to put the manuscript through the various stages of editing and printing under difficult circumstances with the same care and attention to detail that I have come to take for granted in past years.

P. G. B.

Syracuse University

Contents

PART II. QUANTA

PART I
HEAT

Chapter 1

The Kinetic Hypothesis

1.1. Introduction

In ever-increasing measure, modern physics is concerned with the behavior of the ultimate constituents of our physical universe, the elementary particles, and with the laws governing their behavior. Today we believe that the most powerful approach to the physics of aggregates—solids, liquids, gases—is through a study of the molecules, the atoms, and finally the electrons and nuclear particles of which these aggregates are composed. In the perfect experiment, our physical system should be composed of a very few of these particles interacting with each other. Once we understand such a system of a few particles, we may extrapolate their behavior and approach the much more complex system called "one mol of hydrogen" or even "one chicken egg."

Unfortunately, it is very difficult to observe actions of individual elementary particles, and only since 1900 have the experimental techniques required for such work been devised. Earlier, most physical experiments had involved aggregates of very many particles, none of which was either controlled or observed individually. Under these circumstances, the behavior and, in particular, the velocity of any individual particle would differ widely from the average behavior of the aggregate. If even large aggregates of elementary particles obviously obey certain laws of nature, the observed laws must refer to effects that remain after the contradictory behavior of the individual constituent particles has been canceled out mathematically by the application of statistical methods.

The systematic development of the methods that can be used to connect the laws of the aggregates (the macroscopic laws) with those of the individual particles (the microscopic laws) has passed through several stages. Because of the laws of the conservation of linear momentum and angular momentum, it is possible to make assertions concerning the total linear and angular momentum without much information about the internal forces active within the aggregate. The exploitation of these conservation laws leads to the development of elastomechanics and fluid dynamics.[1] The law of conservation of mechanical energy, on the other hand, can be applied only in exceptionally favorable cases. It is true, of course, that the sum of the total kinetic and potential energy of all the constituent particles is conserved. But although the potential energy belonging to certain configurations (such as a compressed or a strained state) can often be ascertained by appropriate experiments, the total kinetic energy of all the particles does not equal one-half the total mass of the aggregate, multiplied by the square of the average velocity, but can readily be shown to be greater than this amount, because of the random motion of the particles. Indeed, this random motion may also make some contribution to the average potential energy.

This excess energy residing in the random behavior of the elementary particles is known as *heat*. Heat energy in turn is subject to certain very general statistical laws, the development of which is known as *thermodynamics*. Naturally, if we can tell for any given process how much of the gross mechanical energy is going to be converted into heat energy, or vice versa, then again we can formulate differential equations governing the future behavior of a body (aggregate of particles), adding to the mechanical equations certain supplementary terms that represent the transformation of energy. As an elementary example, if two ivory balls collide head-on and if we know their velocities immediately preceding the collision, then we can predict their motions following the collision, on the assumption that their collision is perfectly elastic (none of the gross kinetic energy is converted into heat), or else on the assumption that a specified percentage of the mechanical energy is converted into heat; the square root of the percentage of gross kinetic energy preserved in the collision is known as the *coefficient of restitution*.

The laws of thermodynamics represent universal rules concerning the conversion of gross mechanical or electromagnetic energy into random or heat energy. To be applied in any instance, they must

---

[1] A brief presentation of this approach has been given in the author's text *Basic Theories of Physics: Mechanics and Electrodynamics* (Prentice-Hall, 1949), in Chapter 3, "Matter in Bulk." References to this work will be given in the form exemplified by "M&E—Ch.3."

be supplemented by information concerning the particular gross properties of the substances involved, their *equations of state*. The equation of state, in the simplest case of a fluid, relates the temperature (or internal energy, if we choose) to the volume and pressure of the substance. This equation of state can be determined empirically, and in thermodynamics as such, experiment is the *only* method of obtaining it. But if every substance, every macroscopic body, is composed of elementary particles, then the equation of state must be merely one result of the complex internal-force laws between the elementary particles. Actually, knowledge of the internal-force laws should enable us to predict not only the average behavior of the aggregate but also the deviations or fluctuations about that average. To explore the relationship between the *microscopic* events and the laws governing them and the macroscopic averages accessible to our unrefined observation is the task of *statistical mechanics*.

Statistical mechanics enables us to *explain* the basic laws of thermodynamics, which within thermodynamics itself play the role of empirically determined principles, accepted as postulates in the logical structure of the theory. Besides, statistical mechanics permits us to predict the equation of state of a substance if we assume (or obtain from other sources) the force law between the constituent particles. Finally, statistical mechanics has given rise to a theory of the *random fluctuations* of density, pressure, and other gross quantities, which are always observed in any substance if the measuring devices permit the determination of these quantities in a sufficiently small region and if their response is sufficiently rapid that they do not merely register a time average extended over a long period. .

In the later portions of this book, we shall find that the consistent application of the tools of statistical mechanics reveals certain shortcomings in the classical laws of nature. These shortcomings have become the point of departure for modern theoretical physics, which is characterized by the treatment of atomic and subatomic processes with the help of a new conceptual approach, *quantum physics*.

We shall find it necessary to develop statistical mechanics in great generality and with the help of mathematical methods originated by Hamilton.[1] In this chapter, we shall illustrate the poten-

---

[1] M&E—Ch.2.

tialities of the statistical approach with the help of an example we can carry through with relatively simple mathematical techniques. Such an example is afforded by gases.

1.2. Random motion in a perfect monatomic gas

According to the kinetic hypothesis, the individual molecules of which matter is composed are continually engaged in motion regardless of whether the piece of matter as a whole is moving or at rest. These individual motions take place in all directions and at various speeds, so that as far as gross motion is concerned the individual motions and the linear momenta they represent tend to cancel. Apart from gross motion, however, the individual motion of the molecules has a number of important and observable effects. The motion of the ·molecules represents kinetic energy, which contributes to the internal energy of the material. By bombarding the confining walls of a vessel, the moving molecules are responsible for most of what we observe macroscopically as the pressure of a gas; if two bodies are permitted to have contact with each other, so that the molecules at the interface are able to exchange energy through collisions, there will be a net flux of energy, *conduction of heat*, from one body to the other until the energy of molecular motion is shared by them in a particular proportion (we then say that they are at the same temperature). In this section we shall derive an expression for the relationship between internal energy and pressure for a so-called *monatomic perfect gas*.

A monatomic perfect gas is an idealized substance in which there are no forces between individual molecules unless they approach each other to within a very short distance, which we shall set equal to zero. If two molecules "collide" (approach each other close enough to exert forces on each other), then their collision shall be elastic; that is, both the linear momentum and the energy shall be conserved. This last requirement would be trivial, since in mechanical processes energy is always conserved, except that in actual physical processes mechanical energy often is converted into other forms of energy, such as electromagnetic radiation. We shall disregard such possibilities, and we shall also exclude the conversion of energy into internal energy of the molecules. These assumptions are satisfied in good approximation by noble gases at ordinary laboratory temperatures.

Let us consider a quantity of gas in which we observe no gross motion, or no macroscopic flow. We may assume, under these circumstances, that the molecular motion is both *homogeneous* and *isotropic*. By *homogeneity* we mean that the percentage distribution of velocities among the molecules of the gas is the same in every macroscopic space domain within the gas. By *isotropy* we mean that in any given portion of the vessel containing the gas, equal numbers of molecules within any given interval of speed travel in every direction. Finally, we shall assume, as a matter of course, that the density of the gas is also constant throughout the vessel. We shall designate the average number of molecules per unit volume by n.

Let us call the average number of molecules with speeds less than v per unit volume $n(v)$. Naturally, the function $n(v)$ increases monotonically with its argument, and we have

$$n(0) = 0, \qquad n(\infty) = n. \tag{1}$$

Because of our assumption of isotropy, we can immediately assert how many of these velocities will fall within a given infinitesimal solid angle $d\Omega$. The number of molecules whose velocities lie within this solid angle and are less than v must be

$$dn(v) = n(v) \frac{d\Omega}{4\pi}. \tag{2}$$

By differentiating, we can go a step further and determine how many molecular velocities per unit volume lie within a specified infinitesimal solid angle $d\Omega$ and within a specified infinitesimal speed bracket dv. This number is given by the self-explanatory expression

$$dn(v) = \frac{1}{4\pi} n'(v) \, dv \, d\Omega, \tag{3}$$

where $n'(v)$ stands for the derivative $dn(v)/dv$.

Let us designate the mass of an individual gas molecule by m. The kinetic energy of a single molecule is then given by the expression $\frac{1}{2} m v^2$. We shall designate the total kinetic energy of all molecules contained in one unit volume by U. U is then given by the expression

$$U = \frac{1}{2} m \int_{v=0}^{\infty} n'(v) \, v^2 \, dv. \tag{4}$$

We obtain this expression by multiplying the kinetic energy of one molecule in a given infinitesimal speed bracket by the number of molecules per unit volume in that speed bracket and by integrating the result over the domain of all possible speeds.

Expression (4) represents the kinetic energy residing in the random motion of the individual molecules.   In a perfect monatomic gas this kinetic energy is the total internal energy.   In polyatomic gases additional kinetic energy may be contributed by the rotations of the molecules; at higher temperatures, appreciable amounts of internal energy are contained in elastic vibrations and partial or complete dissociation; and at even higher temperatures, all gases exhibit electronic excitation and ionization.   In addition, in all real gases the molecules exert forces on each other at finite distances, with the result that the total internal energy contains a term contributed by the mutual potential energy.   But in this section we shall disregard all these possible deviations from perfect-gas behavior and accept expression (4) as the expression for the density of the internal energy.

The *pressure* of a gas is the force exerted on a unit area of wall. Ideally, we can measure the pressure by cutting a small but finite segment within a plane portion of wall loose from its adjoining portions and by keeping it in place by means of a compressed spring or other source of measurable force.   The pressure is then defined as the force required to keep the wall segment in place, divided by its area.   The force experienced by the wall segment is, of course, caused by the molecules of the gas.   On striking the wall, a gas molecule is acted on by nearby molecules or atoms of the wall material; and if the molecule does not manage to diffuse into the wall, eventually it will be reflected from it.   Because of Newton's third law, the law of equal action and reaction, the change in the linear momentum of the molecule must correspond to an equal but opposite change of momentum of the wall, unless, of course, other forces acting on the wall cancel or modify the effect of the impinging gas molecules.   In our hypothetical device, the force exerted by the gas molecules on the wall segment is just offset by the force of the compressed spring.

In Fig. 1, we see a single molecule possessing the velocity v_1 strike the wall and be reflected from it with a velocity v_2.   The total impulse (change of linear momentum) imparted to the molecule is

$m(\mathbf{v}_2 - \mathbf{v}_1)$, and therefore the impulse imparted to the wall segment is

$$\mathbf{P} = m(\mathbf{v}_1 - \mathbf{v}_2). \tag{5}$$

It is by no means to be expected that each molecule will be reflected from the wall elastically and in accordance with the so-called law of reflection (of optics), so that the angle of incidence equals the angle of reflection. Fortunately, we can obtain an expression for the *average* amount of impulse imparted to our wall segment by all the molecules striking it. For a perfect gas, the velocity distribution in close proximity to the wall must be exactly the same as in the interior of the gas, both for molecules approaching the wall and for molecules traveling away from it. (For a gas with forces between the molecules, this statement requires modification.) To justify this assertion, we shall consider a finite-volume element V in close proximity to the wall segment but not adjacent to it. Let the distance between the wall and the near side of V, δ, be sufficiently great that no molecule inside V is subject to forces by wall molecules. Then the molecules

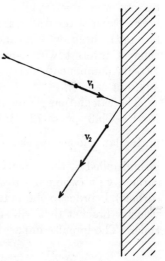

Fig. 1.　Reflection of a molecule by a wall.

inside V are subject to exactly the same forces as those in some other volume deep inside the gas-filled space; there are no forces at all except in very close encounters with other gas molecules. If the velocity distribution and density of the gas molecules in V should differ appreciably from that in the deep interior, then collisions inside V would gradually bring about systematic changes in the velocity distribution. This follows because we have assumed originally that the distribution (3) is the *equilibrium distribution*, that distribution which tends to reproduce itself in random collisions. Any other velocity distribution will be altered by a sufficient number of randomly occurring collisions, in the direction that it will tend to approach more and more the equilibrium distribution (3).

Once we realize that the distribution (3) is the same that will be encountered in close proximity to the wall, we can determine the force that will be exerted on the wall segment by finding out how many molecules per unit time will approach the wall segment and at which velocities, and how many molecules per unit time will recede from the wall segment and at which velocities. Moreover, the plane of the wall segment itself or a plane parallel to it will give us the same result as any other plane surface in the interior of the gas. For reasons of symmetry, all velocity (or momentum) components lying in the plane of the wall segment (or in the plane of an arbitrary surface in the interior) will cancel; that is, equal numbers will enter our zone of interest with equal speed from all directions. But the velocity components at right angles to the chosen plane surface will add, not cancel.

The calculation we require now has been carried out in part in M&E—Ch.3, pages 72–73. Briefly, the number of molecules in a particular velocity bracket $d\Omega\, dv$, which equals $\frac{1}{4\pi}\, n'(v)\, d\Omega\, dv$, must be multiplied by the velocity component at right angles to the chosen surface, $\mathbf{v} \cdot \mathbf{n}$ (where $\mathbf{n}$ is the unit vector perpendicular to the chosen surface), in order to obtain the number of molecules of this particular velocity bracket that will strike a unit area of the surface per unit time. The impulse imparted by these molecules equals

$$\mathbf{dP} = \frac{1}{4\pi}\, (\mathbf{v} \cdot \mathbf{n})\, m\, \mathbf{v}\, n'(v)\, dv\, d\Omega. \tag{6}$$

This expression must now be integrated over all solid angles and over all values of v from 0 to ∞. But since we know that all components not parallel to $\mathbf{n}$ will cancel, we can simplify the integration by first multiplying the integrand by $\mathbf{n}$. The expression for the impulse per unit area per unit time—the pressure—will then become

$$p = \int \mathbf{n} \cdot \mathbf{dP} = \frac{1}{4\pi} \int_{v=0}^{\infty} \int_{\Omega} (\mathbf{v} \cdot \mathbf{n})^2\, m\, n'(v)\, d\Omega\, dv. \tag{7}$$

This integral can be carried out without difficulty. First we shall introduce the angle between the two vectors $\mathbf{v}$ and $\mathbf{n}$, θ, as an explicit variable of integration. We can express the solid-angle element $d\Omega$ in terms of θ by means of the well-known relationship

$$d\Omega = 2\pi \sin \theta\, d\theta. \tag{8}$$

(The integration over the other, trivial, angle, which determines the direction of the v-component parallel to the chosen surface, has already been performed in this equation.)

The expression for the pressure reduces to

$$p = \frac{m}{2} \int_{v=0}^{\infty} v^2 \, n'(v) \, dv \int_{\theta=0}^{\pi} \cos^2 \theta \, \sin \theta \, d\theta$$

$$= \frac{m}{3} \int_{v=0}^{\infty} v^2 \, n'(v) \, dv. \tag{9}$$

Comparison with eq. (4) shows us that our hypothesis concerning the microscopic structure of the monatomic perfect gas leads to the conclusion that at all times the pressure must equal two-thirds of the density of the internal energy. This prediction is borne out by observation, since for monatomic gases the molar heat capacity c_v equals in good approximation $\frac{3}{2}R$, and therefore the internal-energy density is $\frac{3}{2}R \, T/v = \frac{3}{2}p$.

Our result shows that macroscopic relationships can be obtained from assumed microscopic relationships and that, in fact, assumed force laws between molecules can be tested by comparing the resulting equation of state with the one actually observed. On the other hand, the power of such elementary methods of approach is exceedingly limited. We have not yet defined the all-important concept of temperature, nor have we determined the velocity-distribution function $n(v)$. These two tasks are closely related. Two bodies have the same temperature if they will, on the average, transfer zero energy to each other on contact. The equilibrium distribution of velocities is the one which tends to reproduce itself in large numbers of collisions. To define the temperature or to obtain the equilibrium-velocity distribution, we must formulate a specifically statistical theory of the events considered: We must be able to tell what processes will take place *on the average* if we consider a large number of similar but not identical situations. In the next chapter we shall undertake to develop such a theory.

Problems

1. If the average number of molecules per unit volume with a velocity vector within the infinitesimal brackets $dv_x \, dv_y \, dv_z$ is proportional to $e^{-\frac{1}{2}cv^2} \, dv_x \, dv_y \, dv_z$, determine the function $n(v)$ defined in the text of this chapter. Consider n as given.

2. What is the mean kinetic energy of one molecule in the above example? Assuming that a thin rigid wall separates two volumes of gas, having different values for n, m, and the coefficient c in the exponential of the distribution function above, determine the condition that must be satisfied if the forces experienced by the wall on both sides are to balance each other.

3. Assume a slight attractive force between the gas molecules, not sufficient to change their randomly uniform distribution throughout the interior of the confining vessel. If the potential of the attractive force between any two molecules is $V(r)$, determine the average potential energy of the gas. How will the pressure on the confining wall be affected?

Chapter 2

Statistics in Physics

2.1. The concept of probability. Systems and ensembles

If we wish to formulate a theory that will permit us to predict probabilities, we had better first define probability. Surprisingly, many definitions have been proposed in the history of mathematics, and several have been found suitable for the development of an extended mathematical analysis. Likewise, there is a certain freedom of choice in the definition of probability suitable for applications in physics.

In many cases, we can base our definition of probability on some one *ensemble* of similar situations. These similar situations are usually called *systems* in physics. Suppose for instance, that we wish to study the statistical problems of interest to life-insurance companies. Here our unit system is a single person, and the principal event we are interested in is his or her death. To define probability, we can study a certain well-defined group of persons, such as "all persons born in the United States in 1910." With such a well-defined set of systems, we can talk about the number of persons in the ensemble who managed to reach the age of ten years, the number of persons of male sex, and so on. Instead of focusing our attention on the absolute number of persons in the ensemble having the property in question, we may also, and quite conveniently, speak of percentages. We might, for instance, report that 52 per cent of all persons born in 1910 were boys, but that in this group the percentage of men among the survivors in 1945 was only 47. (These are not the correct figures; they are cited only for illustration.) For this case we can now define probability simply as the percentage of persons having a specified property. Our previous statement could be reformulated as follows: Parents expecting a child in 1910 had a 52 per cent probability of having a boy (and a 48 per cent probability of having a girl). A boy born in 1910 had only 47/52 as good a chance to reach the age of thirty-five years as a girl born the same year.

The definition of probability given above is based on the availability of a specific ensemble or population. Should we choose a different ensemble, our probabilities for the same events would change. For instance, should we have determined the percentage of male births in the whole first decade of the twentieth century, the numerical value would have come out differently. Or, to mention a much more practical example, the life-insurance companies can set aside large reserves because their premiums are based on mortality tables that are out of date; in other words, the ensemble of the present policyholders lives very much longer than the ensemble on which the mortality tables are based.

In the above examples there is nothing mysterious about the concept of probability. In many applications, however, we wish to operate with probability considerations when we have no simple ensemble available. Take, as another example, the assertion "In penny matching, there is an equal probability, at any given throw, of turning up heads or tails." Occasionally this statement is cast in the form "Heads and tails have each the *a priori* probability $\frac{1}{2}$." What do we mean by such an assertion? Evidently the assertion is concerned with an observable fact: if we should flip a coin a large number of times, then we expect that heads will turn up in about half the number of tries, tails in the other half. But our assertion is not as precise as predictions in physics usually are; we must carry out "a large number" of experiments, and then the outcome will be "about" half heads and half tails. Percentagewise, we can make the further claim that the larger the number of individual tries, the more closely will the predicted percentage of 50 for either outcome be approximated.

Our assertion deals with observable facts. Therefore it must be possible to show whether it is correct or false. Suppose we should flip the same coin 100 times and get tails in 54 cases, heads in 46 cases. This result would not contradict our original assertion, since in 100 trials the rms[1] deviation from the most probable division (50-50) is ± 5. If we wish to perform a more conclusive test, we should have to increase the number of trials substantially.

---

[1] Standard abbreviation for "root-mean-square."

If we carry out 1000 trials, then the rms deviation from the most probable outcome will be $\sqrt{250} = 15.81 \cdots$. In other words, an outcome of 520 tails vs. 480 heads would be consistent with our original assertion, whereas an outcome of 540 vs. 460 would raise serious doubts. Actually, our original assertion may be slightly in error; that is, if the experiment is carried out a sufficient number of times, there might be a clearly discernible trend favoring one or the other event. Such a deviation could be caused by a slight unbalance in the design of the coin or by the dexterous manner in which the player flips it.

If our assertion clearly concerns observable facts and if its correctness can be judged in the light of experimental evidence, why do we make the assertion that both events are equally probable? Why do we not predict that heads will show twice as often as tails? It is incorrect to claim that our assertion is based on experience in penny matching. Personally, though I have no practical experience with any games of chance, in writing the preceding paragraphs I had no doubts which assertion to put down, and I did not even do library research in penny matching in order to draw on the observations of more experienced persons. If we do not draw on experience, then perhaps we base our assertion on a general philosophical principle, asserting that if a number of outcomes of an experiment are all possible, then their probabilities are equal? I do not think that recourse to such a philosophical principle is either necessary or correct. Actually, we implicitly base our judgment on the validity of certain laws of nature and on an assumed randomness of the detailed starting situations in the individual trials. In the case of the coin, we assume that if we were to distribute in our trials the orientation of the coin and its angular momentum evenly over all possible solid angles, then half of the trials will end with tails. If the player should realize a causal connection between starting orientation and final outcome and if he should consciously favor starting situations that end up in outcomes favorable to him, we should expect a preponderance of favorable outcomes and we should accuse him of cheating. To make cheating as hard as possible, we introduce safeguards that will make the causal connection between the muscular motions of the player and the final outcome of each trial so involved that the player cannot control the outcome.

I think that we can dispense with the notion of a priori probability if we construct an *idealized ensemble of trials*. In the case of penny matching, we could construct such an idealized ensemble by distributing the possible orientations and angular momenta of the coin as it leaves the hand of the player, the height at which it is released, and all the other pertinent variables evenly over all possible values; the resulting ensemble would consist of an infinite number of individual trials. In this case the laws of mechanics would enable us to predict definitely for which ranges of the many variables we should get heads and for which we should get tails. Presumably, half of all the trials would end with either result. If the coin is not balanced, we should be able to predict, after integrating the equations of motion for each possible set of initial conditions, how much the percentage of tails will deviate from 50.

Any actual set of trials will then be a subset of the trials composing our idealized ensemble. Let us consider the probable outcome of an experiment consisting of two trials. We assert that there is a 25 per cent chance of getting tails twice, a 25 per cent chance of getting heads twice, and a 50 per cent chance of getting each result once. This assertion can be interpreted in terms of our idealized ensemble as follows: Consider all possible combinations of two trials belonging to our idealized ensemble; then we shall find that of this infinity of combinations, which form an ensemble of their own (but depend on our original one in an obvious manner), a fourth lead to two heads, another fourth to two tails, and the remaining half to one heads, one tails.

In what follows, we shall operate mostly with hypothetical ensembles composed of an infinity of individual trials or systems. In all cases, we shall assume that each member system obeys known and specified laws of nature. If we endeavor to make statistical predictions concerning the behavior of a mechanical system, we shall construct ensembles consisting of similar mechanical systems, each one composed of the same particles as the actual system of interest to us. The systems of our hypothetical ensemble differ from each other by having different initial conditions. As a result, after a time t, they will have different configurations, and the corresponding constituent individual particles will have different velocities. But if we can integrate the equations of motion of our system for each set of initial conditions, then we can, in principle, predict the distribution of the systems of our ensemble at the time t.

One of the tasks of statistical mechanics is to abbreviate the necessary calculations for cases of physical interest so that results can be obtained with a reasonable amount of labor.

To describe statistical properties of ensembles, both finite and infinite, we do not specify the complete details of every member system; such a complete description is not feasible in most cases, nor is it of interest to the physicist. Instead, we have developed a number of concepts that are useful in that they permit us to describe important properties of ensembles in terms of quantities which can often be predicted without a complete integration of the equations of motion.

Consider a particular dynamical variable of a system, such as the x-coordinate of a specified particle of the system. If we wish to catalogue the values of this coordinate for all our systems, then we should number the systems (if that is possible)[1] and denote the value of x in the nth system by x_n; knowledge of every one of the values x_n at the time t is the most complete knowledge we could possibly acquire. But this description is usually too detailed. A less detailed description is the *distribution* of x in the ensemble, that is, knowledge of the *distribution function* $f(x)$ that specifies how large a fraction of the x_n are less than x. The function $f(x)$ increases monotonically. If x can assume all values from $-\infty$ to ∞, then $f(-\infty)$ will be 0, and $f(\infty)$ will be 1. If x can assume values only between x_1 and x_2, $x_1 < x_2$, then $f(x)$ will rise from 0 to 1 between these two limits.

The distribution function $f(x)$ need not possess a derivative. If it does (and in most cases we consider, such a derivative exists), then the function $f'(x)$ represents the density of distribution of x in our ensemble. The differential $f'(x)\, dx$ equals the (infinitesimal) frac-

---

[1] In an infinite ensemble, it may be necessary to identify the member systems by means of continuously variable parameters instead of or in addition to integral numerals. This contingency does not invalidate the concepts about to be introduced. All that needs to be done to extend the definitions given is to replace the summations by integrations over the continuous parameters or by combinations of integration and summation. In every case, Stieltjes integrals will permit us to carry out the necessary summation procedures in a mathematically unambiguous manner, provided only that some bounded measure for the ensemble as a whole is defined. For example, it must be meaningful to speak of "half of the systems of the ensemble," and so on. We shall always make this assumption.

tion of systems in our ensemble with values of x lying within the interval $x \cdots x + dx$.

Frequently we cannot even determine the distribution function of x, but we can determine the *average value* of x. We call the *ensemble average of x* the arithmetical mean of all the values x_n and designate this ensemble average by the symbol $\langle x \rangle$. In terms of an equation, we have

$$\langle x \rangle = \frac{1}{N} \sum_{n=1}^{N} x_n, \tag{1}$$

where N is the number of systems in a finite ensemble. If the ensemble is infinite, but so that each system can be identified by a numeral (we call such an infinite ensemble *denumerable*), then eq. (1) must be replaced by

$$\langle x \rangle = \lim_{N \to \infty} \left\{ \frac{1}{N} \sum_{n=1}^{N} x_n \right\}. \tag{2}$$

This definition of $\langle x \rangle$ is unambiguous only if the right-hand side converges absolutely toward its limit. Since such an absolute convergence cannot be achieved for many cases of interest to us, we shall give a third definition of $\langle x \rangle$, which is based on the distribution function $f(x)$:

$$\langle x \rangle = \int_{x=-\infty}^{\infty} x \, df(x). \tag{3}$$

This last definition is unambiguous and is equivalent to eq. (1) or (2) whenever either of these two is applicable. But eq. (3) remains meaningful if the infinite ensemble is not denumerable but *continuous*—by far the most important contingency. If $f(x)$ is differentiable, then (3) can also be given the form

$$\langle x \rangle = \int_{x=-\infty}^{\infty} x \, f'(x) \, dx. \tag{4}$$

In addition to the *average* of a given distribution, we are often interested in its *spread*, that is, the amount by which individual values x_n may be expected to deviate from the mean. A convenient measure of the spread is provided by the *variance*, defined as the root-mean-square deviation of x from $\langle x \rangle$. If we form the expression $x_n - \langle x \rangle$ and form its average for the whole ensemble, we find that it vanishes, because there are as many and as great deviations from the mean in one direction as there are in the other:

$$\langle x - \langle x \rangle \rangle = \int_{x=-\infty}^{\infty} (x - \langle x \rangle) \, df(x) = 0. \tag{5}$$

But if we square each individual deviation and then form the average, we form the average of quantities that are all positive, and the result will vanish only if the individual deviations all vanish, in other words if all the x_n are equal. Therefore we define the *mean square spread* by the formula

$$\langle \Delta x^2 \rangle = \langle (x - \langle x \rangle)^2 \rangle = \int_{x=-\infty}^{\infty} (x - \langle x \rangle)^2 \, df(x). \tag{6}$$

A short calculation shows that

$$\langle \Delta x^2 \rangle \equiv \langle x^2 \rangle - \langle x \rangle^2. \tag{7}$$

The variance is the square root of the mean square spread and is also called the *rms spread*.

In addition to ensemble averages, we frequently consider another type of average, *time averages*. Since a mechanical system changes in the course of time, and along with it the values of the dynamical variables, we can form the mean value of the variable x during a specified finite or infinite time interval. The expressions

$$\bar{\bar{x}} = \frac{1}{t_2 - t_1} \int_{t_1}^{t_2} x(t) \, dt,$$

$$\bar{\bar{x}} = \lim_{T \to \infty} \left\{ \frac{1}{2T} \int_{-T}^{T} x(t) \, dt \right\} \tag{8}$$

are called *time averages*. Time averages apply to an individual system, and hence the concept of time average is quite independent of the notion of an ensemble. In the next chapter, however, we shall become acquainted with a special type of ensemble (*quasi-ergodic ensembles*) in which the time average of each individual system equals the ensemble average, in other words, in which the spread of the time averages vanishes. To avoid confusion, in general we shall use different symbols for the two kinds of average: the carets $\langle \ \rangle$ for ensemble averages and the double bar $=$ for time averages.

2.2. Liouville's theorem

Consider an ensemble of mechanical systems identical in structure that at the time t_0 are started with different initial conditions. The "identical structure" implies equal numbers of the various types of constituent particles. For instance, we may consider an ensemble composed of individual systems S, each of which contains exactly 10^{24} protons and 10^{24} electrons. Each individual system represents roughly 1.65 mols of monatomic hydrogen, but without further specifications we are not yet committed to what extent the atoms may be ionized at the time t_0 or to what extent they may have associated to form molecular hydrogen.

We can represent the initial conditions of each member system completely by representing it as a single "representative point" in an appropriate phase space, which in our case will have 12×10^{24} dimensions. As the coordinates in that phase space we can choose the Cartesian coordinates and the linear momentum components of each one of the constituent particles. Our system has 6×10^{24} degrees of freedom.[1] Any canonical transformation will lead to a new set of canonical coordinates that will be equally suitable for the description of the system.

In phase space, our system at the time t_0 is represented by a single point. Its subsequent history is represented by a curve passing through that point. The representative point travels on that curve at a definite velocity. If we call the canonical coordinates used for the description of the phase space q_k and p_k, respectively, with $k = 1, \cdots, f$ (f is the number of degrees of freedom of the system), then the differential equations of the curve of the representative point are given by the *canonical equations of motion*,

$$\frac{dq_k}{dt} = \frac{\partial H}{\partial p_k}, \qquad \frac{dp_k}{dt} = -\frac{\partial H}{\partial q_k} \qquad (k = 1, \cdots, f). \qquad (9)$$

$H(q_k, f_k)$ is the *Hamiltonian function* of our mechanical system. For all the systems of the ensemble, H is the same function of its arguments, but of course at any given time t the values of these arguments are different for different systems.

There is nothing to prevent us from representing all the systems

---

[1] M&E—Ch. 2.

of our ensemble in the same phase space. At the time t_0, complete information about the whole ensemble will be provided by a graphical representation in which each system is represented by one dot on the graph.[1] In short, our ensemble is represented by a cloud of representative points. In the course of time, each one of these points will travel on a curve of its own. If the canonical coordinates of a system, $q_1, \cdots, q_f; p_1, \cdots, p_f$, are given at the initial time t_0, then the equations of motion (9), being first-order differential equations, determine the further history of the system *uniquely*. Geometrically, this further history is represented by a curve in phase space, a *mechanical trajectory*, and we have the result that through each "point" of phase space there passes one and only one possible mechanical trajectory. Thus in phase space the mechanical trajectories form a *field* (or *congruence*) *of curves*, covering the space completely but only once.

Physically, knowledge of both the q_k-coordinates and the p_k-coordinates implies complete information about both initial configuration and initial velocities of our system, and hence the uniqueness of the mechanical trajectory is not a physically novel result. In configuration space, the situation is different. A "point" in configuration space is identified just by the coordinates $q_1, \cdots, q_f$; knowledge of these coordinates alone is insufficient to determine the future of the system completely, and thus we have an infinity of trajectories passing through each point of configuration space, each trajectory differentiated from the others by its particular value of the initial velocity "vector" with the components $\dot{q}_1, \cdots, \dot{q}_f$. The fact that the trajectories in phase space form a field (in the above-defined sense) makes phase space eminently suitable as the framework in which to discuss ensembles of systems.

We shall now consider an ensemble consisting of continuously infinite systems. At a time t_0, we shall assume that they are so distributed in phase space that there exists a smooth function $\mu(q_k, p_k)$ describing their local density; $\mu(q_k, p_k)\, dq_1\, dq_2 \cdots dq_f\, dp_1\, dp_2 \cdots dp_f$ will be the (infinitesimal) fraction of systems of the ensemble whose canonical variables at the time t_0 fall within the specified infinitesimal brackets. In accordance with this defini-

---

[1] The actual preparation of such a graph would encounter certain technical difficulties, particularly the purchase of multidimensional graph paper.

tion, the integral of μ extended over all of phase space must be unity. We shall call μ the *relative density* (or simply *density*) of the systems in phase space. It is an invariant function with respect to canonical transformations; that is, the density of systems at a particular point of phase space is the same in terms of any system of canonical coordinates. We shall omit the proof of this statement; it is based on the fact that the Jacobian of all canonical transformations equals unity.

If we construct an ensemble with a given density function μ at the time t_0, then in principle we must be able to predict the density at any other time t, since the motions of the constituent systems are governed by specific laws, namely, the canonical equations (9). That the prediction is possible in actual fact and not only "in principle" is the content of *Liouville's theorem*.

To obtain the change of μ in the course of time, let us consider a finite volume element in phase space which is bounded by coordinate surfaces and which has, therefore, the shape of a multidimensional parallelepiped. Call the coordinate values at the various bounding surfaces q'_1, q''_1, q'_2, q''_2, $\cdots$, p'_1, p''_1, $\cdots$, so that the double-primed coordinate value in each case exceeds the single-primed corresponding coordinate value (Fig. 2). The fraction of systems of our ensemble contained in this particular volume element V is determined by the volume integral

$$F = \int_{q_1 = q'_1}^{q''_1} \cdots \int_{p_f = p'_f}^{p''_f} \mu(q_k, p_k, t) \, dq_1 \cdots dp_f. \qquad (10)$$

In the course of time, the value of the integral will change because of systems crossing the boundary surfaces. The fraction of systems crossing a coordinate surface depends on the density on that surface, its area, and the value of the velocity component normal to the surface. For instance, the fraction of systems crossing the surface $q''_1 = $ constant in unit time is given by the surface integral

$$I''_1 = \int_{q_2 = q'_2}^{q''_2} \cdots \int_{p_f = p'_f}^{p''_f} \mu(q''_1, q_2, \cdots, p_f, t) \, \dot{q}_1 \, dq_2 \cdots dp_f$$

$$= \int_{q_2} \cdots \int_{p_f} \left(\mu \frac{\partial H}{\partial p_1} \right)_{q''_1} dq_2 \cdots dp_f. \qquad (11)$$

If the velocity component $\dot{q}_1$ is positive on the surface considered, then the integrand of (11) represents a current out of V; if it is negative, then the current is directed into V. A corresponding expression can be obtained for the fraction of systems crossing the surface $q_1' = $ constant; it is

$$I_1' = \int_{q_2} \cdots \int_{p_f} \left(\mu \frac{\partial H}{\partial p_1} \right)_{q'_1} dq_2 \cdots dp_f. \tag{12}$$

In the latter integral, a positive integrand represents systems passing into V, and a negative integrand systems passing out of V. The

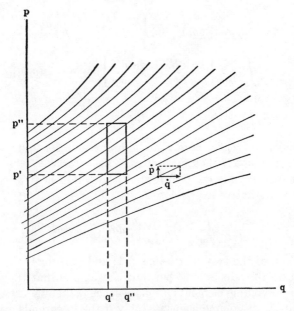

Fig. 2.   Volume element in phase space.

total fraction of systems leaving V in unit time across *both* of the two surfaces just considered is given by the difference $I_1'' - I_1'$. This difference I_1 can be given the form of a volume integral in phase space:

$$I_1 = \int_{q_2} \cdots \int_{p_f} \left[\left(\mu \frac{\partial H}{\partial p_1} \right)_{q''_2} - \left(\mu \frac{\partial H}{\partial p_1} \right)_{q'_1} \right] dq_2 \cdots dp_f$$
$$= \int_{q_1 = q'_1}^{q''_1} \int_{q_2} \cdots \int_{p_f} \frac{\partial}{\partial q_1} \left(\mu \frac{\partial H}{\partial p_1} \right) dq_1 \, dq_2 \cdots dp_f. \tag{13}$$

All together, there are $2f$ pairs of surfaces like the one we have described. If we wish to determine the fraction of systems leaving V per unit time across all of them, we must add $2f$ contributions like (13); this summation can be carried out easily, since the domain of integration is the same in all cases, the whole volume element V. We find for the fraction of systems leaving V per unit time, I, the following expression:

$$
\begin{aligned}
I = I_1 + \cdots + I_{2f} \\
= \int_{q_1} \cdots \int_{p_f} \sum_{k=1}^{f} \left[\frac{\partial}{\partial q_k}\left(\mu \frac{\partial H}{\partial p_k} \right) - \frac{\partial}{\partial p_k}\left(\mu \frac{\partial H}{\partial q_k} \right) \right] dq_1 \cdots dp_f \\
= \int_{q_1} \cdots \int_{p_f} \sum_{k=1}^{f} \left[\frac{\partial \mu}{\partial q_k} \frac{\partial H}{\partial p_k} - \frac{\partial \mu}{\partial p_k} \frac{\partial H}{\partial q_k} \right] dq_1 \cdots dp_f \\
= \int_{q_1} \cdots \int_{p_f} [\mu, H] \, dq_1 \cdots dp_f = -\frac{dF}{dt}.
\end{aligned}
\tag{14}
$$

The symbol $[\mu, H]$ is merely an abbreviation for the preceding lengthy expression; it is known as a *Poisson bracket*.[1]

If we differentiate eq. (10) formally with respect to t, we get for dF/dt the alternative expression

$$
\frac{dF}{dt} = \int_{q_1} \cdots \int_{p_f} \frac{\partial \mu}{\partial t} \, dq_1 \cdots dp_f.
\tag{15}
$$

Comparison of the two expressions (14) and (15) for the change of the fraction of systems in V per unit time shows that they will be equal for all volume elements in phase space (as they must), including infinitesimal volume elements, only if the integrands are equal, that is, if

$$
\frac{\partial \mu}{\partial t} + [\mu, H] = 0.
\tag{16}
$$

This equation may be considered as one possible formulation of Liouville's theorem.

We can obtain a very suggestive interpretation of eq. (16) if we go over to the so-called *substantive* derivative of μ. When we wish to examine the change with time of any quantity in a physical fluid, we can form the time derivative either at a fixed geometrical

---

[1] M&E—pp. 33–34.

point (keeping the space coordinates constant) or at a point that travels along with the streaming fluid. The first of these two time derivatives is often called "local"; the second, "substantive." Substantive derivatives are often identified by the symbol D/Dt. If the velocity is denoted by $\mathbf{v}$, then the local and the substantive derivative of a quantity w are connected with each other by the relationship

$$\frac{Dw}{Dt} = \frac{\partial w}{\partial t} + \mathbf{v} \cdot \nabla w. \tag{17}$$

That is because, in any case,

$$dw = \frac{\partial w}{\partial t}\, dt + \nabla w \cdot \mathbf{dx}, \tag{18}$$

and for substantive differentiation,

$$\mathbf{dx} = \mathbf{v}\, dt. \tag{19}$$

Let us apply the concept of substantive differentiation to phase space. We shall call the substantive derivative of any function of q_k, p_k, and t the rate of change relative to an observer who is moving with the representative points of the surrounding mechanical systems. In this sense, the substantive derivative of a function $w(q_k, p_k, t)$ is given by the expression

$$\frac{Dw}{Dt} = \frac{\partial w}{\partial t} + \sum_{k=1}^{f} \left[\frac{\partial w}{\partial q_k} \dot{q}_k + \frac{\partial w}{\partial p_k} \dot{p}_k \right]$$
$$= \frac{\partial w}{\partial t} + \sum_{k=1}^{f} \left[\frac{\partial w}{\partial q_k} \frac{\partial H}{\partial p_k} - \frac{\partial w}{\partial p_k} \frac{\partial H}{\partial q_k} \right] = \frac{\partial w}{\partial t} + [w, H]. \tag{20}$$

In particular, we find that the substantive derivative of the relative density $\mu(q_k, p_k, t)$,

$$\frac{D\mu}{Dt} = \frac{\partial \mu}{\partial t} + [\mu, H] = 0, \tag{21}$$

vanishes. If an observer in phase space could ride astride one of the representative points and thus move along with the cloud of points that represents our ensemble, he would find that the density of points in his vicinity would remain permanently constant. *Our cloud of points behaves like an incompressible fluid.* This is the most useful form of Liouville's theorem.

Liouville's theorem enables us to divide an ensemble up into separate streamlines. Inside a small tube made up of trajectories, the density remains permanently the same. This fact is independent of the density distribution outside the tube.

Problems

1. To what extent is it possible to collimate a beam of charged particles such as electrons with respect to both localization and momentum by means of electric and magnetic fields in an accelerating device or an electron microscope, once the particles have been injected into the system?

2. Strictly speaking, an ensemble consists of a number of identically composed mechanical systems which, of course, do not interact with each other but exist side by side. The electron cloud in an electronic tube in which space charge is of consequence is therefore not an ensemble. Nevertheless, construct an approximation in which the electrons can be treated as an ensemble in a six-dimensional phase space at each stage. (This approximation method is often called the *Hartree method of the self-consistent field*. It was originally developed for the treatment of spectroscopic problems involving atoms with numerous electrons, but its application to electronic tubes has been carried out with considerable success.)

3. Determine the value of μ for an ensemble of hydrogen atoms of which the center of mass is at rest and the energy of the proton-electron system lies below $-E_0$, assuming that below that energy the density of representative points in the six-dimensional phase space is uniform.

4. Carry out the same determination for a three-dimensional harmonic oscillator (mass m, elastic constant k) if the energy of oscillation is to be less than E_0.

5. Prove that the density of an ensemble in phase space is invariant with respect to canonical transformations.

Chapter 3

Stationary Ensembles

With Liouville's theorem, we have acquired the principal tool for developing statistical mechanics. If we have only partial information concerning the initial conditions of a mechanical system, we must construct an ensemble in which the spread of initial conditions reflects the degree of uncertainty of our information; our ability to predict approximately the future behavior of our actual system corresponds to our ability to compute ensemble averages for the ensemble, and the degree of accuracy of our forecast is represented by the smallness of the variance.

In practice, information about a typical system (such as one mol of a given chemical substance) is usually available to the extent that we know the volume available to the constituent particles and that we know the temperature. The temperature is not a mechanical but a statistical concept. We determine the temperature by permitting our system under observation to come into contact with a "standard" system (a thermometer). If the two systems are at the same temperature, we shall observe no *trend* in the energy flux: *on the average*, the temperature flow from one system to the other vanishes. There remains, however, a finite *spread* in the value of the energy exchanged. If we can apply sufficiently sensitive instruments, we shall observe a kind of *Brownian motion* by the particles in both systems; and if particles of one system knock against particles of the other system, they will transfer microscopic amounts of energy in both directions.

Nevertheless, the requirements of practical applications impress us with the desirability of characterizing statistically the absence of trends. Here we shall need two different concepts. One is the *internal statistical equilibrium* of a system, the state in which we cannot discern macroscopic motion or other macroscopic changes, though microscopic (random) motion of the particles continues.

27

The other concept is *thermal equilibrium between two distinct systems*, the state we usually characterize as that of equal temperatures. Obviously, there is no point in speaking of the essentially external equilibrium between two systems unless each one by itself is in internal equilibrium. Therefore we shall develop the characteristics of internal statistical equilibrium first.

3.1. Stationary distributions

Our first task is to construct ensembles that reflect the property of internal statistical equilibrium. The development of the ensemble in the course of time should exhibit no *trend;* that is, all ensemble averages should remain unchanged. Of course this condition is possible only if the density function $\mu(q_k, p_k, t)$ is independent of t, if $\partial\mu/\partial t$ vanishes permanently throughout phase space.[1]

According to Liouville's theorem in the form (2.16),[2] μ will be independent of t if its Poisson bracket with the Hamiltonian H of the system vanishes; and

$$[\mu, H] \equiv \sum_{k=1}^{f} \left\{ \frac{\partial\mu}{\partial q_k} \frac{\partial H}{\partial p_k} - \frac{\partial\mu}{\partial p_k} \frac{\partial H}{\partial q_k} \right\} = 0 \tag{1}$$

is the necessary and sufficient condition for an ensemble to have a *stationary distribution*, that is, to be in internal statistical equilibrium. We may express this same condition in different words, in accordance with eq. (2.21): at the time t_0 the density must be constant along every curve in phase space that represents a possible mechanical trajectory. This condition is certainly necessary and sufficient. It does not imply that the density μ must be constant throughout phase space, and in fact such an ensemble would not be useful for our purposes. On the other hand, condition (1) is too complicated to lead to any results that can be interpreted in terms

---

[1] If the density function changes even in a limited domain, we can find a partial domain X in which it increases at the time t. If we now construct as a dynamical variable w the function which is defined by the specification that it equals unity inside X and on the enclosing surface of X, and that it vanishes everywhere outside, then the ensemble average $\langle w \rangle$ will certainly have a non-vanishing, positive time derivative. Therefore, *all* ensemble averages will be constant only if μ does not change with time anywhere.

[2] That is, eq. (16) of Chapter 2; this decimal form of reference will be used henceforth.

of macroscopic properties. We must be able to tell more about μ than merely that it is constant along the mechanical trajectories.

Before we go on, we shall specify the kind of mechanical system we are interested in. We shall consider a type of system which is encountered at least in approximation in chemical physics and which represents the simplest conceivable macroscopic situation: a system which is thermally isolated but which interacts mechanically with its surroundings. An example of such a system is a macroscopic quantity of gas enclosed in completely rigid walls (we shall disregard the molecular structure of the walls themselves). The gas molecules, on striking the wall, are capable of exchanging momentum with it; after all, they must be reflected in some fashion into the interior of the gas. But their energy remains conserved at each collision, and as a result the energy of the system as a whole remains constant as well. In other words, in addition to the internal forces of the system we permit the existence of external forces, but they must be conservative. Mathematically, such a system is described by a Hamiltonian that does not depend explicitly on the time t but only on the coordinates q_k, p_k. Automatically, the value of the Hamiltonian, the energy of the system, is constant in time, an "integral of the motion."

The energy $E = H(q_k, p_k)$ is only one of the $2f$ constants that completely identify any one of the field of mechanical trajectories in phase space. Of these $2f$ parameters (which may be chosen as the values of the canonical coordinates at a fixed initial time t_0), $(2f - 1)$ identify a particular trajectory geometrically, and the last one determines the location of the representative point on that trajectory at a particular time. Any set of $2f$ algebraically independent functions of these $2f$ parameters will itself serve as such a set of parameters, and they may be chosen in particular in such a manner that one of them represents the energy.

Most of the remaining parameters cannot be determined by ordinary macroscopic methods of observation, and they are usually unknown. Naturally, if we could determine all $2f$ parameters of a mechanical system by some ingenious experimental technique, we should have converted our problem into one of ordinary analytical mechanics and divested it of its statistical character.

Ordinarily we make the assumption that the energy is the *only* parameter of the $2f$ that can be determined with any degree of accuracy and that all the others are completely unknown. Under these circumstances we must construct our ensemble of systems so that the density μ in phase space depends only on the energy, not on any other characteristic of the trajectories—so that, in other words, for a given value of E the density is uniform. The choice of μ as a function of E only, $\mu(E)$, represents realistically the extent of our ignorance.

Later we shall find that this function $\mu(E)$ is an exponential function of the argument E in many important cases. But before going on with the exposition of the classical theory, we must call attention to the limitations of the assumption made. Because we assume that our system is conservative but that nothing about it is observed except its energy, we represent our information by a density function that depends on the energy only. If this assumption concerning our knowledge is not warranted by circumstances, then we must modify the choice of density function.

To illustrate such a possibility, consider a meteorite in interstellar space. Apart from collisions with the very few atoms found even there (of the order of 1 per cm^3) and from electromagnetic radiations absorbed, scattered, or emitted, all of which we shall disregard, this meteorite is a completely isolated system. Not only is its energy conserved, but also its linear momentum and its angular momentum. Counting each component separately, altogether there are seven macroscopic quantities being conserved, not just one, and there are no reasonable grounds for favoring one over the others. The theory of relativity tells us that the energy with respect to some particular observer is a function of the energy and the linear momentum as measured by some other observer. As a result, it would be much more reasonable in such a case to assume that the density of the hypothetical ensemble should depend on four or seven macroscopic parameters, not just one; and exactly this assumption has to be made if one wishes to formulate statistical mechanics in a relativistically invariant manner.

Energy surface is a common designation for the $(2f - 1)$-dimensional subspace of all points in phase space belonging to the same energy value. Although the assumption of constant density on each energy surface in phase space cannot be justified for any and all situations we may encounter, it appears a good assumption for the typical classical mechanical systems in internal statistical equilibrium as encountered in the laboratory. Historically, the assumption was frequently supported by a hypothesis concerning the structure of trajectories in phase space, known as the *ergodic* or, after a necessary modification, the *quasi-ergodic hypothesis*. According to this, any two trajectories possessing the same energy but otherwise chosen arbitrarily, will at least approach each other below any finite bound, even though they cannot intersect. That is, we can always find at least two points (one on each of the two trajectories chosen) whose absolute coordinate differences $|\Delta q_1|$, $\cdots$, $|\Delta q_f|$, $|\Delta p_1|$, $\cdots$, $|\Delta p_f|$ are all less than ϵ, no matter how small this single number ϵ is chosen. If the quasi-ergodic hypothesis is correct, then a constant μ on each energy surface is the only possible choice consistent with eq. (1), which must be satisfied if the distribution is to be stationary.

A great deal of effort has gone into the examination of the quasi-ergodic hypothesis. A few very simple mechanical systems can be found that obviously do not satisfy it. We could, for instance, construct a "gas" of particles having a zero collision cross section with each other, so that they will never interact. If we enclose this "gas" in perfectly rigid, plane rectangular walls, then each particle will not change its individual energy in the course of time, nor will its linear momentum acquire more than eight distinct values. (On reflection from any wall, two of the linear momentum components will remain unchanged, and the third will merely change its sign: all together, there are eight possible combinations of three signs.) This system is obviously not quasi-ergodic. But we can make it so if we incline the walls very slightly so that the angles become incommensurable with the right angle, and if we replace the noninteracting particles by, for instance, perfectly elastic spheres with a very small radius. Then the directions of the particle momenta will be changed slightly each time a particle strikes three walls, forming a corner, in succession (in a perfectly rectangular corner, the momentum would be exactly reversed); and at every one of the rare collisions of two particles they will have a chance to exchange both momentum and energy. Hence it is probably correct to say that "almost all" conceivable conservative Hamiltonians lead to quasi-ergodic systems.

Even when a system is not quasi-ergodic, there is nothing to prevent us from choosing for μ a function that is constant on each energy surface, unless, of course, we possess specific information concerning some other constant of the motion that restricts our system to part of an energy surface. But only a quasi-ergodic system has the property that *every ensemble average at any time t extended over an ensemble that covers one energy surface with a constant density equals the time average from* $-\infty$ *to* ∞ *of the same quantity for every individual system on the same energy surface.* Suppose we wish to carry out an ensemble average at a time t of some dynamic variable w that depends on the coordinates at least piecewise smoothly. Then we can cover the energy surface at the time t with some grating so that the surface is divided up into cells of equal size.[1] If we choose in each cell a point at random and then form the arithmetical average of the values of w, $[w]$, at these points for all the cells, the result will approach $\langle w \rangle$ without limit if we permit the individual cell sizes to tend to zero. Now if our system is quasi-ergodic, its trajectory will pass through each cell at least once, no matter how fine the grating (of course the grating must remain finite). Thus we can choose our points in the above construction so that they all come to lie on the trajectory of our system. If we now form the time average for t from $-\infty$ to ∞ for any one of the systems represented by the points chosen, its value will be the same as for any other point of the set, since they all lie on the same trajectory and an average extended from $-\infty$ to ∞ for any one of them requires integration over the same entire trajectory. Let us designate this common value by $\bar{w}$. If we form the time average of $[w]$, $\overline{[w]}$, it will be the same as the "bracket average" of $\bar{w}$, $[\bar{w}]$, since the area of an energy surface is ordinarily finite and the operation "bracket averaging" requires only a finite summation: in fact, this double average equals $\bar{w}$ again. To complete our proof, let us consider the change of $[w]$ with time. Let every point of our grating move in accordance with the canonical equations of motion. Then, because of Liouville's theorem, the cell sizes do not change in the course of time,[2] and the set of points at a time t' has the same

---

[1] The area on an energy surface should be measured in terms of $(2f - 1)$ parameters chosen so that together with E they form a set of canonical coordinates in phase space.

[2] Obviously, no representative point can cross a moving cell boundary, so that the fraction of systems in every cell remains constant; but since their density in each cell also remains constant, the size of the cell cannot change, either.

properties it had at the time t. As a result, $[w]$ at the time t' must again approximate $\langle w \rangle$. The latter, however, is time-independent, and therefore $[w]$ must be approximately constant. But if it is, it must equal approximately its own time average, and we have, finally,

$$\bar{w} = \overline{[w]} = [w] = \langle w \rangle. \tag{2}$$

Equation (2) will not hold for a system that is not quasi-ergodic.

After this rather long discussion let us summarize the results we shall need. We shall generally assume that our systems are quasi-ergodic and that time averages can be replaced by ensemble averages extended over one energy surface with constant density. If we consider cases of internal statistical equilibrium, we shall represent the extent of our information by means of an ensemble whose density μ is a function of the system energy only.

3.2. Composite systems

Frequently we are interested in the statistical behavior of systems that are themselves composed of clearly separable systems. We might, for instance, wish to consider a gas that consists of the more elementary systems called molecules. Or we may consider two different chemical substances, a mol of water and above it a mol of helium gas, permitted to exchange heat energy and thus to come to a common temperature. We shall call a *composite system* one that can be considered to be composed of at least two *subsystems* that interact more weakly with each other than the components inside each subsystem do. More specifically, we shall assume that at any given instant the energy of the whole composite system is essentially the sum of the energies of the subsystems, and that the energy of interaction is negligible. We shall permit some small interaction to take place, however, so that energy will shift during sufficiently long time intervals from one subsystem to another. As a whole, the composite system is to be conservative. The purpose of this construction is to derive the *laws of energy interchange between weakly interacting systems*.

Let us consider a composite system Σ consisting of n subsystems $S_1, \cdots, S_n$. The first subsystem is to possess f_1 degrees of freedom, the second f_2, and so on. We can represent the state of the first subsystem by means of its Cartesian coordinates $x_1, \cdots, x_{f_1}$

and corresponding linear momenta $p_1, \cdots, p_{f_1}$, the second subsystem by means of $2f_2$ similar coordinates and momenta, and so on. Each one of the subsystems can then be represented as a single representative point in a phase space appropriate to it. The phase space P_1 for the first subsystem has $2f_1$ dimensions, and so on, with the nth phase space P_n being $2f_n$-dimensional. The totality of all subsystems has $2 \sum_{s=1}^{n} f_s$ coordinates and momenta to describe it. But these coordinates and momenta are, at the same time, a set of canonical coordinates suitable for a description of the composite system Σ. We can construct the $\left(2 \sum_{s=1}^{n} f_s\right)$-dimensional phase space Π in which Σ is represented by a single point. The coordinates used in Π are the same as those used in all the spaces $P_1, \cdots, P_n$. We say that the space Π is the *Cartesian product* of the spaces $P_1, \cdots, P_n$. In geometry this relationship is usually written in the form

$$\Pi = P_1 \times P_2 \times \cdots \times P_n. \tag{3}$$

Before going on with the discussion of our physical problem, we shall look at an example of the "Cartesian product" that is familiar to every reader. Consider the x,y-plane and, separately, the z-axis of an ordinary space. The plane can be considered a two-dimensional space. Each point in that "space" is determined by the two coordinate values x and y. In the same sense, the z-axis is a one-dimensional space. The Cartesian product of these two spaces will be a $(2 + 1)$-dimensional space so constructed that for any combination of two points, one in each factor space, there is one corresponding point in the three-dimensional product space, and vice versa: for each point in the product space there is a corresponding set of two points, one in each factor space. Obviously, the ordinary three-dimensional space has just these properties. For any point in the x,y-plane and any point on the z-axis, we can find precisely one point in three-dimensional space that has the same x- and y-coordinates as the first point and the same z-coordinate as the second point: it is that point of which the two points in the factor spaces are the projections. The relationship between Π and the factor spaces $P_1, \cdots, P_n$ is precisely the same.

For the application of Liouville's theorem to a composite system, we shall also require the relation between the measure of volume in the space Π to that in the spaces P_s. A volume element in the space Π represents physically a state of the composite system that is known within certain (finite or infinitesimal, as the case may be) tolerances. But the state of the composite system is given if the state of each subsystem is given. For the special case where the volume element is a parallelepiped with the infinitesimal edges dx, dp, the volume in Σ is simply the product of all these $\left(2\sum_{s=1}^{n} f_s\right)$ differentials. But it is also the product of the n volume elements in the subspaces, the first one being, for instance, $dx_1 \cdots dx_{f_1} \cdot dp_1 \cdots dp_{f_1}$. In other words, in any integration, the infinitesimal volume element in the space Π that is generated by the differentials of the canonical coordinates is simply the product of the analogous expressions in the n spaces $P_1, \cdots, P_n$.

Let us now turn to the Hamiltonian of the composite system, H. Our original assumption was that the internal interaction of the individual subsystems is large compared with the interaction between two different subsystems. At this point, we can give this assumption mathematical expression. If we continue to use rectilinear particle coordinates and momenta, the total Hamiltonian will be a sum of terms with significances as follows: First there will be the terms quadratic in the momentum components, representing kinetic energy; then there will be terms representing the potential energies between particles belonging to the same subsystem; and finally there will be potential-energy terms belonging to particles of different subsystems. Of these three groups of terms, we can combine the first two into sets of terms that belong to particular subsystems. The set of terms that belongs to the first subsystem we shall designate by H_1, and, generally, the terms of the sth subsystem will be represented by the single symbol H_s. In the third and last group, we shall combine all the terms that represent interaction between the rth and the sth subsystems into a single function h_{rs}. The assumption concerning the relative magnitude of internal and external interactions can now be expressed by the requirement that the sum of the terms h_{rs} is always small compared with the sum of the terms H_s.

It is not particularly difficult to construct composite systems satisfying this requirement. Consider, for instance, a composite system of two loosely coupled harmonic oscillators (undamped harmonic vibrators). The Hamiltonian

$$H = H_1 + H_2 + h_{12}, \tag{4}$$

with

$$H_1 = \frac{1}{2m} p_1^2 + \frac{k_1}{2} x_1^2, \qquad H_2 = \frac{1}{2m} p_2^2 + \frac{k_2}{2} x_2^2, \tag{5}$$

$$h_{12} = \epsilon\, x_1\, x_2,$$

will have the property that for any choice of the canonical variables whatsoever, the term h_{12} will satisfy the inequality

$$|h_{12}| \le \frac{\epsilon}{\sqrt{k_1 k_2}}\, (H_1 + H_2). \tag{6}$$

Therefore, to satisfy our assumption, we simply must choose the coupling parameter ϵ sufficiently small. In practice, however, many composite systems do not satisfy quite so stringent a requirement. In the derivations that follow, it is possible to relax the requirement of loose coupling to an extent that the range of applicability covers a good many situations of physical interest. First, it it is sufficient for the interaction on each energy surface of the composite system to be small, except in regions so small that the product of surface area (in phase space) and magnitude of interaction can be neglected against the product of total energy (for that energy surface) and total surface area. Furthermore, even that relaxed requirement need be satisfied only within a fairly broad range of energies (of the composite system), provided we are interested in situations that do not require us to pass outside that range.

Take, for instance, a gas. The subsystems can be the individual gas molecules. The interaction between two gas molecules is ordinarily small compared with the internal binding energies that hold the molecule together. But the interaction energies might be large for the brief instance of a close encounter or a direct collision. Now it is conceivable that at one instant almost all the gas molecules are engaged in a close encounter; but this set of situations occupies a negligible portion of each energy surface, and hence we may consider a gas as a composite system of only slightly coupled subsystems. If we lower the temperature sufficiently, the gas will condense into a liquid, and then the interaction energy will certainly be an appreciable fraction of the total energy. But if we operate on energy surfaces on which the system is gaseous, we need not be concerned because our assumption does not hold on energy surfaces far removed.

We shall now operate with a Hamiltonian that possesses the form

$$H = \sum_{s=1}^{n} H_s + \sum_{r,s=1,r<s}^{n} h_{rs}, \tag{7}$$

with the inequality (satisfied almost everywhere in a certain energy range)

$$\sum_{r<s} h_{rs} \ll H. \tag{8}$$

Under these circumstances, we can associate energy values—those of the functions H_s—with the individual subsystems, and the sum of these subsystem energies will approximately equal the total energy of the composite system, E:

$$E \sim \sum_{s=1}^{n} E_s. \tag{9}$$

The total energy is, of course, conserved. The subsystem energies, however, will change in the course of time. According to eq. (2.32) or (2.34) of M&E, the rate of change of H_s is determined by its "Poisson bracket" with the total Hamiltonian H,

$$\frac{dH_s}{dt} = [H_s, H]. \tag{10}$$

Inasmuch as the function H_s depends only on a small fraction of the canonical coordinates of the system Σ, most of the terms in the Poisson bracket will contribute nothing. In fact, if we substitute for H the expression (7), we find that none of the H_r will make any contribution, for the simple reason that all but one of those terms have no coordinates in common with H_s, and the last one, H_s, forms a zero Poisson bracket with itself. Of the interaction terms h, on the other hand, only those contribute which have one index equal to s; and eq. (10) reduces to

$$\frac{dH_s}{dt} = \sum_{r \neq s} [H_s, h_{rs}]. \tag{11}$$

If the interaction terms h_{rs} are small, then the changes in the sub-system energies E_s will be slow, but they will assume large values if we are willing to wait long enough.

We have worked so far with Cartesian particle coordinates, because the physical significance of these coordinates is most obvious. However, the individual terms on the right-hand side of eq. (7) are conserved by canonical transformations that do not mix the canonical coordinates belonging to different subsystems. If we carry out a canonical transformation just in the phase space P_1, another just in the subspace P_2, and so on, the totality of these transformations (all of which will be assumed to be time-independent) is a canonical transformation in the phase space II. Because of the independence of the transformations from t, H as well as each one of the H_s remains unchanged in value, and so will the interaction terms h_{rs}.

We are now ready to tackle our principal task. Suppose we construct a stationary ensemble of composite systems Σ by choosing some density function $\mu(E)$ in the phase space II. What can we say about the energy distribution in any one subsystem S_s? The answer will automatically deal with the related problem: Assuming the composite system Σ to be quasi-ergodic, how large a fraction of its time will a subsystem S_s spend in any given energy range?

To treat this question, we shall replace the density function $\mu(E)$ by the energy-distribution function $\mathrm{M}(E)$, which we shall define as the fraction of (composite) systems Σ with energies less than E. Like all distribution functions, $\mathrm{M}(E)$ increases monotonically with its argument from 0 to 1. At the same time, we shall call the volume in II containing all points with energies less than E the *characteristic volume* $X(E)$. The characteristic volume is also a monotonically increasing function of its argument, but for infinite energies it will tend to infinity. The relationship between μ, M, and X is

$$\frac{d\mathrm{M}}{dE} = \mu \, \frac{dX}{dE}. \tag{12}$$

Though $X(E)$ depends only on the form of the Hamiltonian, the function M can be chosen at will from among all functions increasing monotonically from 0 to 1, and its choice, together with $X(E)$, then determines $\mu(E)$.

In each subsystem S_s, we can construct its characteristic volume $X_s(E_s)$. Because of the relationship between the infinitesimal volume elements in the spaces P_s and the space Π,

$$dX = dX_1 dX_2 \cdots dX_n, \qquad (13)$$

we can set up an integral relationship between the functions X_s and the function X:

$$X(E) = \int_{E_1 = -\infty}^{\infty} \frac{dX_1(E_1)}{dE_1} \int_{E_2 = -\infty}^{\infty} \frac{dX_2(E_2)}{dE_2} \cdots$$

$$\int_{E_n = -\infty}^{E - \sum_{s=1}^{n-1} E_s} \frac{dX_n(E_n)}{dE_n} dE_1 \cdots dE_n. \qquad (14)$$

This integral relationship is the key for finding the energy-distribution functions of the subsystems S_s.

The formulas are rather lengthy to write and to read. To abbreviate as much as possible, we shall use the prime to denote derivatives of functions of a single argument, and we shall omit those arguments which are obvious. Equation (14) will then assume the form

$$X(E) = \int_{E_1 = -\infty}^{\infty} \cdots \int_{E_{n-1} = -\infty}^{\infty} \int_{E_n = -\infty}^{E - \sum_{s=1}^{n-1} E_s} X_1' \cdots X_n' dE_1 \cdots dE_n. \qquad (15)$$

If we differentiate this expression, we get

$$X'(E) = \int_{E_1 \cdots E_{n-1} = -\infty}^{\infty} \cdots \int X_1' \cdots X_{n-1}' X_n'\left(E - \sum_{s=1}^{n-1} E_s\right) dE_1 \cdots dE_{n-1}, \qquad (16)$$

and with the help of this result, eq. (12) can be rewritten in the form

$$\mu(E) = M'(E)\left[\int_{-\infty}^{\infty} \cdots \int X_1' \cdots X_{n-1}' X_n'\left(E - \sum_{1}^{n-1} E_s\right) dE_1 \cdots dE_{n-1}\right]^{-1} \qquad (17)$$

Now what about the distribution function for a single subsystem— the function $M_s(E_s)$, which denotes the fraction of systems for which the energy of the subsystem S_s is less than E_s? To obtain M_s, we must integrate $\mu(E)$, eq. (17), over all that part of the phase space II for which the function E_s is less than a certain value. That integral is

$$\mathrm{M}_s(\overset{0}{E_s}) = \int_{E_1=-\infty}^{\infty} \cdots \int_{E_s=-\infty}^{\overset{0}{E_s}} \cdots \int_{E_n=-\infty}^{\infty} \mu\left(\sum_1^n E_s\right)$$

$$X_1' \cdots X_n' \, dE_1 \cdots dE_n. \quad (18)$$

Equations (17) and (18) together provide the answer to our question. If we can work out the necessary integrals, we can tell the fraction of systems of the ensemble for which the subsystem S_s has an energy less than E_s. Before we tackle the general methods for handling the integrals, we shall illustrate the concepts introduced with a few examples. We shall derive the characteristic volumes for three "simple" systems: the free particle in a box, the harmonic oscillator, and the electron in the hydrogen atom. Later we shall calculate the characteristic volume of a composite system which consists of free particles in a box. That system may be considered a model for a perfect gas. For this example we can work out completely the expressions called for in eqs. (17) and (18).

A free particle in a box of volume V possesses a Hamiltonian which, in rectilinear coordinates, has the form

$$H(x, y, z, p_x, p_y, p_z) = \begin{cases} \dfrac{1}{2m}(p_x^2 + p_y^2 + p_z^2) = \dfrac{1}{2m}p^2 \text{ inside the box,} \\ +\infty \text{ outside.} \end{cases}$$

$$(19)$$

The volume of phase space containing all representative points with an energy less than E can be obtained by integrating separately over the space coordinates and over the momentum components. The domain of integration of the spatial coordinates will equal V for any finite energy bound. The volume in the space of the three momentum components ("momentum space") will have the shape of a sphere with the center at the point $(0, 0, 0)$ and having a radius

$$p = \sqrt{2m\,E}. \quad (20)$$

Thus the characteristic volume for a single particle in a box is

$$X(E) = \tfrac{8}{3}\sqrt{2}\,\pi\,V m^{3/2}\,E^{3/2}. \quad (21)$$

The Hamiltonian of a particle that is bound to a fixed point with a harmonic force, that is, a force proportional to the distance from the equilibrium point, has the form (again in rectilinear coordinates)

$$H = \frac{k}{2}(x^2 + y^2 + z^2) + \frac{1}{2m}(p_x^2 + p_y^2 + p_z^2). \qquad (22)$$

This Hamiltonian is a special case of a central force, and the technique of integration is the same in all these cases. The general central-force Hamiltonian is

$$H = \phi(r) + \frac{1}{2m}(p_x^2 + p_y^2 + p_z^2) \qquad (r = \sqrt{x^2 + y^2 + z^2}). \quad (23)$$

$\phi(r)$ is, of course, the potential energy of the particle. That the potential energy is a function of the distance only from the center, r, is what makes the force a central force.[1] To obtain the characteristic volume, we separate the integration again into integration in the space of the coordinates x, y, z and integration in the momentum space. In coordinate space, the volume containing all points with a potential energy less than X is the sphere with the radius $R(\phi)$ at which the potential energy assumes that value. In momentum space, the volume of points whose kinetic energy is less than K is also a sphere, and its volume equals $\frac{8}{3}\sqrt{2}\,\pi\,m^{3/2}K^{3/2}$. The characteristic volume in phase space must be

$$X(E) = \int_{\phi=-\infty}^{E} X_K(E-\phi)\,dX_\phi(\phi) = \int_{K=0}^{\infty} X_\phi(E-K)\,dX_K(K),$$
$$X_K = \tfrac{8}{3}\sqrt{2}\,\pi\,m^{3/2}K^{3/2}, \qquad X_\phi = \tfrac{4}{3}\pi\,[R(\phi)]^3. \qquad (24)$$

For any special function $\phi(r)$ that is given to us, we must then attempt to carry out one or the other form of the integral (24). The limits of integration are determined by the fact that X_K vanishes for all negative values of its argument.

Returning now to the Hamiltonian of the harmonic oscillator,

---

[1] In Newtonian mechanics, a particle will experience a central force whenever it is attracted by a single particle that is fixed. Moreover, the general two-body problem (two particles attracting or repelling each other) can always be reduced to the form of a central-force problem if we introduce, instead of the Cartesian particle coordinates, the coordinates of the joint center of mass and the coordinates of one particle relative to the other or relative to the center of mass. This technique was illustrated in M&E—Ch. 1, on the example of planetary motion.

eq. (22), we find that the potential energy equals $\frac{k}{2} r^2$ and that the function X_ϕ is, therefore,

$$X_\phi(\phi) = \tfrac{8}{3} \sqrt{2}\, \pi \left(\frac{\phi}{k}\right)^{3/2}. \tag{25}$$

Because of the formally similar way in which r and p enter into the Hamiltonian (22), it makes no difference for the integration which of the two forms (24) we employ. Choosing the first, we get

$$X(E) = \frac{64}{3}\, \pi^2 \left(\frac{m}{k}\right)^{3/2} \int_{\phi=0}^{E} (E - \phi)^{3/2}\, \phi^{1/2}\, d\phi$$

$$= \frac{8}{3\pi} \left(\frac{E}{\nu}\right)^3 \int_0^1 (1 - x)^{3/2}\, x^{1/2}\, dx, \tag{26}$$

$$\left(\nu = \frac{1}{2\pi} \sqrt{\frac{k}{m}}, \quad x = \frac{\phi}{E}\right).$$

The last integral is a dimensionless number. Its value can be determined without difficulty, for instance if we substitute for x the new variable $x = \sin^2 \theta$. The resulting integral over trigonometric functions can be evaluated by means of a short calculation or by the use of a table of integrals. Its value is $\pi/16$. ν, which has been introduced into the second line of eq. (26), is the resonance frequency of the oscillator. The final form of $X(E)$ is

$$X(E) = \frac{1}{6} \left(\frac{E}{\nu}\right)^3. \tag{27}$$

Our third example is the electron in the hydrogen atom. If we assume, for the purpose of this calculation, that the center of mass is at rest, disregarding the contribution of translatory motion to the energy, then the Hamiltonian for the motion of the proton and the electron about the common center of mass is

$$H = \frac{p^2}{2m} - \frac{e^2}{r}. \tag{28}$$

The coordinates and momentum components appearing in this expression are actually *relative* coordinates and momentum components, that is, those of the electron, but are diminished by the values of the corresponding quantities for the proton. The symbol

m stands in this case not for the mass of the electron but for the so-called *reduced* electron mass, which is defined as

$$m = m_e \frac{m_p}{m_p + m_e}, \tag{29}$$

where m_e and m_p are the masses of the electron and the proton, respectively.

In our present case, we can again apply the formula (24) for the central-force case, with the potential energy being equal to $-e^2/r$. Because the potential energy is always negative and the volume function X_ϕ infinite for all non-negative values of its argument, the integral (24) can be finite only for negative values of the energy E. With the potential-energy volume being

$$X_\phi(\phi) = \tfrac{4}{3}\pi\, e^6\, |\phi|^{-3} \qquad (\phi \leq 0), \tag{30}$$

we have, for negative values of E only,

$$X(E) = \int_{k=0}^{\infty} \tfrac{4}{3}\pi\, e^6 (|E| + K)^{-3} \cdot 4\sqrt{2}\,\pi\, m^{3/2}\, K^{1/2}\, dK$$

$$= \frac{16}{3}\sqrt{2}\,\pi^2\, m^{3/2}\, e^6\, |E|^{-3/2} \int_0^{\infty} \frac{\sqrt{x}\, dx}{(1 + x)^3} \tag{31}$$

$$\left(x = \frac{K}{|E|}, \qquad E < 0\right).$$

The numerical value of the last integral is $\pi/8$, and hence the function $X(E)$ for the non-ionized hydrogen atom is

$$X(E) = \tfrac{2}{3}\sqrt{2}\,\pi^3\, m^{3/2}\, e^6\, |E|^{-3/2} \qquad (E < 0), \tag{32}$$

being infinite for $E = 0$ and for all positive energies. We can prevent $X(E)$ from ever becoming infinite if we enclose our hydrogen atom in a vessel with a finite volume. Then, if the electron becomes ionized, it remains still confined to the interior of the vessel, and the system remains susceptible to a statistical treatment.

The preceding example teaches us something about the suitability of systems for a statistical treatment that is based on the concept of stationary ensembles. We cannot treat systems that have characteristic volumes which become infinite for finite energies. Otherwise, a composite system that possesses even one subsystem with that property will have the tendency to throw all its energy into that subsystem. Let us consider, for a moment, a system composed of several hydrogen atoms that are capable of interacting with each other slightly. The characteristic volume of each subsystem remains finite only as long as the energy of that subsystem is negative. So let us endow the composite system with a negative total energy; that is, let us start with a situation where all of the electrons are firmly bound to their respective protons. If we let the composite system start with this situation, energy will be transferred back and forth between the various subsystems; and if this interaction continues long enough, some one of the hydrogen atoms will acquire enough energy to become ionized. As soon as that happens, its electron will leave the neighborhood of its proton permanently, and the composite system will be effectively reduced to $(n - 1)$ atoms. Now again, after a time, another atom will become ionized, and so forth, until there is only one atom left intact, which has acquired all the negative energy originally distributed throughout the composite system. Obviously, there can be no permanent stationary distribution of energy in an ensemble of this kind.

The situation is completely different if we place our hydrogen atoms inside a vessel with rigid walls from which no electrons can escape. In that case also, a certain number of atoms will become ionized; but the free electrons will cross and recross the interior of the vessel, and occasionally one of them will approach a free proton closely enough to be captured. Thus, depending on the number of hydrogen atoms in the interior and depending on the total energy of the system, eventually we shall find a stationary distribution of the ensemble constructed of systems of *confined* hydrogen atoms, in which a certain percentage of atoms is intact and the remainder ionized. The smaller the vessel and the smaller the total energy available, the greater will be the percentage of intact atoms.

Returning to our general problem, we wish to treat the integrals in eqs. (17) and (18) so that we can make predictions concerning the percentage of subsystems S_s possessing energies less than $\overset{0}{E_s}$. These two expressions contain an integral in common that represents the characteristic volume of a composite system identical with Σ, except that it does not contain the subsystem S_s. We shall call this function Y_s, where the index s now refers to the *missing* subsystem. Y_s is given by the expression

$$Y_s(E) = \int_{E_1=-\infty}^{\infty} \cdots \int_{E_{s-1}=-\infty}^{\infty} \int_{E_{s+1}=-\infty}^{\infty} \cdots \int_{E_n=-\infty}^{E-\sum_1^n{}' E_r} X_1' \cdots X_{s-1}'$$

$$X_{s+1}' \cdots X_n' \, dE_1 \cdots dE_{s-1} \, dE_{s+1} \cdots dE_n. \quad (33)$$

The prime attached to the summation symbol that appears in the last integral limit is intended to indicate that in the sum E_s is to be omitted. In other words, this expression is identical with (15), except that one of the subsystems has been omitted. The derivative of Y_s is given by an expression analogous to (16),

$$Y_s'(E) = \int_{E_1=-\infty}^{\infty} \cdots \int_{E_{s-1}} \int_{E_{s+1}} \cdots \int_{E_{n-1}=-\infty}^{\infty} X_1' \cdots X_{s-1}'$$

$$X_{s+1}' \cdots X_n'\Big(E - \sum_{r=1}^{n-1}{}' E_r\Big) dE_1 \cdots dE_{s-1} \, dE_{s+1} \cdots dE_{n-1}. \quad (34)$$

With the help of this new volume function, eqs. (17) and (18) can be written in the form

$$\mu(E) = \mathrm{M}'(E) \left[\int_{E_s=-\infty}^{\infty} X_s'(E_s) \, Y_s'(E - E_s) \, dE_s \right]^{-1},$$

$$\mathrm{M}_s(\overset{0}{E_s}) = \int_{E_s=-\infty}^{\overset{0}{E_s}} \int_{\bar{E}=-\infty}^{\infty} \mu(E_s + \bar{E}) \, X_s'(E_s) \, Y_s'(\bar{E}) \, dE_s \, d\bar{E}$$

$$= \int_{E=-\infty}^{\infty} \mu(E) \int_{E_s=-\infty}^{\overset{0}{E_s}} X_s'(E_s) \, Y_s'(E - E_s) \, dE_s \, dE,$$

$$\left(\bar{E} = \sum_1^n{}' E_r, \ E = \sum_1^n E_r \right).$$

$$(35)$$

If we substitute the first expression into the second, we get, finally, for $\mathrm{M}_s(\overset{0}{E_s})$ the integral

$$\mathrm{M}_s(\overset{0}{E_s}) = \int_{E=-\infty}^{\infty} \frac{\int_{E_s=-\infty}^{\overset{0}{E_s}} X_s'(E_s) \, Y_s'(E - E_s) \, dE_s}{\int_{E_s=-\infty}^{\infty} X_s'(E_s) \, Y_s'(E - E_s) \, dE_s} \, d\mathrm{M}(E). \quad (36)$$

The expression (36) represents a considerable simplification. The distribution depends on an integral over a fraction of which the denominator is independent of $\overset{0}{E_s}$; this denominator is, in effect, a normalizing factor, assuring us that for $\overset{0}{E}_s \to \infty$ the integrand, and therefore M_s itself, tends to unity. Actually, nothing is lost if we specialize the energy distribution of our ensemble and assume that all composite systems of the ensemble have the same energy $\overset{0}{E}$. $M(E)$ is then a *step function*, defined by the requirement that its value be zero for all arguments less than $\overset{0}{E}$ and unity for all arguments greater than $\overset{0}{E}$. With such a special disposition of $M(E)$, eq. (36) takes the form

$$M_s(\overset{0}{E}_s, \overset{0}{E}) = \frac{\int_{-\infty}^{\overset{0}{E}_s} X'_s(E_s) \, Y'_s(\overset{0}{E} - E_s) \, dE_s}{\int_{-\infty}^{\infty} X'_s(E_s) \, Y'_s(\overset{0}{E} - E_s) \, dE_s}, \tag{37}$$

in which the percentage of subsystems S_s with energies less than $\overset{0}{E}_s$ depends on $\overset{0}{E}_s$, the total energy available $\overset{0}{E}$, and, of course, on the shapes of the functions X'_s and Y'_s.

Equation (37) is the most concise form we can obtain for the subsystem energy distribution M_s. The nature of the sth subsystem enters in the form of its characteristic volume X_s. But quite obviously, the energy distribution is also affected by the nature of the rest of the system Σ, and that influence is represented by the function Y_s. We shall now show that for very large composite systems, that is, for systems consisting of large numbers of subsystems, the function $Y_s(E - E_s)$ can be approximated by an exponential function.

3.3. The Boltzmann Factor

In this section we shall study the form of the characteristic volume of a composite system and apply our results to eq. (37). Since in this formula it is not Y_s itself but its derivative that determines the partial energy distribution, we shall immediately consider integrals of the form (16) and (34). These integrals are apparently so awkward because the multiple integrals cannot be represented as products of single integrals. Thus the relative role played by the constituent subsystems cannot be ascertained by mere inspection. Our first aim must be to convert the integral (16) into such a form that the individual subsystems enter more simply and, incidentally, more symmetrically.

This purpose can be accomplished by means of a technique that is usually called the technique of *Laplace transforms* and which is closely akin to the theory of the Fourier integral. If the individual characteristic volumes (or rather their derivatives X_s') had Fourier transforms, then our task would be extremely simple. But these functions increase monotonically to infinity for large positive values of the argument, and hence a Fourier transform is not defined. Consideration of such examples as (21) and (27) shows, however, that the function $e^{-\alpha E_s} X_s'(E_s)$, where α is some arbitrary positive number, possesses a Fourier transform in many important cases. In fact, all that is necessary is that X_s' vanish for all negative values of the energy (or at least for all values less than some arbitrary value $-\overset{0}{E}$) and that it increase more slowly than the exponential function. We shall then call the function

$$\xi_s(\omega_s) = \int_{-\infty}^{\infty} X_s'(E_s) e^{-(\alpha + i\omega_s) E_s} \, dE_s \tag{38}$$

the Laplace transform of X_s'. Because of the Fourier integral theorem, X_s' may be recovered from its Laplace transform by means of the formula

$$X_s'(E_s) = \frac{e^{\alpha E_s}}{2\pi} \int_{-\infty}^{\infty} \xi_s(\omega_s) e^{i\omega_s E_s} \, d\omega_s. \tag{39}$$

We shall now substitute the Laplace transforms into eq. (16). The result of this substitution is

$$X'(E) = \left(\frac{1}{2\pi}\right)^n e^{\alpha E} \int \cdots \int_{E_1, \cdots, E_{n-1} = -\infty}^{\infty} \int \cdots \int_{\omega_1, \cdots, \omega_n = -\infty}^{\infty} \prod_{s=1}^{n} \{\xi_s(\omega_s)\}$$

$$e^{i\left[\omega_n E + \sum_1^{n-1} (\omega_s - \omega_n) E_s\right]} \cdot d\omega_1 \cdots d\omega_n \, dE_1 \cdots dE_{n-1}. \tag{40}$$

Although the number of integrations apparently has been increased, the integrand now is the product of a large number of factors, and each set of variables (E_s, ω_s), $s = 1, \cdots, (n-1)$, appears in only one factor. Such a separable integral is

$$I_s = \frac{1}{2\pi} \int_{E_s = -\infty}^{\infty} e^{-i\omega_n E_s} \int_{\omega_s = -\infty}^{\infty} \xi_s(\omega_s) e^{i\omega_s E_s} \, d\omega_s \, dE_s \tag{41}$$

which equals $\xi_s(\omega_n)$ because of Fourier's integral theorem. Thus, we can carry out all but one of the integrations of (40) immediately, and we are left with the integral

$$X'(E) = \frac{1}{2\pi} e^{\alpha E} \int_{\omega = -\infty}^{\infty} e^{i\omega E} \prod_{s=1}^{n} [\xi_s(\omega)] \, d\omega. \tag{42}$$

This expression shows that the Laplace transform of $X'(E)$ is simply the product of the Laplace transforms of the characteristic volumes of the constituent subsystems.

We shall use this relationship to determine the characteristic volume derivative $X'(E)$ of a composite system of which every subsystem S_s has a characteristic volume derivative of the form

$$\begin{aligned} X'_s(E_s) &= a_s E_s^{n_s}, \qquad n_s > 0, \quad \text{if} \quad E_s \geq 0, \\ X'_s(E_s) &= 0 \qquad\qquad\qquad\quad \text{if} \quad E_s \leq 0. \end{aligned} \tag{43}$$

That means that free particles in a box as well as harmonic oscillators form suitable subsystems. We shall not assume that the subsystems are all alike. The Laplace transform of (43) is

$$\xi_s(\omega_s) = a_s n_s! (\alpha + i\omega)^{-(n_s+1)}, \tag{44}$$

and the Laplace transform of $X'(E)$ is the product of all the factors (44). For the function $X'(E)$ itself, with little effort we can get the expression

$$X'(E) = \frac{\displaystyle\prod_{s=1}^{n} a_s n_s!}{\left(\displaystyle\sum_{s=1}^{n} n_s + n - 1\right)!} E^{\left(\sum\limits_{s=1}^{n} n_s + n - 1\right)} \qquad (E \geq 0). \tag{45}$$

Next we shall substitute this expression into eq. (37), applying the formula to the system $(\Sigma - S_s)$. We need not assume that S_s itself obeys eq. (43). We can dispense with the constant coefficients in (45), since they will cancel out. The function for the distribution of E_s will be

$$M_s(\overset{0}{E}_s, \overset{0}{E}) = \frac{\displaystyle\int_{E_s=0}^{\overset{0}{E}_s} X'_s(E_s) \, (\overset{0}{E} - E_s)^{n-2+\sum\limits_{r}' n_r} \, dE_s}{\displaystyle\int_{E_s=0}^{\overset{0}{E}} X'_s(E_s) \, (\overset{0}{E} - E_s)^{n-2+\sum\limits_{r}' n_r} \, dE_s}, \tag{46}$$

if $\qquad\qquad X'(E_s) = 0 \qquad$ for $\qquad E_s \leq 0.$

Both in the numerator and in the denominator, the principal contribution to the integrals will come from fairly small values of E_s, because, at least for fairly complex systems, with large values of the exponent, the function Y'_s decreases so rapidly if E_s assumes any considerable value that the product of the two characteristic functions will become very small compared with its value for $E_s \sim 0$. As a matter of fact, since we assume that our subsystem S_s likewise has nonvanishing values of X'_s only for positive values of the subsystem energy, the product will be zero at $E_s = 0$ and will tend to a maximum for a value of E_s that is small compared with the total energy E; after passing this maximum it will rapidly drop to very small values. We shall, therefore, expand $Y'_s(E - E_s)$ into a power series in ascending powers of E_s, a power series that will converge very well in the range of values that make the principal contribution to the integrals we are interested in.

Furthermore, we shall introduce the quantity

$$\nu = \frac{1}{n-1} \sum{}' n_r + 1, \tag{47}$$

which represents the average contribution of each subsystem to the exponent of E in the expression for Y'_s. Likewise, we shall introduce the average energy per subsystem,

$$\epsilon = \frac{1}{n-1} \overset{0}{E}. \tag{48}$$

Once we have introduced the quantities ν and ϵ into (46), we shall be able to exhibit separately the effect of the average characteristics of the constituent subsystems (their contributions to the all-important exponent and their share of the total energy) and the effect of the total number of constituent subsystems. The expression (46) will then take the form

$$\mathrm{M}_s(\overset{0}{E}_s, \overset{0}{E}) = \frac{\displaystyle\int_0^{\overset{0}{E}_s} X'_s(E_s)\left(1 - \frac{E_s}{(n-1)\epsilon}\right)^{(n-1)\nu-1} dE_s}{\displaystyle\int_0^{\overset{0}{E}} X'_s(E_s)\left(1 - \frac{E_s}{(n-1)\epsilon}\right)^{(n-1)\nu-1} dE_s},$$

with
$$\left(1 - \frac{E_s}{(n-1)\,\epsilon}\right)^{(n-1)\nu - 1} = 1 - \frac{1}{\epsilon}\left(\nu - \frac{1}{n-1}\right)E_s$$

$$+ \frac{1}{2!}\frac{1}{\epsilon^2}\left(\nu - \frac{1}{n-1}\right)\left(\nu - \frac{2}{n-1}\right)E_s^2 - \cdots . \quad (49)$$

This power series will tend to the exponential series if we let the number n of constituent subsystems increase without changing their average characteristics ν and ϵ.   In the limit, we get

$$\lim_{n\to\infty}\{M_s(\overset{0}{E_s})\} = \frac{\int_0^{\overset{0}{E_s}} X_s'(E_s)\, e^{-\frac{\nu}{\epsilon}E_s}\, dE_s}{\int_0^{\infty} X_s'(E_s)\, e^{-\frac{\nu}{\epsilon}E_s}\, dE_s}. \quad (50)$$

Physically, we can interpret our result as follows: A single system with a known characteristic volume X_s can interact with a very large complex composite system composed of such constituents as harmonic oscillators and particles free to move within a finite region.   If we are permitted to increase the number of subsystems without limit (provided, however, that the percentages of particular types of subsystems remain unchanged and that the total energy is increased in proportion to the size of the composite system), then the energy distribution of the system under consideration S_s will approach (50).   The composite system $(\Sigma - S_s)$ is a particular type of *temperature bath*.   Naturally, we shall want to know how large the bath must be chosen before the asymptotic expression (50) is a good approximation of (49).   Later we shall also attempt to generalize the type of constituent subsystem suitable for the construction of temperature baths.

Let us first examine the goodness of the approximation (50) to the rigorous formula (49).   The principal contribution to the integral comes from a region in which the exponential in (50) is comparable to unity.   Depending on the exact shape of X_s', the approximation of the binomial series by the exponential series needs to be good only in a region in which the argument $(\nu/\epsilon)\cdot E_s$ lies between 0 and a value f which is greater than one and of the order of $|E_s\cdot V_s''/V_s'|$.   The approximation will be worst at the upper limit. At this upper limit, both the binomial and the exponential series will decrease after f terms; if we wish to break off the exponential series at such a point that the relative error (error divided by the true value of the function) is less than some small number δ, then the standard formulas for rest-term estimates tell us that we shall retain $N(\delta)$ terms, where

$$e^f f^{N+1} \leq (N + 1)! \; \delta. \tag{51}$$

Now we can estimate the error produced when we replace the binomial series by the exponential series. The percentage error produced in the Nth term of the series equals

$$\Delta = 1 - \left(1 - \frac{1}{\bar{N}}\right)\left(1 - \frac{2}{\bar{N}}\right) \cdots \left(1 - \frac{N}{\bar{N}}\right) \quad [\bar{N} = \nu(n - 1)]. \tag{52}$$

This error can be estimated very roughly, but sufficiently well for a consideration of the parameters affecting our approximation as

$$\Delta \sim \frac{1}{2}\frac{N^2}{\bar{N}} = \frac{1}{2}\frac{N^2}{\nu(n - 1)}, \tag{53}$$

provided it is small compared with unity. Suppose, for instance, that we have constructed a temperature bath of one mol of a near-perfect monatomic gas. In that case, the number N is $\frac{3}{2}$ times Avogadro's number, or, very roughly, 10^{24}. The discrepancy between the exponential and the binomial series will, therefore, become serious after about 10^{12} terms of the series expansion. For such an enormous number of terms, the error due to the breaking off of the series is completely negligible if f is small compared to N. Only when f approaches about $\frac{1}{4}N$ does it become necessary to consider the error given by eq. (51). Thus in our present case we should be justified in using the exponential function for a range of f up to about 10^{11}. On the other hand, f is a measure for the complexity of the subsystem S_s under consideration. It is of the same order of magnitude as the number of degrees of freedom of the subsystem. Thus, if we brought an organic macromolecule of, say, 10^8 molecular weight into contact with our one-mol temperature bath, its energy distribution would be given by eq. (50) with virtually perfect accuracy.

The introduction of exponential factors into the computation of energy distributions was first proposed by Boltzmann; accordingly, we shall call the exponential exp $\{-(\nu/\epsilon)E_s\}$ the *Boltzmann factor*.

So far, we have derived the occurrence of the Boltzmann factor for a very restricted situation: that the characteristic volume of the temperature bath is proportional to a positive power of the energy. This result can be extended to all characteristic volumes that possess merely one property; the integral

$$I = \int_{-\infty}^{\infty} X'_s(E) \, e^{-\alpha E} \, dE \tag{54}$$

must converge for each subsystem for all positive values of α. Under these circumstances, we can derive the Boltzmann formula as an asymptotic expression that is approached if the temperature bath is made sufficiently large.

To do so, we shall make use of the so-called *central limit theorem*, which occupies a key position in the theory of probability. The central limit theorem explains the significance of Gauss's error function; it states that if a non-negative function $f(x)$ possesses the three integrals

$$I_0 = \int_{-\infty}^{\infty} f(x) \, dx,$$

$$X I_0 = \int_{-\infty}^{\infty} x f(x) \, dx, \tag{55}$$

$$(\Delta^2 + X^2)I_0 = \int_{-\infty}^{\infty} x^2 f(x) \, dx,$$

then the "integral involutions" $f_n(x)$,

$$f_2(x) = \int_{-\infty}^{\infty} f(x - x_1) \, f(x_1) \, dx_1,$$

$$f_3(x) = \int\int_{-\infty}^{\infty} f(x - x_1) \, f(x_1 - x_2) \, f(x_2) \, dx_2 \, dx,$$

$$\cdot$$
$$\cdot$$
$$\cdot$$

$$f_n(x) = \int_{-\infty}^{\infty} f_{n-1}(x - x') \, f(x') \, dx', \tag{56}$$

tend, for large values of n, asymptotically to

$$f_n(x) \rightarrow \frac{I_0^n}{\sqrt{2\pi n}\, \Delta} \, e^{-\frac{1}{2}\frac{(x - nX)^2}{n\, \Delta^2}}. \tag{57}$$

That is, if to a "sharp" function, Dirac's delta function, we apply a "spreading" process, one in which through an integral transformation the delta function is spread into the distribution $f(x)$,

$$f_1(x) = \int_{-\infty}^{\infty} f(x - x_0) \, \delta(x_0) \, dx_0, \tag{58}$$

and if we repeat the same spreading operation on the result again and again, then ultimately we shall get a Gaussian distribution if only the spreading function itself possesses a "center of gravity" X and an rms spread Δ. For finite values of n, the approximation will be best near the center of gravity, nX.

Now let us apply the central limit theorem to the function $e^{-\alpha E} X'(E)$. First of all, it is clear that if the integral (54) converges, then the other two integrals listed in (55) will converge as well. That is because for a given value of α we shall always, beyond a certain positive value of x, have the inequality

$$x^n e^{-\alpha x} < e^{-\frac{\alpha}{2} x}, \qquad x \geq \left(\frac{2n}{\alpha}\right)^2; \qquad (59)$$

and since the integral (54) is assumed to converge for all positive values of the factor α, we have, for sufficiently large values of x',

$$\int_{x'}^{\infty} x^n e^{-\alpha x}\, dx < \int_{x'}^{\infty} e^{-\frac{\alpha}{2} x}\, dx < \infty, \qquad x' \geq \left(\frac{2n}{\alpha}\right)^2. \qquad (60)$$

Next, it is clear that the characteristic volume derivative of composite systems is obtained from that of the constituents by integral involutions. If we introduce in expression (16) the following new variables of integration

$$
\begin{aligned}
E_1 &= E - x_1, & x_1 &= E - E_1, \\
E_2 &= x_1 - x_2, & x_2 &= E - E_1 - E_2, \\
&\;\; \cdot & &\;\; \cdot \\
&\;\; \cdot & &\;\; \cdot \\
&\;\; \cdot & &\;\; \cdot
\end{aligned}
\qquad (61)
$$

$$E_{n-1} = x_{n-2} - x_{n-1}, \qquad x_{n-1} = E - \sum_{s=1}^{n-1} E_s,$$

$X'(E)$ turns into

$$X'(E) = \int \cdots \int_{x_1, \cdots, x_{n-1} = -\infty}^{\infty} X'_1(E - x_2) X'_1(x_1 - x_2) \cdots$$

$$X'_{n-1}(x_{n-2} - x_{n-1}) X'_n(x_{n-1})\, dx_1 \cdots dx_{n-1}. \qquad (62)$$

The same relation holds for the functions $e^{-\alpha E} X'(E)$. We shall now construct a sequence of ever-increasing temperature baths by taking the first temperature bath first once, then twice, then three times, and so on. This method of constructing the sequence gives a definite meaning to the requirement that, except for size, all temperature baths of the sequence be similar. To this sequence we can now apply the central limit theorem directly; we have, for the $\bar{n}$th temperature bath in our sequence, the asymptotic expression

$$X'_{\bar{n}}(\bar{n}\,\bar{\epsilon} - E) \sim \frac{I_0^{\bar{n}}\, e^{\alpha(\bar{n}\bar{\epsilon}-E)}}{\sqrt{2\pi\bar{n}}}\, e^{-\frac{1}{2}\frac{[\bar{n}(\bar{\epsilon}-\epsilon^*)-E]^2}{\bar{n}\Delta^2}}$$

$$= \frac{I_0^{\bar{n}}\, e^{\alpha\bar{n}\bar{\epsilon}}}{\sqrt{2\pi\bar{n}}}\, e^{-\frac{1}{2}\frac{\bar{n}}{\Delta^2}(\bar{\epsilon}-\epsilon^*)^2}\, e^{\left(\frac{\bar{\epsilon}-\epsilon^*}{\Delta^2}-\alpha\right)E}\, e^{-\frac{1}{2}\frac{E^2}{\bar{n}\Delta^2}}. \tag{63}$$

I_0 and ϵ^* stand for the integrals

$$I_0 = \int_{-\infty}^{\infty} e^{-\alpha E}\, X'_1(E)\, dE,$$

$$\epsilon^* = \frac{1}{I_0} \int_{-\infty}^{\infty} e^{-\alpha E}\, X'_1(E)\, E\, dE. \tag{64}$$

$\bar{\epsilon}$ is the total energy, divided by $\bar{n}$. The definition of Δ^2 is also obvious. The last factor in (63) will tend to unity as we let $\bar{n}$ go to infinity.

The approximation will improve with increasing $\bar{n}$ (and become perfect for infinite $\bar{n}$) for the point $\bar{n}\,\epsilon^*$ and for points which, on an absolute energy scale, have a fixed distance from $\bar{n}\,\epsilon^*$. Therefore eq. (63) is valid only if we choose the parameter α so that ϵ^* coincides with $\bar{\epsilon}$. We shall call this choice β, which obviously is a function of $\bar{\epsilon}$. If we go with $\alpha = \beta$ into eq. (63), omit the last factor (since it will tend to unity when the whole approximation becomes valid), and substitute the result into eq. (37), all the factors in (63) that are independent of E will cancel, and we shall be left with

$$\mathrm{M}_s(\overset{0}{E}_s,\ \overset{0}{E}) = \frac{\int_{-\infty}^{\overset{0}{E}_s} X'_s(E_s)e^{-\beta E_s}\, dE_s}{\int_{-\infty}^{\infty} X'_s(E_s)e^{-\beta E_s}\, dE_s}, \qquad \beta = \beta(\bar{\epsilon}). \tag{65}$$

This formula, our final result, again contains a Boltzmann factor.

3.4. Temperature.   Canonical ensembles

The result of our discussion so far is that if a system in which we are interested is in contact with a temperature bath of sufficient size, and if the system and the bath are otherwise isolated (so that the total energy is constant), then the probability of finding the system with an energy less than $\overset{0}{E}_s$ is given by eq. (65).   This distribution function depends on the detailed structure of the bath as well as on the total energy available, because these two circumstances together determine the value of the constant β.   But actually, if we had two temperature baths of quite different chemical composition available for experiment, then in general two different values of the total energy would exist, each appropriate to one of the baths we have, so that we could achieve the same energy distribution in a particular system by bringing it in contact with either temperature bath and, in each case, making available the correct amount of total energy.   In other words, we can dispense with all knowledge of the detailed structure of a bath and the total energy available if we have some other means of determining β.   Given knowledge of that parameter, we can predict the energy distribution of a system brought in contact with the bath, provided only that we have knowledge of the characteristic volume of the *system*. Inasmuch as the bath will interest us only to the extent that it determines the energy distribution of systems brought in contact with it, and since the constant β is a property of the bath only, not of the system, from now on we shall characterize baths merely as having a particular value of this parameter.

If there is a single parameter β that determines the energy distribution of any (sufficiently small) system in contact with a particular bath, then this parameter must be directly connected with what we usually call the temperature.   As a matter of fact, two baths having the same value of β will, if permitted to interact thermally, transfer on the average zero energy to each other.   We can verify this assertion immediately if we assume that the thermal contact is accomplished by means of a (small) system that we couple alternately with one and then with the other system.   Every time we couple and then uncouple the system with one bath, there will be a net change in energy of the system (and therefore also of the bath).   But when we consider a large number of these cycles, we know that the energies on uncoupling from bath No. 1 will follow the distribution (65) with a particular value of β. That distribution is, of course, identical with the distribution of energies found at the instants of coupling with bath No. 2, since between uncoupling from No. 1 and coupling with No. 2 the energy cannot change. But when we take the distribution of energies at the instants of uncoupling from No. 2, that distribution must again be (65), with the same value of β (since we had assumed that our two baths are endowed with the same β-value). Hence, on the average the amounts of energy transferred to No. 2 and taken out of No. 2 cancel. The same result holds, of course, for bath No. 1. It follows that β really has the properties ordinarily associated with a temperature scale. We must assume that β is some function of the (mercury thermometer) temperature θ, and vice versa.

Let us now return from a consideration of baths to our system, the one we formerly called S_s. We shall say that the system possesses a temperature θ if it is in contact with a bath at the temperature $\theta(\beta)$; this statement means that the energy of the system, in the course of time, must have a distribution given by the formula

$$\mathbf{M}(E,\ \theta) = \frac{\int_{-\infty}^{E} e^{-\beta(\theta)E'}\, X'(E')\, dE'}{\int_{-\infty}^{\infty} e^{-\beta(\theta)E'}\, X'(E')\, dE'}, \tag{66}$$

Thus, when a small system has a definite energy (when it is isolated), it does *not* have a temperature; when it has a temperature, it has an *energy distribution*.

Willard Gibbs showed how we may think of the temperature as the property of an ensemble of isolated systems, without the benefit of a temperature bath. His proposal is simple. We must construct an ensemble of (small) systems, the ones we are interested in, but we must not place all of them on the same energy surface; rather, we must distribute them on all energy surfaces in accordance with the formula (66). Then all ensemble averages will be exactly the same as if each system were in contact with a temperature bath. An ensemble formed according to this prescription is called a *canonical ensemble*.

Let us determine the density of a canonical distribution in the phase space of the system. If this density be called $\mu(E)$ (our distribution is to be stationary), then the fraction of systems with energies less than $\overset{0}{E}$ must be

$$M(\overset{0}{E}) = \int_{-\infty}^{\overset{0}{E}} \mu(E)\, dX(E) = \int_{-\infty}^{\overset{0}{E}} \mu(E) X'(E)\, dE. \qquad (67)$$

Comparison of the two integrals (66) and (67) for the same function $M(\overset{0}{E})$ shows that the density function $\mu(E)$ is

$$\mu(E) = \frac{e^{-\beta E}}{\displaystyle\int_{-\infty}^{\infty} e^{-\beta E'}\, X'(E')\, dE'}. \qquad (68)$$

The denominator in this formula is independent of E; as we said before, it is essentially a normalization factor. However, this denominator is a function of β and hence of the temperature θ. This integral occurs in innumerable relationships of statistical mechanics and has been given a name of its own. It is called the *partition function* or, less frequently, the *sum over the states*. The latter expression is a rather awkward translation of *Zustandssumme*. We shall denote the partition function by the symbol Z, so that

$$Z \equiv \int_{-\infty}^{\infty} e^{-\beta E}\, X'(E)\, dE. \qquad (69)$$

Z is a function of β; of course, it also depends on the characteristic volume of the system we are considering. Later we shall study the change in Z brought about by a change in the mechanical characteristics of the system [as reflected in the form of $X'(E)$]. But first we shall form the first and second partial derivatives of Z with respect to β. We have

$$\frac{\partial Z}{\partial \beta} = -\int_{-\infty}^{\infty} E\, e^{-\beta E}\, X'(E)\, dE \qquad (70)$$

and

$$\frac{\partial^2 Z}{\partial \beta^2} = +\int_{-\infty}^{\infty} E^2\, e^{-\beta E}\, X'(E)\, dE. \qquad (71)$$

These two expressions enable us to find both the average energy and the rms spread of the energy of a system for a given value of θ if we know the partition function as a function of β. To this end, we have to apply eqs. (2.3) and (2.6), which define ensemble averages and rms spreads in terms of the distribution function. We find for the average energy of the system

$$\langle E \rangle = \int_{-\infty}^{\infty} E \, d\mathrm{M}(E) = \int_{-\infty}^{\infty} E \, X'(E) \, \mu(E) \, dE$$

$$= \frac{1}{Z} \int_{-\infty}^{\infty} E \, X'(E) \, e^{-\beta E} \, dE = -\frac{1}{Z} \frac{\partial Z}{\partial \beta} = -\frac{\partial}{\partial \beta} (\ln Z), \quad (72)$$

and for its mean square spread

$$\langle \Delta E^2 \rangle = \int_{-\infty}^{\infty} [E^2 - \langle E \rangle^2] \, d\mathrm{M}(E) = \frac{1}{Z} \int_{-\infty}^{\infty} [E^2 - \langle E \rangle^2] X'(E) \, e^{-\beta E} \, dE$$

$$= \frac{1}{Z} \frac{\partial^2 Z}{\partial \beta^2} - \frac{1}{Z^2} \left(\frac{\partial Z}{\partial \beta} \right)^2 = \frac{\partial}{\partial \beta} \left(\frac{1}{Z} \frac{\partial Z}{\partial \beta} \right) \tag{73}$$

$$= \frac{\partial^2}{\partial \beta^2} (\ln Z).$$

Thus, if we know the partition function of a system, we can compute the average energy of the system (for a given β) as well as its average energy fluctuation.

We shall apply these formulas to three types of system: to a single particle in a box, to a composite system consisting of many of these particles (that is, a perfect monatomic gas), and finally to a general composite system possessing a Hamiltonian that depends quadratically on some of the canonical coordinates.

Let us begin with a single particle in a box. We have determined the characteristic volume in eq. (21). If we substitute this expression in the defining equation for the partition function, (69), we get

$$Z = 4 \sqrt{2} \, \pi \, V m^{3/2} \int_0^{\infty} e^{-\beta E} E^{1/2} \, dE, \tag{74}$$

considering that $X'(E)$ is zero for all negative values of the argument. The integral can be converted into a standard type if we introduce a new variable of integration, $x = \sqrt{2\beta E}$. The partition function then becomes

$$Z = 4\pi V m^{3/2} \beta^{-3/2} \int_0^{\infty} e^{-1/2 x^2} x^2 \, dx = \frac{4}{\sqrt{2}} \pi^{3/2} V m^{3/2} \beta^{-3/2},$$

$$\ln Z = \text{const} - \frac{3}{2} \ln \beta. \tag{75}$$

The last integral has been evaluated by means of a recursion formula that can be found in any calculus text. The average energy and its rms spread are now found to be

$$\langle E \rangle = \frac{3}{2} \cdot \frac{1}{\beta} \tag{76}$$

and

$$\langle \Delta E^2 \rangle = \frac{3}{2} \frac{1}{\beta^2} = \frac{2}{3} \langle E \rangle^2,$$

$$\frac{\langle \Delta E^2 \rangle}{\langle E \rangle^2} = \frac{2}{3}. \tag{77}$$

Equation (76) tells us that the average energy of the particle in a box is inversely proportional to β, and this result enables us to establish a tentative relationship between the parameter β and the so-called gas temperature scale.

In a perfect gas, we know from experience that the energy is proportional to the pressure, and this result was also derived from the microscopic model of a perfect monatomic gas in Chapter 1. The gas scale is based on the pressure (if the volume is kept fixed), so that the temperature of the gas is *defined* as being proportional to the pressure.[1] Thus in a perfect gas the average energy of the gas, which must be a multiple of the average energy of each molecule, is proportional to the gas temperature θ_g. Therefore we can conclude that

$$\beta = \frac{1}{\kappa \theta_g}. \tag{78}$$

Right now, we shall not bother to determine the constant κ. Later we shall introduce a more fundamental temperature scale than the gas scale, the so-called Kelvin scale, and then we shall obtain again a relationship similar to (78). At that time we shall determine the universal parameter occurring in that equation.

Before we go on to the next example, we shall do something that we could not have done in Chapter 1, except with a tremendous effort: we shall determine the velocity distribution of the atoms in a perfect monatomic gas. We shall take a macroscopic quantity of

---

[1] The constant of proportionality is determined by historic reasons. Although it would be possible to relate the temperature scale directly to our parameter β, setting the constant of proportionality in this relationship equal to 1, such a scale has never been introduced in practice.

gas and consider a single atom in it. Once we have established statistical equilibrium, we may consider the remainder of the gas as a temperature bath in which this one atom is immersed. Then the probability that our single atom will have an energy less than $\overset{0}{E}$ is given by the function $M(\overset{0}{E})$, eq. (63), which in our case reduces to

$$M(\overset{0}{E}) = \frac{\int_0^{\overset{0}{E}} e^{-\beta E} \sqrt{E} \, dE}{\int_0^{\infty} e^{-\beta E} \sqrt{E} \, dE}. \tag{79}$$

In this model, all the energy is kinetic energy, and $\overset{0}{E}$ is simply equal to $\frac{1}{2m} \overset{0}{p^2}$. Thus the probability that a given atom will have a linear momentum of a magnitude less than $\overset{0}{p}$ or a velocity less than $\overset{0}{v}$ is

$$M_p(\overset{0}{p}) = \frac{\int_0^{\overset{0}{p}} e^{-\frac{\beta}{2m}p^2} p^2 \, dp}{\int_0^{\infty} e^{-\frac{\beta}{2m}p^2} p^2 \, dp} = \sqrt{\frac{2}{\pi}} \, \beta^{3/2} m^{-3/2} \int_0^{\overset{0}{p}} e^{-\frac{\beta}{2m}p^2} p^2 \, dp,$$

$$\tag{80}$$

$$M_v(\overset{0}{v}) = \sqrt{\frac{2}{\pi}} \, \beta^{3/2} \int_0^{\overset{0}{v}} e^{-\frac{m}{2}\beta v^2} v^2 \, dv.$$

This probability distribution holds for every atom with the mass m. Thus M_v will also represent the *fraction of atoms of mass m in our gas with velocities less than* $\overset{0}{v}$. And by differentiating the last line of eq. (80), we can find the infinitesimal fraction of atoms of mass m with absolute velocities (speeds) between v and $v + dv$:

$$dM_v = \sqrt{\frac{2}{\pi}} \, \beta^{3/2} e^{-\frac{m}{2}\beta v^2} v^2 \, dv. \tag{81}$$

This formula for the velocity distribution in a perfect gas was first derived by Maxwell and is called a *Maxwellian velocity distribution*.

We shall now go over to our second example, the composite system of n particles which are almost noninteracting. Applying eq. (45), right away we can get for the function X'_n the form

$$X'_n(E) = A \, E^{\frac{3}{2}n-1}, \tag{82}$$

since every one of the constants n_s equals $\frac{1}{2}$. Thus the partition function must be

$$Z = A \int_0^\infty e^{-\beta E} E^{\frac{3}{2}n-1} \, dE = A \, \beta^{\frac{3}{2}-n} \int_0^\infty e^{-x} x^{\frac{3}{2}n-1} \, dx$$

$$(x = \beta E), \qquad (83)$$

$$\ln Z = B - \frac{3}{2} n \ln \beta,$$

where A and B stand for constants of no further interest to us. For $\langle E_n \rangle$ we get

$$\langle E_n \rangle = \frac{3}{2} \, n \, \frac{1}{\beta} = n \, \langle E_1 \rangle. \qquad (84)$$

This result was to be expected. The average energy of n very nearly independent systems must be n times the average energy of any one of them. But for the mean square spread and for the relative mean square spread we get

$$\langle \Delta E_n^2 \rangle = \frac{3}{2} \, n \, \frac{1}{\beta^2} = n \langle \Delta E_1^2 \rangle = \frac{2}{3n} \langle E_n \rangle^2,$$

$$\frac{\langle \Delta E_n^2 \rangle}{\langle E_n \rangle^2} = \frac{2}{3n} = \frac{1}{n} \frac{\langle \Delta E_1^2 \rangle}{\langle E_1 \rangle^2}. \qquad (85)$$

This result is merely one instance of the smoothing effect of large numbers of constituent systems. Although each molecule in a gas undergoes very considerable fluctuations of energy, the energy distribution of a large number of them is relatively stable; that is, it is very unlikely that an overwhelming number of them will assume above-average or below-average energies *at the same time*. For one mol of a gas, the internal energy will have an rms fluctuation of no more than 10^{-12} of its average value, an amount that can be observed only under very special experimental conditions.

3.5. The equipartition law

Our third application of expression (72) for the average energy of a system is one in which (at least) one of the canonical variables q_k, p_k appears in the Hamiltonian quadratically. This case is of great practical importance, because in many important physical models variables enter in such a manner. For instance, if we use Cartesian coordinates, then the particle momentum components contribute to the Hamiltonian quadratic terms; in the harmonic oscillator, even the location coordinates enter quadratically. If we wish to examine a system in which the particles are bound to each other by elastic forces that tend to maintain fixed distances between them (such a system is a good model of a crystal), then the differences between the coordinates of neighboring particles make quadratic contributions to the Hamiltonian, and so on. We shall now single out one coordinate that appears in this manner, and call it x. The Hamiltonian of our system will then have the form

$$H = \bar{H} + \frac{c}{2} x^2. \tag{86}$$

The function $\bar{H}$ depends on the remaining $(2f - 1)$ canonical coordinates, but not on x. c is some constant. The characteristic volume $X(E)$ of the system (86) is that volume in which the sum of the energy terms $\bar{E}$ and E_x (the first being the value of $\bar{H}$, the second being equal to $\frac{c}{2} x^2$) does not exceed E. The volume element in phase space equals the product of the coordinate and momentum differentials, dq_k and dp_k, and one of these is dx. If we introduce for the product of the remaining $(2f - 1)$ differentials the abbreviating notation $d\bar{X}$, then the infinitesimal volume element in phase space is $d\bar{X} \, dx$.

Now into the $(2f - 1)$-dimensional domain of integration whose volume element is $d\bar{X}$ we can introduce a function that is akin to a characteristic volume, namely, the integral over that region in which $\bar{E}$ does not exceed a preassigned value. We shall call this function $\bar{X}(\bar{E})$. The domain in phase space in which $\bar{E}$ lies within an infinitesimal bracket $d\bar{E}$ and, at the same time, E_x lies within an infinitesimal bracket dE_x must have a volume

$$dX = \bar{X}'(\bar{E}) \, d\bar{E} \, dx = \sqrt{\frac{2}{cE_x}} \, \bar{X}'(\bar{E}) \, d\bar{E} \, dE_x,$$

$$dx = d\left(\sqrt{\frac{2}{c} E_x}\right). \tag{87}$$

Thus $X(E)$ must be

$$X(E) = \int_{E_x=0}^{\infty} \int_{\bar{E}=-\infty}^{E-E_x} \bar{X}'(\bar{E}) \, d\bar{E} \, \frac{dE_x}{\sqrt{E_x}}, \tag{88}$$

and its derivative X' comes out as

$$X'(E) = \int_{E_x=0}^{\infty} \bar{X}'(E - E_x) \frac{dE_x}{\sqrt{E_x}}. \tag{89}$$

With this expression, we shall determine the partition function. We have

$$Z(\beta) = \int_{E=-\infty}^{\infty} e^{-\beta E} \int_{E_x=0}^{\infty} \bar{X}'(E - E_x) \frac{dE_x}{\sqrt{E_x}}$$

$$= \int_{E'=-\infty}^{\infty} e^{-\beta E'} \bar{X}'(E') dE' \cdot \int_{E_x=0}^{\infty} e^{-\beta E_x} \frac{dE_x}{\sqrt{E_x}} = \sqrt{\frac{\pi}{\beta}} \, \bar{Z}(\beta), \tag{90}$$

$$E' = E - E_x.$$

In this expression, $\bar{Z}$ designates an integral that is formed from $\bar{X}'$ the same way the partition function is formed from X'. For the average energy we get

$$\langle E \rangle = -\frac{\partial}{\partial \beta} (\ln Z) = -\frac{\partial \ln \bar{Z}}{\partial \beta} + \frac{1}{2\beta} = \langle \bar{E} \rangle + \langle E_x \rangle,$$
$$\langle E_x \rangle = \frac{1}{2\beta} = \frac{1}{2} \kappa \, \theta_g. \tag{91}$$

Naturally, the average energy is the sum of the averages of the two partial energies $\bar{E}$ and E_x. Regardless of the physical significance of the canonical variable x, the system behaves mathematically as if it consisted of two entirely separate systems, the one with the Hamiltonian $\bar{H}$, the other with the Hamiltonian $\frac{c}{2} x^2$. But the remarkable aspect of eq. (91) is that each canonical variable that contributes just a quadratic term to the Hamiltonian (and does not appear in it otherwise) adds to the average energy of the system the same amount of energy, just $\frac{1}{2} \kappa \, \theta_g$, no matter how small or how large the coefficient c. This law is called the *equipartition law*. We shall now discuss some of its implications.

Our previous example, the free atom in a monatomic gas, is a special case of the equipartition law. The Hamiltonian of a single mass point consists of three quadratic terms and nothing else, so the energy per atom should be $\frac{3}{2} \kappa \, \theta_g$, just as we found in eq. (76). One mol of such a gas contains N atoms (N being Avogadro's number, 6.02×10^{23}), so its internal energy should be $\frac{3}{2} N \kappa \, \theta_g$.

If we increase the temperature of a body by permitting it to increase its random motion, without changing its volume, shape, or other macroscopic characteristics that affect its energy, we call the amount of energy required to increase the temperature one degree (of whatever temperature scale we happen to work with) its (*internal*) *heat capacity*. If the body happens to be one mol of a well-defined chemical substance, then we call this quantity the *specific* or *molar heat*. In gases (where this distinction is important) we speak of the *specific heat at constant volume*, c_v, to distinguish it from the specific heat at constant pressure, c_p. According to our results so far, c_v for a monatomic gas should equal $\frac{3}{2} N \kappa$ if the temperature is measured on the gas scale. As a matter of fact, the molar heats of all monatomic gases are very nearly constant, equal to $\frac{3}{2} R$; R is the gas constant, roughly 2 calories per degree centigrade or, in cgs units, 8.3×10^7 ergs/°C. Comparison of our result from the theoretical treatment of the microscopic model with measured values thus leads to the result that the constant κ equals R/N.

The equipartition law enables us to go over to gases that are not monatomic. Consider a diatomic gas, such as oxygen, O_2, or carbon monoxide, CO. Such a molecule has an energy that is composed additively of its translatory energy and its rotational energy. The average translatory energy again will be $\frac{3}{2} \kappa \theta_g$. As for the rotational energy, a diatomic molecule (a dumbbell) has two degrees of freedom; and if we introduce spherical coordinates, its rotational energy is given by the expression

$$H_{\text{rot}} = \frac{1}{2I} \left(p_\theta^2 + \frac{1}{\cos^2 \theta} \, p_\phi^2 \right)$$
$$\left(0 \leq \phi \leq 2\pi, \qquad -\frac{\pi}{2} \leq \theta \leq \frac{\pi}{2} \right), \quad (92)$$

where I is the moment of inertia about an axis at right angles to the line that connects the two molecules. The four canonical coordinates in this partial phase space are θ, p_θ, ϕ, and p_ϕ. ϕ does not occur at all, and p_θ occurs in such fashion that we can apply the equipartition law immediately. For the remaining term, a short calculation that runs exactly like all those performed earlier in this chapter shows that its contribution also equals $\frac{1}{2} \kappa \theta_g$. Thus the average rotational energy of a diatomic molecule comes out as $\kappa \theta_g$, and the total specific heat c_v of a diatomic gas must be

$$c_v = \tfrac{3}{2}R + R = \tfrac{5}{2}R. \tag{93}$$

This result is again confirmed by the experimental evidence.

As for gases whose molecules are composed of more than two atoms, all those whose atoms do not lie on one straight line have an additional rotational degree of freedom; theory predicts—and experiment confirms—that the specific heat of such a gas must equal $3R$. Thus, the equipartition law predicts with considerable accuracy the specific heats of all gases that are nearly perfect.

Unfortunately, we have achieved this success only by the application of a discretion that is the better part of valor. We have not taken into account the complete Hamiltonian of the polyatomic molecules; if we had, we should have obtained results manifestly at variance with the facts. Naturally each atom, each molecule contains electrons, whose contribution has not been considered at all. If we should take them into account in the simplest possible case, the monatomic hydrogen gas (which is stable at very high temperatures), we should get a very large contribution from the average energy of these electrons, both the ionized and the non-ionized ones. But we could argue that very likely our whole picture of the electronic motion is wrong; and as long as we take a wholly classical point of view, we are quite unable to account for any of the features of atomic spectra. In other words, our theoretical result in the case of electronic motion might be due to a faulty microscopic model.

But in addition, in polyatomic molecules the atoms are certainly able to shift their relative positions. There must be strong but finite forces that tend to restore an equilibrium position. At high temperatures, molecules will occasionally be strained to the point that they do not revert to their equilibrium positions; that is when we observe dissociation.

In a diatomic molecule, the two atoms must attract or repel each other in such a manner that some particular distance represents a minimum of potential energy. If we know nothing about the nature of these forces, we can assume that the potential energy vs. distance curve looks somewhat like the one in Fig. 3. If we carry out a power expansion of $\Phi(r)$ about the point $r = r_0$, we must get a series like this:

$$\Phi(r) = \Phi_0 + \frac{k}{2}(r - r_0)^2 + \frac{k'}{6}(r - r_0)^3 + \cdots. \tag{94}$$

If we replace the actual potential energy by the function

$$\bar{\Phi} = \Phi_0 + \frac{k}{2}(r - r_0)^2, \tag{95}$$

then we shall represent the true Hamiltonian very nearly correctly for small deviations from the equilibrium distance r_0. But $\bar{\Phi}$ is

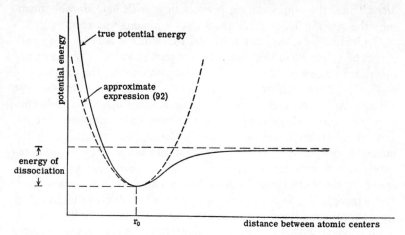

Fig. 3. Hypothetical potential energy of a diatomic molecule.

the potential energy of a harmonic oscillator. It is true that this harmonic oscillator is not tied to a center but to an equilibrium distance; but a fairly short calculation shows that for temperatures that are sufficiently low (large values of β) the potential energy makes a contribution that corresponds to a single degree of freedom obeying the equipartition law. The internal kinetic energy (including rotational energy) will make a contribution of $\frac{3}{2} R$; and so, with a potential energy (95), the specific heat of a diatomic gas would be

$$c_v = \tfrac{3}{2} R + (\tfrac{1}{2} R + \tfrac{3}{2} R) = \tfrac{7}{2} R, \tag{96}$$

even if we disregard completely any contributions from electronic motion. $\bar{\Phi}$ is undoubtedly not the correct expression for the potential energy for any but the smallest deviations from equilibrium distance. But Fig. 4 shows that at any energy level above the lowest the actual volume in the partial phase space of the internal degrees of freedom is likely to be larger than the corresponding

characteristic volume indicated by (95).   As a result, the system
would actually be more often at high energy levels than we have
assumed in using the potential (95).   In other words, the specific
heat predicted by eq. (96), if incorrect, should be replaced by an
even higher value!

Today we can understand both the success of the classical
theory and its failure, but only on the basis of quantum mechanics.

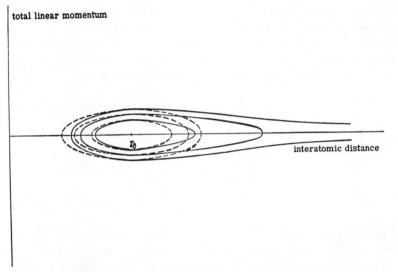

Fig. 4.   Energy surfaces in the simplified internal phase space of a
diatomic molecule.

Historically, the need to apply the equipartition law "with discretion" was the principal reason for the first attempt at a quantized
theory of nature by Planck.   We shall have to say more about these
things in the second part of this book.   Now we shall relate another
accomplishment of the classical equipartition law.

A reasonable model of a crystallized material is a system of
particles that are held in a certain configuration by elastic forces.
Each particle will have, in addition to its kinetic energy, a potential
energy that is a minimum when that particle has a certain position
relative to its nearest neighbors.   Schematically, if we number all
particle coordinates and momenta through from 1 to $3n$ (if there be
a total of n particles involved), the Hamiltonian must have the form

(in Cartesian coordinates)

$$H = \sum_{i=1}^{3n} \frac{1}{2\mu_i} p_i^2 + \Phi(x_i),$$

(97)

$$\mu_1 = \mu_2 = \mu_3 = m_1, \ \mu_4 = \mu_5 = \mu_6 = m_2, \cdots .$$

The potential energy depends on the configuration, on *relative* coordinates only. For certain values of the coordinates, the potential energy will be a minimum; these values represent the stable configuration of the crystal lattice. Let the equilibrium value for x_i be y_i. Then for small deviations of the lattice configuration from its equilibrium value, the potential energy will be represented by the first terms in the multiple power series expansion,

$$\Phi = \Phi_0 + \tfrac{1}{2} \sum_{i,k=1}^{3n} c_{ik}\,\xi_i\,\xi_k \qquad (\xi_i = x_i - y_i),$$

(98)

and the whole Hamiltonian has the form

$$H = \tfrac{1}{2} \sum_{i,k=1}^{6n} c_{ik}\,\xi_i\,\xi_k,$$

(99)

$$\xi_{3n+1} \equiv p_1, \ \xi_{3n+2} \equiv p_2, \cdots .$$

Naturally, for physical reasons, most of the coefficients c_{ik} will be zero. The Hamiltonian (99) can be "diagonalized"; that is, we can introduce new variables by means of a linear homogeneous coordinate transformation,

$$\eta_k = \sum_{i=1}^{6n} \alpha_{ki}\,\xi_i,$$

(100)

so that in terms of the new variables the Hamiltonian becomes a sum of squares

$$H = \tfrac{1}{2} \sum_{k=1}^{6n} c_k\,\eta_k^2.$$

(101)

The transformation may not be canonical, but whether it is or not is unimportant. In any case, we can represent a volume element in phase space by means of the new coordinate differentials, multiplying their product merely by the (constant) Jacobian of the transformation. To the transformed Hamiltonian we can apply the equipartition law, and our result is that the energy of a crystal lattice due to random vibration must be, at least in first approximation, equal to $3n\kappa\theta_g$. If we have one mol of a substance of which each molecule contains $\bar{n}$ atoms, then the molar heat capacity of that substance should be $3R\bar{n}$. This law is known as the *Dulong-Petit law*. Measurements have shown that it is satisfied by a large number of solid substances at sufficiently high temperature. It is again an indication of the limitations of classical physics that the Dulong-Petit law is also satisfied quite well by metals, even though in addition to the lattice points (ions) a metal contains a "gas" of practically free electrons. If the behavior of these electrons could be described classically, their contribution to the heat capacity would be of the same order of magnitude as that of the lattice vibrations.

Problems

1. Consider a harmonic oscillator in two dimensions whose elastic constants k_x and k_y are different. To what extent is this system quasi-ergodic?

2. Consider the same question for a mass point moving under the influence of an inverse-square law of attraction (a) if there is no other perturbing force, (b) if the perturbing force is very small and is also a central force, (c) if the perturbing force is a very weak uniform field of force (both magnitude and direction being the same everywhere).

3. The Hamiltonian for the molecules of a gas is approximately

$$H = h + \frac{1}{2m}\mathbf{p}^2 + mgz$$

under the influence of the field of gravity of the earth, and the coordinate z cannot assume negative values. The function h is the Hamiltonian for the internal degrees of freedom only. How does the presence of the last term affect the mean energy of the gas molecules? What about the density as a function of z, and how about the velocity and internal-energy distributions as functions of the elevation?

Chapter 4

Thermodynamics, First Law

4.1. Heat transfer and mechanical work

The discipline of thermodynamics deals with the *macroscopic* changes that may be perpetrated on a highly complex system. These changes are essentially of two kinds. On the one hand, we can change the total energy possessed by the complex system without changing its other characteristics; we then speak of *heat transfer* without the performance of work. On the other hand, it is also possible to change the gross conditions of the system, for instance by changing the shape of the volume to which it is restricted, or by impressing on the system an electromagnetic field. In all these cases, of course, the Hamiltonian of the system (as a microscopic system) is being changed in its functional dependence on the canonical variables, and this change will in general also result in a change of total energy. These changes we usually call the *performance of work*, the word "work" standing for macroscopically observable transfers of energy. Naturally, any change may involve both the performance of work and the transfer of heat.

Macroscopically, we know perfectly well how to characterize these two types of change. In a *heat transfer*, we permit the system under scrutiny to receive or to give off heat to neighboring systems by conduction or by radiation without experiencing a change in volume or shape and without undergoing a change in the applied external forces. The most common *performance of work*, on the other hand, consists of compression and expansion. Other types of work performance include changes in shape (such as the forging of metals), polarization and magnetization, and dropping through a gravitational potential. We call the performance of work without simultaneous heat transfer an *adiabatic process*. This name is only one of several names of Greek origin used in thermodynamics, and the necessity of knowing the significance of all of them is one of the more incidental sources of confusion for the beginner in this subject. We call changes that take place without a change in volume *isochoric*, those in which the temperature is being kept constant *isothermal*, and those changes where the pressure remains unchanged *isobaric*. It may be of some slight help to the reader to know that the prefix *iso-* stands for constant, and that while *diabasis* is the Greek word for "passage," the prefix *a-* is a negative, just like the English prefix *un-*. Thus an adiabatic process is one in which there is no passing over, no transfer (of heat).

In thermodynamics, it is customary to call the energy of a system, to the extent that it cannot be represented as gross kinetic energy, gross potential energy, or gross electromagnetic energy, its *internal energy U*. For any given temperature, this internal energy is subject to random fluctuations, but its average, in the absence of gross motion and external forces, is equal to $\langle E \rangle$. In thermodynamics, we usually deal with systems of sufficient size and complexity that the variance of the energy within the canonical ensemble is very small compared to its mean value. To this extent, we may set the thermodynamic quantity U equal to $\langle E \rangle$ and consider it a function of the temperature, without committing an appreciable error quantitatively. It is because of the smallness of the variance that we may consider the *system variable U* a function of the *ensemble parameter θ*.

Before we can attempt to translate the macroscopic terminology of thermodynamics into the language of statistical mechanics, we must make one more reservation. Thermodynamics deals with complex systems and their changes; but each of these systems is always considered as represented by a canonical ensemble. Thus at any given moment we must have statistical equilibrium or at least a very good approximation to equilibrium. Therefore we must restrict ourselves to the consideration of processes that take place sufficiently slowly so that at each stage the system can be approximated by an equilibrium state. It is often said that thermodynamics treats *infinitely slow processes*. We must imagine that if necessary each member system of the ensemble can be coupled (loosely) to every other member of the ensemble to reestablish the canonical distribution of energies whenever in the course of a finite process the deviation from canonical distribution becomes appreciable. Furthermore, we must assume that measurements will normally determine time averages of the quantities in question, so that every observation and measurement actually determines an *average of a stationary, canonical distribution.*

This restriction is necessary if we are to be able to describe a system in terms of macroscopic parameters only and if we are to make predictions in terms of these same parameters. It has often been objected that thermodynamics cannot deal with *fast changes* in which the systems of an originally canonical ensemble will assume an (instantaneous) distribution that is far from being canonical. This objection is probably well taken. In using thermodynamic methods, we must keep this restriction in mind and guard against applying thermodynamic laws uncritically where they might not hold.

A canonical ensemble is completely known if its Hamiltonian function is given to us and if we know, in addition, the value of the parameter β. Changes that take place must, therefore, be changes in one or the other of these characteristics, or in both. If a system exchanges energy with its surroundings without changing its volume or its shape and without any change in the external macroscopic forces, then its Hamiltonian as a function of the canonical coordinates in phase space must remain unchanged. Heat transfer without the performance of work must be reflected in the representative ensemble by a change in the value of β only.

When we deal with the most common subjects of thermodynamic investigations, gases and liquids, a pure heat transfer can be characterized by the fact that the *volume* remains unchanged, where constancy of gravitational and electric potentials, etc., is taken for granted. The dependence of the internal energy, $\langle E \rangle$, on β is, therefore, called the *isochoric dependence* of the energy on β. Since β is usually replaced by some other temperature scale (the gas scale, for instance), the most common measure of this dependence is the *isochoric heat capacity*, C_v, defined as the isochoric derivative of the internal energy with respect to the adopted temperature,

$$C_v = \frac{\partial \langle E \rangle}{\partial \theta} = \frac{d\beta}{d\theta} \frac{\partial \langle E \rangle}{\partial \beta} = -\frac{d\beta}{d\theta} \frac{\partial^2 \ln Z}{\partial \beta^2}. \tag{1}$$

How can we characterize the performance of work in terms belonging to statistical mechanics? In a change of any type, the systems of our ensemble must be interacting in some fashion with the out-

side world.   In the absence of such interaction, the systems form a
stationary ensemble, and nothing can change.   If our systems are
coupled "loosely" with the outside (that is, if the contribution of
the interaction terms to the Hamiltonian is always small compared
with the energy of the system), interaction with the outside world
either can be known in detail, or it may be purely random; finally,
it may be a mixture of both.   Let us illustrate the significance of
these distinctions by means of an example.   Consider a gas which
is enclosed in a vessel whose walls are rigid, except for one window.
We shall use this window to install interaction devices.   Let us first
install in this window a piston held in place by strong springs, and
have the molecules of our gas impinge on one side of this piston
and on the other side the molecules of some other gas that is also
otherwise confined by perfectly rigid walls.   The piston will be set
swinging by the impinging molecules, and in turn it will tend to
impart momentum to the gas molecules in amounts determined
by its instantaneous motion.   This type of interaction will impart
to the system we are interested in energy by means of random
processes exclusively.   Nevertheless, there is a trend in the change in
energy: If the auxiliary gas is at a higher temperature than the first
gas (if its β-value is smaller), then it will tend to transfer energy
to the first gas; if its temperature is lower, it will draw off energy.
This statement will be proved by a detailed computation below, but
first we shall give an example of the other type of interaction.   Suppose that again we install a piston, but by means of a weight we
press this piston toward the interior of our gas (in this instance, we
do not require a second gas).   Then, depending on the magnitude
of the weight, the average acceleration due to the impinging gas
molecules will exceed the force of the weight, will be less, or will
be equal.   Accordingly, the piston will carry out an average net
motion away from the gas, into it, or none at all; and at the end of
this process (when the piston has come up against a built-in stop,
let us say), the gas will occupy a different volume than it did before.
Its Hamiltonian H and its characteristic volume $X(E)$ will be new
and different functions, and the process just described will belong
to the second type: we have *performed work* on the gas.

In more general terms, the performance of work corresponds to a
microprocess that changes the Hamiltonian (as a function of the
canonical coordinates) of the system and its characteristic volume.

In view of the general theorem of mechanics that the rate of change of the energy of a system with time-dependent Hamiltonian equals the partial time derivative of H,

$$\frac{dH}{dt} = \frac{\partial H}{\partial t} \tag{2}$$

[see M&E, eq. (2.35), p. 34], the same change in the Hamiltonian carried out on every system of a canonical ensemble leads to a change in energy given by the integral

$$\frac{d\langle E \rangle}{dt} = \frac{1}{Z} \int \frac{\partial H}{\partial t} e^{-\beta E} \, dX, \tag{3}$$

or, if we wish to eliminate the time scale and write our expression simply in terms of a variation of the Hamiltonian H,

$$\delta_{\text{ad}}\langle E \rangle = \frac{1}{Z} \int \delta H(q_k, \, p_k) \, e^{-\beta H(q_k, p_k)} \, dX. \tag{4}$$

Before we go on with the general theory, let us return to our example of the piston forming part of the boundary of a perfect gas. We shall now carry out the necessary calculations that confirm our intuitive assertion that the piston will transfer energy to the gas both when it is used to compress the gas and when it merely is permitted to swing between two gas volumes at different temperatures. If the piston is capable of swinging only in the direction normal to its face, we can determine the energy transferred between the piston and an individual gas molecule by solving a collision problem between two bodies in one dimension only (since there is no exchange of momentum in the direction parallel to the face of the piston) and by assuming that the collision is perfectly elastic.[1] Call the mass of the gas molecule m, that of the piston M, and their

---

[1] An inelastic collision between two macroscopic bodies is one in which part of the gross motion is converted into random motion of the constituent molecules. In atomic collisions, we call an *inelastic collision* one in which some of the energy of translatory motion is converted into some form of internal energy, whether rotational, vibrational, electronic, or nuclear. In our example, it is of course quite possible to have inelastic collisions: some of the gas molecules might be adsorbed on the surface of the piston, the piston will heat up, and so on. However, all these complications contribute nothing to our problem, and we shall work with a (nonrealizable) piston that is internally completely rigid and merely capable of moving on guide rails as a whole.

velocity components at right angles to the piston just before the collision v and V, respectively. Immediately after the collision, their velocity components will be given by the formulas

$$v' = 2\bar{v} - v, \qquad V' = 2\bar{v} - V,$$

$$\bar{v} = \frac{mv + MV}{m + M}, \tag{5}$$

where $\bar{v}$ stands for the velocity of the common center of mass of the system piston-molecule. Since we are interested in the transfer of energy in the collision, we shall determine the difference in kinetic energy of the gas molecule before and after the collision. For this increase in kinetic energy of the gas molecule as a result of its collision with the piston, we find the expression

$$\Delta T = \frac{m}{2} (v'^2 - v^2) = 2m\bar{v}(\bar{v} - v)$$

$$= \frac{2mM}{(m + M)^2} (mv + MV)(V - v) \tag{6}$$

$$= \frac{4mM}{(m + M)^2} \left[-\frac{m}{2} v^2 + \frac{M}{2} V^2 - \frac{1}{2} (M - m)vV \right].$$

Again, both v and V represent velocities prior to the collision.

Having obtained this general expression for the energy transfer during an individual collision, we must evaluate the average transfer of energy during a large number of collisions. The time average of the piston velocity, taken over a period long enough to average over the random fluctuations in piston velocity, will be denoted by $\bar{\bar{V}}$. We can assert confidently that positive and negative deviations of V from $\bar{\bar{V}}$ are equally probable, since V depends on previous collisions, but not the one just taking place. Therefore we can assert that the average energy transferred from the piston to the system of gas molecules per collision equals

$$\langle \Delta T \rangle = \frac{4mM}{(m + M)^2} \left[\frac{M}{2} \overline{\overline{V^2}} - \left\langle \frac{m}{2} v^2 \right\rangle - \frac{1}{2} (M - m)\langle v \rangle \bar{\bar{V}} \right], \tag{7}$$

where the double bar denotes time averages and the carets an average over all the molecules of the gas that strike the piston. We are now ready to treat separately the several situations in which we are interested.

If the piston is held in place by a sufficiently strong spring, the collisions will set it swinging, but they will not produce a permanent dislocation of the piston, and the average of the piston velocity (including the sign) will vanish. As a result, the last term in eq. (7) will be zero, and the average energy transferred per collision from the piston to the gas will be proportional to the difference between the average kinetic energy of the piston and the average kinetic energy (normal to the piston) of the individual gas molecules. If there were only one gas and the piston, the condition of statistical equilibrium would be that this difference vanishes—a result that also follows directly from the equipartition law. But let us consider the case of the piston between two volumes of gas. Denote the quantities belonging to the second gas by primes. Then, if the numbers of gas molecules striking the piston from either side per unit time are n and n', respectively, the kinetic energy accumulated by the piston per unit time must be

$$\dot{T}_P = \frac{4nmM}{(m+M)^2}\left(\left\langle\frac{m}{2}v^2\right\rangle - \frac{M}{2}\overline{V^2}\right) + \frac{4n'm'M}{(m'+M)^2}\left(\left\langle\frac{m'}{2}v'^2\right\rangle - \frac{M}{2}\overline{V^2}\right)$$

$$\sim \frac{2}{M}\left(nm^2\langle v^2\rangle + n'm'^2\langle v'^2\rangle\right) - 2(nm + n'm')\overline{V^2}. \tag{8}$$

If the piston is to be in a state of stationary velocity fluctuations— if the situation is to represent a statistically constant stream of energy from one to the other gas across the piston—then the rate of energy accumulation of the piston must vanish, and we have

$$\frac{M}{2}\overline{V^2} \sim \frac{nm}{nm + n'm'}\left\langle\frac{m}{2}v^2\right\rangle + \frac{n'm'}{nm + n'm'}\left\langle\frac{m'}{2}v'^2\right\rangle. \tag{9}$$

If we substitute this expression for the average kinetic energy of the piston back into the formula for the rate at which the first gas accumulates energy, we find for this rate

$$\dot{T}_1 \sim \frac{4nn'mm'}{M(nm + n'm')}\left(\left\langle\frac{m'}{2}v'^2\right\rangle - \left\langle\frac{m}{2}v^2\right\rangle\right). \tag{10}$$

The direction of the energy stream is from the gas with the greater energy per degree of freedom to that with the lesser energy per degree of freedom, as we would expect.

It might appear strange that the laws of mechanics, which make no distinction between the past and the future, which permit any process to run forward as well as backward, nevertheless seem to lead to a definite asymmetry in our statistical problems, the approach toward statistical equilibrium in the future, not in the past (the stream of energy tends to reduce the temperature difference between the two gases *in the future*); but a brief review of our present example reveals the source of asymmetry. It is the assumption that the molecules approaching the piston are representative of the velocity distribution in the interior, whereas those reflected by the piston are not. This assumption then makes a definite distinction between the assumed velocity distributions of the molecules before and after collision with the piston; if we assume that the velocity distribution before collision is the same as elsewhere in the gas, then the laws of mechanics, together with the requirement that the piston shall not accumulate increasing amounts of energy, definitely lead to the result that the velocity distribution of molecules leaving the piston is different (unless the two gases happen to be at the same temperature) from the velocity distribution throughout the gas. Had we assumed instead that the velocity distribution of the molecules leaving is the same as the over-all distribution, we should have found that the energy stream is toward the hotter gas, clearly an assumption and a result rejected by our physical intuition and experience. We shall need to examine this problem of asymmetry later in greater generality.

Let us now turn to the question what happens if the piston is also subject to a macroscopic force and, as a result, carries out a net motion. Let this force be F and let the piston velocity, time-averaged over the fluctuations, be $\overline{\overline{V}}$. We shall assume again that the kinetic energy carried by the piston is stationary as well as its velocity $\overline{\overline{V}}$. In other words, neither the average velocity nor the mean square velocity of the piston (which includes the contribution of its random motion) is to exhibit a trend to change. These two conditions take the mathematical form

$$0 = \dot{T}_P \sim \frac{4nm}{M}\left(\left\langle \frac{m}{2}v^2\right\rangle - \frac{M}{2}\overline{V^2} + \frac{1}{2}M\langle v\rangle \overline{\overline{V}}\right) + F\overline{\overline{V}}, \qquad (11)$$

$$0 = M\dot{\overline{\overline{V}}} = F + nm(\langle v\rangle - \langle v'\rangle) \sim F + 2nm(\langle v\rangle - \overline{\overline{V}}). \qquad (12)$$

From the second of these two conditions, we find immediately that the imposed force F must be directed into the gas and equal to the impulse transferred per unit time by the impinging gas molecules. If we substitute the second condition into the first, we find further that the kinetic energy of random motion of the piston must equal that of one degree of freedom of one gas molecule, as expected:

$$0 \sim \frac{4nm}{M}\left[\left\langle\frac{m}{2}\,v^2\right\rangle - \frac{M}{2}\,(\overline{V^2} - \overline{V}^2)\right]. \tag{13}$$

Finally, the energy acquired by the gas molecules per unit time turns out to be simply the average work done by the force F on the piston and, through it, on the gas:

$$\dot{T}_1 \sim \frac{4nm}{M}\left(\frac{M}{2}\,\overline{V^2} - \left\langle\frac{m}{2}\,v^2\right\rangle - \frac{1}{2}\,M\langle v\rangle\overline{V} = F\overline{V} \right.$$
$$= 2nm\overline{V}(\overline{V} - \langle v\rangle) \sim -2nm\overline{V}\langle v\rangle. \tag{14}$$

In other words, the work done under these conditions equals in good approximation the product of the impulse transferred per unit time by the impinging gas molecules to a stationary piston and the actual time-averaged velocity of the piston. Again, this result is consistent with the usual statement that the mechanical work performed on a gas by compression equals the product of its pressure by the effected reduction in volume. Our result is, however, valid only in the case of slow and stationary piston displacement. If we expand a gas slowly, it will perform work and lose internal energy in accordance with our formulas. If we withdraw the piston very quickly (a situation we can realize in practice by opening a cock that lets the gas stream into an evacuated space), the work done by the gas will be less, and in the extreme case of sudden and complete withdrawal the gas will do no work at all.

We are now ready to carry the general theory a little further. Let us return to eq. (4), which represents the change in energy caused by the performance of mechanical work without the simultaneous transfer of heat. If work is performed in this manner, the temperature will in general change; this change in temperature can be determined easily by the requirement that it must be just right so that the internal energy will change by the amount predicted by eq. (4). If we compare two ensembles with slightly different Hamiltonian functions and slightly different values of β, then the difference in their internal energies, assuming both to be canonical, will be

$$\delta\langle E\rangle = -\delta\left(\frac{\partial \ln Z}{\partial \beta}\right) = \delta\left\{\frac{1}{Z}\int H\,e^{-\beta H}\,dX\right\}$$

$$= -\frac{\partial^2 \ln Z}{\partial \beta^2}\,\delta\beta + \frac{\langle E\rangle}{Z}\int \beta\,\delta H\,e^{-\beta H}\,dX$$

$$+ \frac{1}{Z}\int (1 - \beta H)\,\delta H\,e^{-\beta H}\,dX \tag{15}$$

$$= C_v\,\delta\theta + \frac{1}{Z}\int [1 + \beta(\langle E\rangle - E)]\,\delta H\,e^{-\beta E}\,dX,$$

because of eq. (1). This expression must be equated to the right-hand side of eq. (4), and we find that the change in θ as the result of an adiabatic process is given by

$$C_v\,\delta\theta = \frac{\beta}{Z}\int (E - \langle E\rangle)\,\delta H\,e^{-\beta E}\,dX. \tag{16}$$

In a mixed process (performance of work as well as transfer of heat), the amount of heat transferred to the system must equal the total gain in energy, diminished by the amount of work performed on the system:

$$\delta Q = C_v\,\delta\theta + \frac{\beta}{Z}\int (\langle E\rangle - E)\,\delta H\,e^{-\beta E}\,dX. \tag{17}$$

or $\qquad\delta Q = \delta\langle E\rangle - \frac{1}{Z}\int e^{-\beta E}\,\delta H\,dX = \frac{1}{\beta}\,\delta(\beta\langle E\rangle + \ln Z). \tag{18}$

We have now established the principal relations leading from statistical mechanics to thermodynamic concepts. Our next task is to pronounce laws governing the processes possible with actual thermodynamic objects. Naturally, these laws must contain only macroscopically defined quantities.

4.2. Equations of state

Consider a given amount of fluid at rest. Ordinarily, its macroscopic state is described completely if we know the volume available to the fluid, and its temperature. If we disregard such unusual conditions as the presence of very strong electric or magnetic fields, the same amount of the same type of fluid will always be found to be in the same "state" (gaseous or liquid, or a definite mixture of both); it will have the same pressure and the same internal energy. The equation that gives us the pressure of the fluid as a function of its volume and its temperature is called its *equation of state*.

That knowledge of just two parameters (volume and temperature) should completely characterize the gross behavior of a fluid is in itself a remarkable fact.   This fact is made possible only because of the restrictions under which thermodynamics operates in general, and because of the simple properties of fluids as compared with solids or vitreous materials.   The general restrictions are those we have discussed in the preceding section; we consider that the fluid and our information about it are represented adequately by a canonical ensemble.   Hence, knowledge of the temperature as well as of the Hamiltonian function completely determines the thermodynamic properties.   But knowledge of the Hamiltonian is generally a complicated business; here we can use to advantage the special properties of the fluid.   Under ordinary circumstances, the Hamiltonian depends only on the available volume; if we know the volume as well as the temperature, then the canonical ensemble that is to represent the extent of our knowledge about the system is determined completely.

Let us assume, for the time being, that we know the partition function Z as a function of these two parameters, which we shall call θ and V.   Then we have, as before, for the mean energy of the system

$$\langle E \rangle = - \frac{\partial \ln Z(V, \theta)}{\partial \theta} \frac{d\theta}{d\beta} \equiv U(V, \theta). \tag{19}$$

The mean energy, too, is a function of V and θ. We shall now ascertain expressions that will characterize the two basic changes of which our fluid system is capable.   Any actual change can be represented as a combination of these two.   We may start with the observation that our thermodynamic system (our ensemble) depends only on two parameters and that the two possible changes are therefore a change in temperature at constant volume (isochoric processes) and a change in volume at constant temperature (isothermal processes).   The change in energy as a result of a combination of these two (infinitesimal) processes is, of course, given by

$$dU = \frac{\partial U}{\partial V} dV + \frac{\partial U}{\partial \theta} d\theta,$$

$$\frac{\partial U}{\partial \theta} \equiv C_v. \tag{20}$$

The other possible approach is for us to think of the *mechanism* of change, and then the two possible basic processes are the performance of work (adiabatic processes) and the transfer of heat (isochoric processes). The latter type of process already has been characterized, but we must find an expression for the work performed in an adiabatic process.

Let us consider first a system that in addition to the temperature is described by a number of macroscopic parameters $R_1, \cdots, R_n$. In the case of a chemically pure fluid, there is only one such parameter, the volume. The Hamiltonian of the system, in addition to being a function of the phase space coordinates q_k, p_k, depends then on these n macroscopic parameters R_i. The amount of work done in an infinitesimal adiabatic process is then equal to the ensemble average of the δH induced by an infinitesimal change of these macroscopic parameters,

$$\delta_{\text{ad}}\langle E \rangle = \frac{1}{Z} \sum_{i=1}^{n} \delta R_i \int \frac{\partial H(q_k,\, p_k,\, R_l)}{\partial R_i} \, e^{-\beta H} \, dX, \qquad (21)$$

in accordance with eq. (4). This expression can be readily transformed in such a manner that the only phase-space integral to be performed is the partition function. We may write the most general change in Z in the form

$$\begin{aligned}
\delta Z &= -\int (\beta \, \delta H + H \, \delta\beta) \, e^{-\beta H} \, dX \\
&= -Z[\langle E \rangle \, \delta\beta + \beta \, \delta_{\text{ad}}\langle E \rangle],
\end{aligned} \qquad (22)$$

and we have, therefore, quite generally, for the right-hand side of eq. (4),

$$\delta_{\text{ad}}\langle E \rangle = -\frac{1}{\beta} [\langle E \rangle \, \delta\beta + \delta \ln Z]. \qquad (23)$$

In our particular case, where the adiabatic changes can be characterized by the changes in a finite number of macroscopic parameters R_i, this expression reduces to

$$\begin{aligned}
\delta_{\text{ad}}\langle E \rangle &= -\frac{1}{\beta} \left[\langle E \rangle \, \delta\beta + \frac{\partial \ln Z}{\partial \beta} \, \delta\beta + \sum_{i=1}^{n} \frac{\partial \ln Z}{\partial R_i} \, \delta R_i \right] \\
&= -\frac{1}{\beta} \sum_{i=1}^{n} \frac{\partial \ln Z}{\partial R_i} \, \delta R_i,
\end{aligned} \qquad (24)$$

and for the case of a pure fluid to the even simpler expression

$$\delta_{\rm ad}\langle E \rangle = -\frac{1}{\beta}\frac{\partial \ln Z}{\partial V}\,\delta V. \tag{25}$$

In this last equation, the coefficient of δV represents the amount of work done per unit reduction of volume under stationary conditions. But this work done per unit reduction in volume is commonly known as the *pressure*. Thus for the pressure of a fluid we have the expression

$$p = \frac{1}{\beta}\frac{\partial \ln Z}{\partial V}. \tag{26}$$

In thermodynamics, it is customary to designate the amount of (infinitesimal) work done by dW. Equations (24) and (25) may, therefore, be given the form

$$dW = -\sum_{i=1}^{n} Y_i\,dR_i, \qquad Y_i = \frac{1}{\beta}\frac{\partial \ln Z}{\partial R_i}; \tag{27}$$
$$dW = -p\,dV.$$

The symbol d indicates that the quantity to which it is attached is not a dynamical or thermodynamic function; that is, there is no property "work" defined either as a function on phase space or as an ensemble average.

Likewise, the amount of heat transferred to a system is designated by Q or, in the case of an infinitesimal process, by dQ. The sum of heat transferred to a system and work performed on the system must equal the total increase in internal energy, or

$$dQ = dU - dW = dU + \sum_{i=1}^{n} Y_i\,dR_i$$

$$= -d\left(\frac{\partial \ln Z}{\partial \beta}\right) + \frac{1}{\beta}\sum_{i=1}^{n}\frac{\partial \ln Z}{\partial R_i}\,dR_i$$

$$= \sum_{i=1}^{n}\left(\frac{1}{\beta}\frac{\partial \ln Z}{\partial R_i} - \frac{\partial^2 \ln Z}{\partial \beta\,\partial R_i}\right)dR_i - \frac{\partial^2 \ln Z}{\partial \beta^2}\,d\beta \tag{28}$$

$$= \frac{1}{\beta}\,d\left(\ln Z - \beta\frac{\partial \ln Z}{\partial \beta}\right) = -\frac{1}{\beta}\,d\left[\beta^2\frac{\partial}{\partial \beta}\left(\frac{1}{\beta}\ln Z\right)\right],$$
$$Z = Z(\beta;\,R_1,\,\cdots,\,R_n).$$

For the case of a simple fluid, this formula reduces to

$$dQ = dU + p\,dV. \tag{29}$$

These formulas are the equivalents of the statistical relations (17) and (18).

In thermodynamic measurements, we cannot in general determine the internal energy directly, though we can measure its change in the course of various processes. What we can measure easily is the temperature, with the help of a calibrated comparison system (a thermometer), the volume and other parameters determining shape, and the pressure or similar macroscopic parameters [designated by Y_i in eq. (27)], by measuring the counterforce required to keep a piston at rest. The totality of the equations expressing the dependence of the stress parameters Y_i on the strain parameters R_i and on the temperature θ is called the *equation of state* of the (macroscopic) system:

$$Y_i = Y_i(\theta; R_1, \cdots, R_n). \tag{30}$$

For a simple fluid, the equation of state reduces to a single relationship:

$$p = p(\theta, V). \tag{31}$$

The equation of state provides somewhat less complete information about a macroscopic system than knowledge of the partition function as a function of the temperature and the macroscopic parameters R_i. Equations (30), together with (27), represent a set of differential equations whose integration leads to the partition function, but not uniquely. The principal value of the equation(s) of state lies in the circumstance that it summarizes information that can be obtained by straightforward measurements of a macroscopic character. If in addition to the partition function the internal energy is known as a function of the macroscopic parameters, then integration determines the partition function except for a constant factor. But since the partition function enters almost all thermodynamic formulas in the form of a logarithm, this constant factor is usually not very significant.

Before concluding this section, we must justify the procedure in which we considered the local Hamiltonian a continuous and differentiable function of the volume V. If we use, for instance, rectilinear coordinates and ordinary momenta as our q_k's and p_k's, then this condition is assuredly not satisfied: the walls of a vessel, if they are to be impenetrable, must be represented by positive infinite values of H for any coordinate combination that would place any of the system molecules outside the vessel. However, it is easy to carry out a canonical transformation, essentially a change of scale, so that in terms of the new coordinates the spatial volume is always described in the same manner (that it is, for instance, a cube of length 1 in coordinate units) and that the actual volume V appears as a parameter in the expression for the Hamiltonian for all values of the q_k's inside the unit cube. In terms of such coordinates, then, the derivations given are mathematically sound.

4.3. The first law

The first law of thermodynamics is the macroscopic expression of the conservation law of energy. From the microscopic point of view (that is, if we approach thermodynamics from statistical mechanics), it is trivial. But if we start from purely macroscopic observations, we must pronounce the conservation of energy as a law logically separate from the equation of state.

We start with the existence of an equation of state (30 or 31) and with additional measurements which tell us about the amount of work performed as well as the amount of heat transferred for any (infinitesimal) change in the system parameters. As for the amount of work performed, the correct macroscopic formulation is provided by eqs. (27). The amount of heat transferred can be determined by a calorimetric experiment: If our fluid is in contact with a surrounding fluid of standard heat capacity,[1] then the amount of heat transferred to our fluid is equal to the heat withdrawn from the calorimetric fluid, and this amount we can in turn determine by noting the drop in temperature of the calorimetric fluid as well as its quantity. Thus, for any conceivable infinitesimal process,

---

[1] Ordinarily, water is used as a standard for defining the unit amount of heat: one calorie is the amount of heat required to heat one gram of water one degree centigrade; the equivalent number of mechanical units of energy, ergs, must then be determined by a separate experiment, such as Joule's experiment, in which water is heated by stirring with a carefully measured force acting through a known displacement. To simplify our discussion and to keep the formulas free of conversion factors, we shall assume that such determinations have been made and that the heat transferred can be expressed directly in ergs or an equivalent mechanical unit.

we can determine the amount of work done (by forcing any change in volume to take place against an appropriately loaded piston) as well as the heat transferred. We can summarize the results of such measurements for the heat transferred in a formula

$$dQ = C_v \, d\theta + \sum_{i=1}^{n} J_i \, dR_i, \tag{32}$$

where C_v has the same significance as before; both J_i and C_v are functions of R_i and θ which must be determined empirically.

The difference between the heat transferred to the system and the work performed by it,

$$dQ - dW = C_v \, d\theta + \sum_{i=1}^{n} (J_i - Y_i) \, dR_i, \tag{33}$$

is, according to our previous discussions, the increase in U. But in a systematically thermodynamic approach (that is, using only macroscopic observations and concepts), we get the differential expression (33) without reference to U. From that point of view, to claim that this expression is an exact differential is a logically new assertion; and this assertion constitutes the *first law of thermodynamics*. The assertion of the first law of thermodynamics can also be formulated thus: If we carry out on our system a series of changes resulting in a finite change in temperature as well as volume, then, though both the total amount of heat transferred to the system and the total amount of work performed by the system will depend on the exact manner in which we have passed from the initial state of the system to the final state, the *difference* between these two quantities depends only on the initial and the final state and *is independent of the intermediate stages*.

We shall give a third formulation of the first law that makes use of the concept of a cycle. A succession of (finite) changes in a thermodynamic system is called a *cyclic process* or just a *cycle* if the final state is identical with the initial state. In a cycle, we generally do not retrace every step taken, but we arrange matters so that the intermediate states are not coincident. We can, for instance, first compress a gas adiabatically, thereby raising its temperature; we can then permit it to cool without expansion by bringing it in contact with a temperature bath having its initial temperature; and finally we can expand our gas isothermally to its original volume.

The first law then asserts that the net amount of heat transferred to a system in a cycle (which is in general different from zero and is negative in the example just given) equals the net amount of work performed by it. Thus a cleverly arranged cycle, a "thermal engine," may convert heat into mechanical work, but it cannot produce work out of nothing.

Mathematically, the first law can be formulated [by the assertion that the difference between the two (*inexact*) differentials dQ and dW is an *exact differential*. We call this exact differential dU and the quantity defined by it (except for an arbitrary additive constant) the internal energy U. The mathematical formulation of the first law is then

$$dU = dQ - dW. \tag{34}$$

This equation accomplishes two distinct purposes within the framework of thermodynamics. On the one hand, it asserts a (thermodynamic) law of nature, that the difference between the two inexact differentials on the right is an exact differential; on the other, eq. (34) serves as the defining equation of the internal energy. Being identical with eq. (28), it carries no information that does not follow directly from statistical-mechanical considerations.

If for a simple fluid we were to prepare a graph with V and θ as the coordinates, then any series of changes we carry out will be represented by a curve in the V, θ-plane. The quanties Q and W, the finite amounts of heat transferred and of work performed, respectively, will be integrals along this curve, and the value of the integrals depends on the whole curve. But the integral ΔU, the increase in internal energy, depends only on the end points of the curve; if these end points coincide, if we have a cyclic process, then the integral ΔU vanishes altogether. Thus, if we somehow normalize the constant of integration (if we call some state "the reference state" and assign to it zero internal energy), then U is defined for each point of the graph plane, and quite irrespective of any particular curve passing through that point. Whenever a quantity that is originally defined as a path integral in the "phase diagram" is actually definable as a point function and independent of the choice of integration path, we call that quantity a *variable of state*. With this terminology, we may also formulate the first law by simply asserting that the internal energy is a variable of state.

If the differential expression for dU, eq. (33), is to be an exact differential, then the coefficients C_v and $(J_i - Y_i)$ are the partial derivatives of U with respect to the arguments θ and R_i, respectively, and as such are subject to the conditions that

$$\frac{\partial C_v}{\partial R_i} - \frac{\partial (J_i - Y_i)}{\partial \theta} = 0, \qquad \frac{\partial (J_i - Y_i)}{\partial R_j} - \frac{\partial (J_j - Y_j)}{\partial R_i} = 0, \qquad (35)$$

$$i, j = 1, \cdots, n.$$

In fact, condition (35) is both necessary and sufficient to assure mathematically that dU is really an exact differential and U a variable of state.

Equations (33) through (35) exhaust the power of the first law of thermodynamics. As far as applications go, we are frequently interested in processes in which not the volume V (or other parameters R_i) but the pressure p (or the corresponding variables Y_i) is kept constant. The pressure remains constant (and the volume changes) in the great majority of processes that result in chemical reactions or in changes of state, such as the evaporation or the freezing of liquids, the condensation of gases, the melting and the sublimation of solids, or the change of a solid from one mode of crystallization to another. Ordinarily, all these changes are accomplished under atmospheric pressure, not in a bomb of constant volume. For the treatment of such processes, it is convenient to introduce new variables of state.

Let us hold a system under constant pressure (or under constant stresses Y_i). If we change the temperature under these conditions, the heat transferred from a suitable temperature bath must serve both to account for the change in internal energy and for the work performed:

$$dQ = dU + p\,dV = d(U + pV),$$

$$dQ = dU + \sum_{i=1}^{n} Y_i\,dR_i = d\left(U + \sum_{i=1}^{n} Y_i R_i\right). \qquad (36)$$

The first line holds for a simple fluid (and will hold in all the following equations), the second line for the more general thermodynamic system. The conversion into an exact differential is possible because we are restricting ourselves to processes in which p or the Y_i are being kept constant. We call this type of process *isobaric*.

The quantity Ψ,

$$\Psi = U + p\,V,$$

$$\Psi = U + \sum_{i=1}^{n} Y_i\,R_i, \tag{37}$$

is known as the *enthalpy* or the *heat content*.   It is a variable of state, just like the internal energy.   That is, it depends only on the present state of the thermodynamic system, not (like the heat transferred, for instance) on the history leading to that state.

So far, we have used as our independent thermodynamic variables the conventional temperature θ. (or occasionally β) and the parameters R_i or the volume V, because they determine the Hamiltonian of the system and the canonical distribution.   But in phenomenological thermodynamics, these parameters are merely some of the variables of state of the system.   Generally, any set of $(n+1)$ independent variables of state will serve to characterize the (macroscopic) state of the system uniquely, and all other variables may be represented as functions of these arbitrarily chosen $(n+1)$.   In the case of a simple fluid, this number is 2.   For this most important case of all, a special notation has been developed, which can readily be extended to the system with $(n+1)$ thermodynamic "degrees of freedom."   We agree that any symbol once introduced characterizes a certain variable of state (say U means the internal energy) regardless of the choice of independent variables.   When partial derivatives are written down, we place them within parentheses and append to the lower right in the form of subscripts those remaining independent variables which are to be considered constants for purposes of partial differentiation.   For instance, if we consider, as heretofore, the internal energy as a function of temperature and volume, we have

$$dU = \left(\frac{\partial U}{\partial \theta}\right)_V d\theta + \left(\frac{\partial U}{\partial V}\right)_\theta dV,$$

$$dU = \left(\frac{\partial U}{\partial \theta}\right)_R d\theta + \sum_{i=1}^{n} \left(\frac{\partial U}{\partial R_i}\right)_\theta dR_i. \tag{38}$$

If we wish to express the change in internal energy with temperature in an isobaric process, we had better choose θ and p (or the Y_i) as the independent variables.   A short calculation, which will be left to the reader, shows then that

$$\left(\frac{\partial U}{\partial \theta}\right)_p = \left(\frac{\partial U}{\partial \theta}\right)_V + \left(\frac{\partial U}{\partial V}\right)_\theta \left(\frac{\partial V}{\partial \theta}\right)_p,$$

$$\left(\frac{\partial U}{\partial \theta}\right)_Y = \left(\frac{\partial U}{\partial \theta}\right)_R + \sum_{i=1}^{n} \left(\frac{\partial U}{\partial R_i}\right)_\theta \left(\frac{\partial R_i}{\partial \theta}\right)_Y.$$

(39)

Previously, we introduced, as the internal heat capacity C_v of a system, the amount of heat required to raise the temperature one unit step in an isochoric process. We shall now define as the *isobaric heat capacity* C_p the amount of heat to be transferred to raise the temperature one unit step in an isobaric process. According to eqs. (32) and (36), these two different heat capacities are

$$C_v = \left(\frac{\partial U}{\partial \theta}\right)_V, \qquad C_p = \left(\frac{\partial \Psi}{\partial \theta}\right)_p,$$

$$C_v = \left(\frac{\partial U}{\partial \theta}\right)_R, \qquad C_p = \left(\frac{\partial \Psi}{\partial \theta}\right)_Y.$$

(40)

Both heat capacities can be determined experimentally, but not with the same degree of ease. Ordinarily, it is easier to keep the pressure constant than the volume, especially for liquids and solids, where the thermal expansion of the specimen is the same order of magnitude as that of the material of the confining vessel or clamps. Applying the defining equation for the heat content (37) and the chain rule of differentiation [as in the derivation of eq. (39)], we can easily find a relationship between the two heat capacities. This relationship is

$$C_p = C_v + \left(\frac{\partial V}{\partial \theta}\right)_p \left[p + \left(\frac{\partial U}{\partial V}\right)_\theta\right],$$

$$C_p = C_v + \sum_{i=1}^{n} \left(\frac{\partial R_i}{\partial \theta}\right)_Y \left[Y_i + \left(\frac{\partial U}{\partial R_i}\right)_\theta\right].$$

(41)

The distinction between C_v and C_p assumes particular importance when a substance changes its state—when, for instance, a liquid evaporates. If we lock a liquid within completely rigid walls and raise the temperature gradually, the pressure will increase continuously, though beyond a certain temperature very rapidly. But if we keep the same liquid under constant pressure and raise the temperature, then, for moderate pressures at least, there will come a temperature, *the boiling point*, at which the volume increases a finite and usually very large amount before the temperature can increase any further. We then say that the liquid has been *evaporated*, that it has changed completely into the gaseous form. While this change from the liquid to the gaseous state takes place, the system absorbs a finite amount of heat; this amount is called the *heat of evaporation*. Fundamentally the same situation is encountered whenever a substance changes its state (freezes, for instance) or its mode of crystallization. The general term used for the finite change in the heat content Ψ (which equals the amount of heat transferred to the system) is *heat of formation*. When the heat of formation is positive, the corresponding change of state is called *endothermic;* in an endothermic change, heat is withdrawn from the surroundings. In the opposite case, when heat is released to the surroundings, we call the change *exothermic*.

Generally, it is fairly easy to measure the heat of formation, $\Delta\Psi$, in calorimetric experiments. It is normally to be expected that the internal energy changes also. We can compute this change in internal energy very easily if in addition to the heat of formation we know the change in volume. We have then

$$\Delta U = \Delta\Psi - p\,\Delta V,$$

$$\Delta U = \Delta\Psi - \sum_{i=1}^{n} Y_i\,\Delta R_i. \tag{42}$$

In some transitions the change in internal energy is even greater than the change in heat content. Ice, for instance, occupies a greater volume than the corresponding amount of water. Thus in the transition from ice to water, whereas the heat of fusion is about 79.7 calories per gram, the *reduction* in volume in atmospheric pressure makes a small additional positive contribution to the increase in internal energy, which amounts to about 2×10^{-3} calorie per gram.

Problems

1. Knowing the heat of formation of gaseous H_2O at normal pressure and at 100°C (to be obtained from any table of physicochemical constants), and assuming that at 1 atm and at 100°C steam satisfies the equation of state for a perfect gas, determine the change in internal energy for 1 gram or for 1 mol.

2. Assume that in a gas the attractive force between any two molecules is negligible except in the event of very close approach. With this assumption and setting the mutual potential energy between two molecules as $-V(r)$ (where the function V need not be specified, except that it vanishes for all values of $r > r_0$), derive expressions for the partition function, internal energy, and pressure as functions of V and θ (or β). Derive expressions for C_v and C_p.

3. Under what circumstances would you consider the concept of surface energy (and the corresponding concept of surface tension) physically meaningful? Making the necessary assumptions, proceed to develop a theory of these quantities on the basis of statistical mechanics.

4. Consider a simple cubic lattice consisting of only one kind of atoms. Assume that the equilibrium density is known (and therefore the equilibrium distance between neighboring molecules) and also the isothermal bulk modulus. Determine the ratio between work done and heat transferred in the event of isotropic isothermal compression.

5. In the above model, how much heat would be developed in adiabatic compression? What about the change in temperature if it were technically feasible to dilate the material isotropically and adiabatically?

6. Determine differential expressions for the infinitesimal increase in temperature resulting from an infinitesimal adiabatic compression, both in terms of the change in volume and in terms of the amount of work done.

7. Compare the adiabatic and the isothermal bulk moduli with each other.

Chapter 5

Thermodynamics, Second Law

5.1. Introduction

The first law of thermodynamics represents the translation of the law of conservation of energy into thermodynamic language. At the time of its discovery, in the middle of the nineteenth century, the first law was a tremendous accomplishment because at that time the atomistic nature of heat energy was not yet clearly established. But once the kinetic hypothesis of heat had found general acceptance, the first law was nothing but a natural and easily understood consequence of the basic laws of mechanics.

The second law, on the contrary, cannot be derived from purely mechanical laws. It carries the stamp of the essentially statistical nature of heat. Moreover, we shall find that its self-consistent formulation is possible only for ensembles of systems that are not in statistical equilibrium. We shall find two formulations of the second law. One can be derived by straightforward argument from the foundations of statistical mechanics; this formulation merely asserts the *existence* of a certain variable of state, the *entropy*. Although this formulation of the second law suffices to derive a certain number of thermodynamic relationships, the customary formulation of the second law in thermodynamics goes far beyond the assertion of the *existence* of the entropy. According to the second formulation, all thermodynamic processes involving a system that is *isolated thermally* from its surroundings (no heat can be transferred) will *increase* its entropy. Ordinarily, when we talk of the second law of thermodynamics, we are referring to the second (and stronger) formulation. In this strong form, the second law implies the notion of the *irreversibility* of thermodynamic processes. If in an isolated system the entropy is bound to increase in any actual process, then the system can progress from some initial state A to a final state B having a greater entropy, but it cannot return to the state A without violating the second law.

Obviously, irreversibility cannot be a property of the underlying mechanical laws of our micromodel.   The micromodel simply obeys the laws of mechanics (and electrodynamics), and any possible mechanical or electrodynamical process runs just as well backward as forward; all the laws of nature we have encountered so far maintain a complete symmetry between past and future.   Furthermore, the basic law for the behavior of an ensemble, Liouville's theorem, possesses the same symmetry.   Equilibrium ensembles naturally cannot give rise to asymmetries between past and future because, as ensembles, they do not change at all.   Finally, it is clear, because of Liouville's theorem, that a nonequilibrium ensemble cannot "approach" equilibrium in the course of time: if initially the distribution over an energy surface is not constant, it will never become constant, nor will it have a tendency to "smear out."   On the contrary, all minima and maxima of the density distribution on an energy surface in phase space, while changing their locations in the course of time, will retain exactly their deviations from the mean density.   As a matter of fact, we could, if we wanted to, introduce new coordinates in phase space by means of a canonical transformation such that the new momenta and location coordinates would all be constants of the motion (constant along each mechanical trajectory).   In terms of such a canonical coordinate system, it is obvious that a nonequilibrium ensemble preserves all the essential features of its density distribution.

Nevertheless, thermodynamic processes in nature tend to proceed in one direction only.   If two substances are brought into thermal contact with each other, heat passes from the hotter to the colder substance, not the other way around.   If gas molecules are permitted to pass freely between two regions of lesser and greater pressure, the net motion will be into the region of smaller pressure.   Friction tends to convert mechanical energy into heat energy, and so forth.   Thus one of the most striking features of processes involving heat energy is that they do discriminate between past and future.   It will be our task to explain this characteristic in terms of arguments that flow naturally from our theoretical foundation.   We have already had an inkling of the nature of such arguments in Section 4.1.   There we found that energy passes from one system to another at lower temperature if initially each system is assumed to be representative of a canonical ensemble.   Naturally, the ensemble that we obtain by forming the Cartesian product of the two original ones will not be canonical and will never become canonical; but a single system, if it is quasi-ergodic, will have time averages that are equal to the ensemble averages of a stationary ensemble. We shall discuss this argument more thoroughly at the end of the chapter.

In the meantime, we shall first discuss the existence and the physical significance of the entropy function.

5.2. Thermodynamic weight

Intuitively, the second law is concerned with ensembles that fall short of being canonical, that deviate from equilibrium. If we are eventually to make statements concerning the approach (in a certain sense) of such systems toward equilibrium, we must first develop some ensemble function that may be considered a measure for the deviation from canonical distribution. Such a function should, within certain limits, assume its greatest (or its smallest) value for a canonical distribution. If it has this property, then its deviation from that maximum will be a measure for the deviation of a particular ensemble from canonical distribution.

Naturally, there are infinitely many canonical distributions for a given system, and any function of the desired nature must be compared to a particular one of these canonical distributions. Not yet having constructed the desired measure of "noncanonicity," we are free to set up our requirements in that respect at will. But it appears natural to compare our given distribution with the one canonical distribution having the same mean energy $\langle E \rangle$. If we do so, we can construct our measure without too much difficulty. Let us suppose that the measure F be some integral over phase space of the general form

$$F = \int f[\mu(q_k, p_k); q_k, p_k] \, dX. \tag{1}$$

Our task is then to determine the function f so that the integral is greater for a canonical distribution μ_c than for any other choice consistent with our assumptions. Any distribution function μ must satisfy two requirements: its integral over the whole phase space must equal unity, and the mean energy of the ensemble computed with its help must equal the preassigned value $\langle E \rangle$:

$$\int \mu(q_k, p_k) \, dX = 1, \qquad \int \mu \, H(q_k, p_k) \, dX = \langle E \rangle \tag{2}$$

We shall treat our problem as a maximum problem with subsidiary conditions, and we shall introduce the two subsidiary conditions (2) through the method of Lagrange's multipliers. For the change in F if we should vary $\mu(q_k, p_k)$ we get

$$\delta F = \int \frac{\partial f}{\partial \mu} \delta\mu(q_k, p_k) \, dX. \tag{3}$$

But $\delta\mu$ is subject to the two requirements that

$$\int \delta\mu \, dX = 0, \qquad \int H \, \delta\mu \, dX = 0. \tag{4}$$

If we call the two Lagrange's multipliers α and γ, then our requirement that δF should vanish for any variations of μ consistent with eqs. (4) leads to the condition at each point of phase space that

$$\frac{\partial f[\mu; q_k, p_k]}{\partial \mu} + \alpha + \gamma H = 0. \tag{5}$$

Our maximum problem is peculiar in that we know the solution. The unknown in this case is the problem! We must find a function f such that eq. (5) is satisfied for

$$\mu = \frac{1}{Z} e^{-\beta H}. \tag{6}$$

The logarithm of the density (6) is a linear function of H. Thus we may be able to solve our problem by setting tentatively

$$\frac{\partial f}{\partial \mu} = a \ln \mu + b \tag{7}$$

and

$$f = f_0 \, \mu \ln \left(\frac{\mu_0}{\mu} \right). \tag{8}$$

Since the constant f_0 contributes nothing to the problem of maximization, we shall drop it. Our proposed measure function then turns out to be the integral

$$F = \int \mu \ln \left(\frac{\mu_0}{\mu} \right) dX, \tag{9}$$

where the remaining constant μ_0 remains undetermined, but it will be retained since it is not dimensionless.

The integral (9) has only one stationary value, and that is the canonical distribution. For the canonical distribution, F becomes

$$F_c = \int \mu_c \ln \left(\frac{\mu_0}{\mu_c} \right) dX = \ln \mu_0 + \ln Z + \beta \langle E \rangle,$$

$$\mu_c = \frac{1}{Z} e^{-\beta E}.$$

(10)

The question arises whether this value constitutes a minimum or a maximum of F or is a saddle point. If it were the latter, F would be useless as a measure, because then noncanonical distributions might have F-values equal to that of the canonical distribution. Actually, the value (10) is the largest value of which the integral is capable, provided that we consider only normalized distributions having the same value $\langle E \rangle$. We shall now prove this fact.

Suppose we consider a continuous sequence of distributions $\mu(\alpha; q_k, p_k)$. α is a parameter that identifies individual distributions in the sequence. We shall arrange matters so that for $\alpha = 0$ the distribution is canonical. For all other values of α, the distribution is noncanonical, but it will remain normalized, and all distributions of the sequence are to have the same value of $\langle E \rangle$. Naturally, F will be defined for each distribution in our sequence, and it will be a function of α. We shall form the first and the second derivative of F with respect to α, and in particular we shall determine the values of these two derivatives for the value $\alpha = 0$. By direct computation, we have

$$\frac{dF}{d\alpha} = \int \frac{\partial f}{\partial \mu} \frac{\partial \mu}{\partial \alpha} dX = \int \frac{\partial \mu}{\partial \alpha} \left[\ln \left(\frac{\mu_0}{\mu} \right) - 1 \right] dX$$

(11)

and

$$\frac{d^2F}{d\alpha^2} = \int \left[\frac{\partial f}{\partial \mu} \frac{\partial^2 \mu}{\partial \alpha^2} + \frac{\partial^2 f}{\partial \mu^2} \left(\frac{\partial \mu}{\partial \alpha} \right)^2 \right] dX$$

$$= \int \left[\left(\ln \frac{\mu}{\mu_0} - 1 \right) \frac{\partial^2 \mu}{\partial \alpha^2} - \frac{1}{\mu} \left(\frac{\partial \mu}{\partial \alpha} \right)^2 \right] dX.$$

(12)

The dependence of μ on α is subject to the two conditions (2). If we differentiate these two conditions twice with respect to α, we get for the second derivative of μ the two integral conditions

$$\int \frac{\partial^2 \mu}{\partial \alpha^2} dX = 0, \qquad \int \frac{\partial^2 \mu}{\partial \alpha^2} H \, dX = 0.$$

(13)

Except for the two conditions (2), the dependence of μ on α is arbitrary. If we now substitute into eq. (12) the canonical distribution μ_c, $\dfrac{d^2F}{d\alpha^2}$ reduces to

$$\frac{d^2F}{d\alpha^2}\bigg|_{\alpha=0} = \int \left[\frac{\partial^2\mu}{\partial\alpha^2} (\ln \mu_0 + \ln Z + \beta H - 1) - \frac{1}{\mu_c}\left(\frac{\partial\mu}{\partial\alpha}\right)^2 \right] dX$$

$$= -\int \left(\frac{\partial\mu}{\partial\alpha}\right)^2 \frac{dX}{\mu_c} < 0, \qquad \frac{\partial\mu}{\partial\alpha} \not\equiv 0.$$

(14)

In this simplification we have used the two relationships (13). We find then that the second derivative of F with respect to α is negative definite for a canonical distribution no matter how we choose the infinitesimal deviation from canonicity that is represented by the parameter α. Thus the canonical distribution represents a true maximum with respect to neighboring noncanonical distributions.

Moreover, we can prove that the canonical distribution represents an absolute maximum with respect to any other distributions satisfying the two conditions (2). To do so, we must make use of the fact that the canonical distribution represents the *only* stationary distribution with respect to variations compatible with conditions (2), and furthermore, that if F is finite, it depends continuously and differentiably on the distribution μ. In order to carry out this proof, let us arrange all distributions consistent with the conditions (2) in sets so that all distributions in one set deviate "the same amount" from a canonical distribution. For instance, we may define each set as one containing all distributions having the same value of Δ^2:

$$\Delta^2 = \int (\mu - \mu_c)^2 \mu_c \, dX. \tag{15}$$

Naturally, the number of these sets is infinite, since Δ^2 is capable of assuming each value between 0 and ∞. Inasmuch as μ_c leads to a local maximum, we may assume that for all values of Δ^2 less than some δ^2, every member distribution of every set with $0 \leq \Delta^2 \leq \delta^2$ will have an F less than F_c. As a result, we may be certain that within this range of Δ^2, at least, there will be some distribution or distributions having a maximum value of F within its or their set. Call this maximum value $F(\Delta^2)$. In the vicinity of $\Delta^2 = 0$, this function must decrease with increasing value of the argument.

Within each set, and for the maximum distribution(s) $F = \bar{F}$, F will be stationary with respect to arbitrary variations of μ [which must, of course, be consistent with eqs. (2) as well as with the condition that it does not lead outside the set under consideration, $\Delta^2 =$ constant]; and since it cannot be stationary with respect to all variations (only the canonical distribution itself is stationary), the derivative of $\bar{F}$ with respect to Δ^2 cannot vanish away from μ_c. Thus, if

$$\frac{d\bar{F}}{d(\Delta^2)} < 0 \qquad (16)$$

near 0, it will decrease in the whole domain of distributions bounded by $\Delta^2 = \delta^2$. But that is not all. Obviously, on that boundary everywhere

$$F \leq F(\delta^2) < F_c. \qquad (17)$$

Thus we find that the value δ, defined as that value beyond which there are some $F > F_c$, simply does not exist: our domain includes all distributions for which F does not become negatively infinite. Hence for all non-canonical distributions without restriction F is always less than F_c, given by eq. (10).

Having proved this important property, we now know that the deviation of F from F_c is a measure of noncanonicity. And we shall generally adopt the function over the distribution

$$\Phi(\mu) = \ln Z + \beta\langle E\rangle + \int \mu \ln \mu \, dX \geq 0 \qquad (18)$$

as our measure of noncanonicity.

The quantity e^F,

$$K = e^{-\int \mu \ln\left(\frac{\mu}{\mu_0}\right) dX} = \mu_0 \, e^{-\int \mu \ln \mu \, dX}, \qquad (19)$$

is often called the *thermodynamic weight* or the *thermodynamic probability* of a given distribution. This terminology has its roots in a different approach to the whole problem of canonical distributions, an approach that was adopted by the founders of the statistical theory of heat, primarily Boltzmann.

Boltzmann discovered the Boltzmann factor by an argument that is not based at all on the consideration of ensembles. He investigated the distribution of identical subsystems (say molecules) that were loosely coupled to form a composite system (a macroscopic amount of matter). He argued as follows: Assuming that the composite system is ergodic, it will on the average occupy a given volume in phase space for a length of time proportional to that volume. In terms of the phase spaces of the subsystems (all of which are replicas of each other), we can get a very good picture of the distribution-in-time by first subdividing each sub-system phase space into small cells of equal volume. The Cartesian product of one cell of the phase space of subsystem 1 by one cell of the phase space of subsystem 2, and so on, and finally by one cell of the phase space of subsystem N (N being the number of molecules in our composite system) is then a typical cell in the big phase space, and these cells likewise all possess equal volume. Our composite system will then spend the same percentage of time (if we wait long enough) in each one of these standard cells in the big phase space, and we say that these cells have equal *a priori probability*.

Boltzmann then proceeded to derive the average distribution of the molecules over their phase spaces by pointing out that different combinations of "occupation numbers" (n_1 molecules in their first cells, n_2 molecules in their second cells, and so on) covered widely varying numbers of cells in the big phase space and would thus be maintained by the composite system as a whole for very different lengths of time. As a matter of fact, an estimate that we shall not carry out here shows that the overwhelming majority of standard cells corresponds to occupation numbers in the immediate vicinity of the "most probable distribution," that is, the combination of occupation numbers possessing the largest number of standard cells.

Let us quickly determine the number of standard cells correspond-ing to a set of occupation numbers $n_1, n_2, \cdots$, consistent with the obvious requirement that

$$\sum_{k=1}^{\infty} n_k = N \tag{20}$$

In order to place n_1 molecules into the first cell, we must lift n_1 mole-cules out of a total number of N. This can be done in

$$P_1 \doteq \frac{N!}{n_1! \, (N - n_1)!} \tag{21}$$

different ways. As the next step, we must lift out of the remaining $(N - n_1)$ molecules n_2 and place them into the second cell of the small phase spaces. We find then that we can occupy the first two cells with n_1 and n_2 molecules, respectively, in

$$P_1P_2 = \frac{N!}{n_1!\,(N-n_1)!}\,\frac{(N-n_1)!}{n_2!\,(N-n_1-n_2)!}$$
$$= \frac{N!}{n_1!\,n_2!\,(N-n_1-n_2)!} \tag{22}$$

different ways. If we continue this procedure indefinitely, we shall eventually exhaust the whole supply of molecules, and we find that the total number of standard cells of the big phase space belonging to our distribution of molecules among the cells of the little phase space is given by the expression

$$P = \prod_{k=1}^{\infty} P_k = \frac{N!}{\displaystyle\prod_{k=1}^{\infty} (n_k!)}. \tag{23}$$

For an isolated system (the gas to be enclosed in walls that are perfect heat insulators), the total energy E is also constant. Thus, if the average energy of states in the first cell is ϵ_1, and generally in the kth cell ϵ_k, then the occupation numbers, in addition to eq. (20), must satisfy the further condition

$$\sum_{k=1}^{\infty} n_k\epsilon_k = E. \tag{24}$$

With these two restrictions, we must now attempt to maximize P of eq. (23).

Strictly speaking, our problem requires the examination of all possible integers for $n_1, \cdots, n_k, \cdots$; but the problem is considerably simplified if we replace the factorials by the asymptotic expressions known as Stirling's formula and if we treat the occupation numbers as if they were continuously variable. According to Stirling's formula, for large numbers n the expression

$$n! \sim \sqrt{2\pi n}\left(\frac{n}{e}\right)^n \tag{25}$$

is a very good approximation. Substituting, we find then that

$$\ln P \sim N \ln N - \sum_{k=1}^{\infty} n_k \ln n_k. \tag{26}$$

Maximizing P itself is equivalent to maximizing its logarithm. Thus we find that the most probable distribution of the molecules is characterized by the requirement that

$$\delta P = - \sum_{k=1}^{\infty} (\ln n_k + 1)\, \delta n_k = 0, \tag{27}$$

where the variations of the n_k are restricted by the two auxiliary conditions

$$\sum_k \delta n_k = 0, \qquad \sum_k \epsilon_k\, \delta n_k = 0. \tag{28}$$

If we apply the method of Lagrange multipliers, as before, we find that

$$\ln n_k = \alpha - 1 - \gamma \epsilon_k,$$
$$n_k = A\, e^{-\gamma \epsilon_k}, \tag{29}$$

where α and γ are again the two Lagrange multipliers. These two multipliers are determined by the requirement that the two auxiliary conditions be satisfied. Substituting first into eq. (20), we find

$$A = \left(\sum_{k=1}^{\infty} e^{-\gamma \epsilon_k} \right)^{-1}. \tag{30}$$

As for the other parameter, γ, we cannot in general solve for it in closed form, but it is obvious that the condition obtained from eq. (24),

$$E = \frac{\displaystyle\sum_{k=1}^{\infty} \epsilon_k\, e^{-\gamma \epsilon_k}}{\displaystyle\sum_{k=1}^{\infty} e^{-\gamma \epsilon_k}} \tag{31}$$

has only one solution.

If we choose our equal-volume cells very small in order to increase accuracy and finally go over to the limit of infinitesimal cell size, the quantity P of eq. (23) approaches, except for a constant factor, the expression K of eq. (19), and the sum (26) goes over into the integral F, eq. (9). In order to establish the complete parallelism between the Boltzmann results and ours, we must reinterpret Boltzmann's composite system as an ensemble in contact with a temperature bath; the temperature bath is in this case the totality of all the other members of the ensemble. Our procedure, to start right away with ensembles and to develop the notion of canonical distribution as an ensemble distribution and not as the most probable distribution of the components of a composite system, was originated by Gibbs and is considerably more powerful than the original Boltzmann ideas. Our procedure also circumvents the need for introducing expressions like P of eq. (23) that increase beyond limit as the cell size is decreased unless they are artificially kept finite with the help of a normalization factor. Later, in quantum mechanics, we shall encounter situations in which the standard cells have a fixed finite size; but in that case again, we shall use the Gibbs concepts and look for average rather than for most probable distributions.

For an ensemble of closed systems, the integral F, eq. (9), is constant in the course of time, because of Liouville's theorem. For a system that is in contact with its surroundings, we can obtain a very important result provided the ensemble distribution is and remains canonical. In that case, F_c is given by the expression (10) at all times; but if we go back to eq. (4.18), we find that the amount of heat transferred to a canonical ensemble equals

$$\delta Q = \frac{1}{\beta}\, \delta F_c. \tag{32}$$

In other words, the amount of heat transferred to a canonical ensemble, though not a variable of state itself, becomes one if we multiply it by β. And the product $\beta\, \delta Q$ represents the change in F_c.

5.3. The second law

Suppose we have two canonical ensembles representing systems of different types at different temperatures; that is, their β-values are different. Naturally, these two ensembles can coexist and each remain canonical only as long as they are insulated from each other. If these two ensembles are now brought into thermal contact, the composite systems will also possess a distribution, but that distribution will not be canonical and will not become canonical if the new composite systems are kept insulated from their surroundings. But we can easily determine the value of F for the composite system, since the relationship between the density in the composite phase space and the densities in the two component phase spaces is simply

$$\mu = \mu_1\mu_2, \qquad dX = dX_1\,dX_2. \tag{33}$$

We have, therefore, quite generally,

$$F = \int \int \mu_1\mu_2 \ln\left(\frac{\mu_1^0\mu_2^0}{\mu_1\mu_2}\right) dX_1\,dX_2$$

$$= \int \int \mu_1\mu_2 \left(\ln\frac{\mu_1^0}{\mu_1} + \ln\frac{\mu_2^0}{\mu_2}\right) dX_1\,dX_2 = F_1 + F_2 \tag{34}$$

$$(\mu_0 = \mu_1^0\mu_2^0).$$

The function F is simply additive.

The composite ensemble is not canonical; but we can convert its distribution into a canonical distribution if we permit it to come into thermal contact with a temperature bath that has been chosen so that on the average the amount of heat energy transferred between the composite system and the bath is zero. In that case, $\langle E \rangle$ will not change, but the distribution will become canonical. We have proved previously that if the values of $\langle E \rangle$ belonging to an arbitrary and a canonical distribution are equal, then F_c is always greater than F. It follows that F_c for the composite system will exceed the sum of the F_c-values of the two components provided the $\langle E \rangle$-value of the composite system equals the sum of the mean energies of the component ensembles. *This statement is equivalent to the second law of thermodynamics.* In thermodynamics, we assume implicitly that a system can always be represented by a canonical ensemble having the mean energy possessed by our actual system.

So far, we have started with two component systems at different temperatures. This assumption is, however, quite unnecessary. Suppose, for instance, that we start with two component systems consisting of one mol of oxygen and two mols of hydrogen gas, respectively. If they are originally at the same temperature and then mixed, the resultant mixture will be far from canonical. One of the reasons is that in this case the energy surfaces are not connected, and the H_2O gas having the same energy is fairly inaccessible in phase space. But let a spark act as a catalyst, and suddenly we find that our mixture radically changes its distribution in phase space and that it finally settles, in a completely adiabatic process, into a distribution having a much higher temperature than the original components. Again, the final F_c will be considerably greater than the sum of the F_c-values of the two original component systems.

Inaccessible domains of phase space are by no means rare. Consider a supercooled liquid. Such a system takes an extremely long time to reach that domain of phase space in which a really stable distribution is possible. In the meantime, the motion of the representative point in a limited portion of phase space is so rapid that the system appears quasi-ergodic in that portion of phase space, and we can assign to the system a temperature for almost any practical purpose, though strictly speaking the distribution-in-time is not canonical. If the system suddenly gains access to the whole of its energy surface, the resulting distribution will almost always have a different temperature and, according to our general proof, it will have an increased value of F_c. When a distribution is not strictly canonical but is canonical with respect to a limited domain of phase space from which the remainder is poorly accessible, we call that distribution, as well as the state of one system represented by that distribution, *metastable*.

We shall give our results yet another interpretation, one that is valid on the assumption of quasi-ergodicity. If we assume that a system in contact with a temperature bath forms a quasi-ergodic composite system, then the system itself will have a distribution-in-time that is identical with a canonical ensemble distribution. Likewise, if we form the time average of F for such a system (in its phase space, without the phase space of the temperature bath), then that time average must equal F_c. Under these circumstances, we may associate with any system that has a given energy the value F_c of the canonical distribution with the same mean energy. Thus F_c becomes a thermodynamic variable of state, just like the pressure (which also has only statistical significance). We call this variable the *entropy*. The customary symbol is S. In the case of a metastable system, we assign the time average F'_c that corresponds to quasi-ergodic motion on the restricted energy surface. With these definitions, it is then correct to state that in the absence of heat transfer from the surroundings the establishment of thermal contact between components originally isolated from each other, or the transition of a system from a metastable state into a more stable one, or any similar process produces an increase in the entropy.

What happens if heat can be transferred from the surroundings?

In that case we can always represent the total process as a sequence of infinitesimal processes, each one constituting either pure heat transfer or pure internal adjustment. The result, because of eq. (32), is

$$\delta S > \beta \, \delta Q. \tag{35}$$

In thermodynamics, the inequality (35) represents the most general formulation of the second law.

Let us briefly summarize the results obtained in this section. We have found a phase space integral, F, which depends on the assumed distribution of an ensemble in phase space and which is an integral of the motion. For a given value of the mean energy of the ensemble, F assumes its absolutely largest value for the canonical distribution belonging to that value for $\langle E \rangle$. We have designated this largest value of F for a given value of $\langle E \rangle$ by F_c.

If we consider F_c as a function of the Hamiltonian of the system (or of the macroscopic parameters characterizing it) and of the mean energy, it may be considered a thermodynamic variable of state, depending, as it does, only on the usual $(n + 1)$ macroscopic parameters. Taken with this meaning, F_c has the important property that its change is directly related to the heat transferred from the outside to the system (assumed to be represented by a canonical ensemble) by means of eq. (32). In any heat exchange with the outside, the (infinitesimal) amount of heat transferred to the system, though not itself an exact differential, forms an exact differential when multiplied by β. We find that in any nonsimple system (such as the composite of two systems originally isolated from each other, a system in metastable equilibrium, and so on) the internal changes leading to an approach of the macroscopic parameters to their equilibrium values will cause the value of F_c to increase. Altogether, in any thermodynamic process involving both internal reorganization and heat exchange with the surroundings, the inequality (35) will be satisfied. The restrictive word "thermodynamic" in this sentence means that all processes considered must proceed sufficiently slowly that either the system as a whole or at least its components may be represented at each stage by canonical ensembles. The value of δS is determined by the temperature of that component (if the system as a whole does not possess one temperature) which receives heat.

5.4. Thermodynamic derivation. Kelvin scale

In thermodynamics proper, the second law can be obtained from an entirely different starting point. Because of its transcending importance, we shall report these derivations in addition to the one from statistical mechanics. The purely thermodynamic derivation has the advantage of employing concepts somewhat closer to the procedures of the experimenting physicist.

Two things need to be shown: that the heat transferred, multiplied by a certain function of the temperature, becomes the derivative of a variable of state; and that this variable of state, for internal processes of an isolated system, whether simple or composite, always increases.

All thermodynamic proofs of these two assertions start with the observation that certain (macroscopic) processes in nature are always observed to take place in one direction only: heat is transferred from the hotter to the colder body, diffusion always leads to more complete mixing, friction always converts mechanical into heat energy, and so forth. None of these processes are ever observed to operate in reverse. The task of distilling from these diverse processes their common characteristics and of clothing these characteristics into one all-embracing statement occupied several generations of physicists and physical chemists. The final formulation is the assertion of *the impossibility of a perpetuum mobile of the second kind: It is not possible to construct a cycle that does nothing but withdraw heat energy from a temperature bath and convert it wholly into (macroscopic) mechanical energy.* In this statement, the restriction to cycles is important. After all, a gas that expands adiabatically and that cools in the process does nothing but convert part of the heat energy of its molecules into macroscopic energy. But, according to our primary assumption, it is impossible to accomplish this conversion in a cycle, that is, in a process that in the end returns the thermodynamic system to its original state.

This formulation of the basic statement has surprising generality. It does imply the *irreversibility* of certain processes, because the reverse of the *perpetuum mobile* of the second kind is obviously possible: to construct a cycle that does nothing but convert mechanical energy wholly into heat energy. Joule's paddle wheel, which turns in a viscous liquid and heats it up, is such a mechanism, and it must therefore be irreversible. That is to say, we cannot undo the results of operating Joule's paddle wheel in any manner so that at the end of our operations nothing has changed in the universe except that the weight (that drove the paddle wheel originally) has been raised back to its starting level and the liquid has been cooled correspondingly. Naturally, if we permit ourselves to bring about other changes somewhere in our auxiliary equipment, we can go back to the starting situation; but in that case our auxiliary devices have not carried out a cycle. It follows that for an isolated system we can arrange its possible states in a hierarchy; for any given set of two states, A and B, it is either possible to go back and forth between A and B; or we can go from A to B, but not from B to A; or we can go from B to A, but not from A to B; all without producing permanent changes elsewhere.[1]

If all states can be arranged thus in a hierarchy, then there must exist a parameter, a variable of state, that characterizes the position of a given state within that hierarchy. Without yet having properly determined that parameter, which we shall call the entropy S, we shall agree that if transitions are possible between two states A and B in either direction, then we shall assign them the same value of S; if transition from A to B is possible, but not vice versa, we shall assign B a larger value of S than A; and so forth. In this manner, we have partially defined S so that it is bound to increase for all irreversible processes of a closed system and that it remains unchanged in a reversible process. We must now attempt to relate S to the other variables of state.

To do so, we shall consider a rather complex system, consisting of four components. Two components will be two temperature baths, at two different temperatures measured on some conventional scale and designated by θ_1 and θ_2, θ_1 being the higher temperature of the two. One component will be a "machine" capable of exchanging heat with either of the two baths and of performing work in accordance with the two laws of thermodynamics. Such a "machine" can be very elaborate, but it can also be very simple,

---

[1] In order not to get into difficulties with the first law of thermodynamics, we shall always include with our system some repository of mechanical energy: a weight that can be raised and lowered, a spring that can be wound up or released, or some similar device. Then we can always use that repository to make all conceivable states of the thermodynamic portion of the system energetically possible.

being, for instance, just a quantity of gas in a cylinder fitted with a piston. The performance of work will consist of displacements of the piston, and the exchange of heat will be accomplished by plain conduction through the cylinder walls. The fourth component of our assembly will be the repository of mechanical energy that we need in order not to run afoul of the first law.

In all the processes that we consider, we shall always let the machine go through an integral number of cycles. That is, at the end of each process the machine shall have returned exactly to its original state; volume and temperature of the gas, for instance, must be the same at the end as they were at the start. The only differences between the different states of our composite system that we shall consider can be described fully by the amounts of heat withdrawn from or delivered to the two baths, and changes in the amount of energy in the repository. In order to simplify matters further, we shall also assume that both baths are so large that their temperatures do not change appreciably in the course of the experiment. By making all these assumptions, we relieve ourselves of the need of discussing the contribution of the machine to the entropy of the composite system, and we need not worry about finite changes in the temperature of a bath.

Clearly, we cannot hope to carry out a process in which we withdraw heat from one bath, convert it into energy, and deposit all this energy in the repository. That is just the kind of process excluded by our original assumption. However, there are processes in which we can withdraw heat from the hot bath, convert part of that heat into mechanical energy (which we deposit), and transfer the balance to the cool bath. In fact, any steam engine in which the condensed water is returned to the boiler provides an example. We shall call the ratio between the mechanical energy produced and the amount of heat withdrawn from the hot bath the *efficiency* of our machine, for obvious reasons. No machine can have an efficiency equal to 1. But it is possible to construct machines of zero efficiency, for instance if we simply permit heat to pass directly from the hot to the cool bath. The efficiency is thus some fraction between 0 and 1.

We can run our machine in such a manner that it carries out an irreversible process, and, ideally at least, we can run it reversibly. In the latter case it is possible to bring our composite system back to the original state by running the machine in reverse. An example of a reversible process is the well-known Carnot cycle, a series of purely isothermal and purely adiabatic processes carried out with a gas in a cylinder with piston; every step of the Carnot cycle can be reversed, and thus the cycle is reversible as a whole. We shall now prove that the efficiency of an irreversible cycle is always less than the efficiency of a reversible cycle, in other words, that the reversible cycle is the most efficient cycle conceivable.

Let us first run an irreversible cycle until an amount of heat Q_1 has been withdrawn from the hot bath and an amount of work W has been performed. The amount of heat deposited in the cool bath naturally is

$$Q_2 = Q_1 - W. \tag{36}$$

The efficiency of our cycle is equal to W/Q_1. Now let a reversible cycle run in reverse until exactly all of Q_2 has been withdrawn from the cool reservoir. To do so, we have to furnish an amount W' of mechanical energy, and consequently, we shall deliver an amount of heat Q_1',

$$Q_1' = Q_2 + W', \tag{37}$$

to the hot reservoir. The efficiency of the second process equals W'/Q_1'. At the end of the second process, the net change in the state of the cool bath is zero. The net effect on the hot bath is that an amount of heat equal to $Q_1 - Q_1'$ has been withdrawn, and the net effect on the repository of energy is that an equal amount of mechanical energy has been deposited. If our original assumption about the impossibility of a *perpetuum mobile* of the second kind is to be valid, then the quantity $Q_1 - Q_1'$ must be negative; altogether, under these circumstances, mechanical energy must have been converted into heat, not vice versa. Hence we can conclude that

$$Q_1' > Q_1, \qquad W' > W, \qquad \frac{W}{Q_1} < \frac{W'}{Q_1'}, \tag{38}$$

and that was the assertion to be proved. By exactly the same argument, we can also show that if there are two different ways to run a reversible cycle between the hot and the cool bath, these two reversible cycles must have the same efficiency. Otherwise, we could construct a *perpetuum mobile* of the second kind by letting the less efficient process run backward and by combining it with the more efficient cycle run forward. We conclude then, finally, that the efficiency η of a reversible cycle is not only the greatest efficiency attainable but is also a quantity that is entirely independent of the detailed nature of the reversible cycle employed. η will be a universal function of the temperatures of the two baths. We shall now consider a series of processes that will tell us just how η depends on these two arguments.

Consider three temperature baths, at temperatures θ_1, θ_2, and θ_3, and establish reversible cycles running between any two of them. Let the first bath be the hottest and the third the coolest. If we withdraw an amount Q_1 from the hottest bath, do some work W_1 by means of a reversible cycle, and deliver the balance of energy Q_2 to the second bath, and if we then withdraw that same amount again, let another reversible cycle do an amount of work W_2, and deposit the remaining energy Q_3 in the coolest bath, the net effect of our two processes will be that there is no change in the second bath, that a total amount of work $W_1 + W_2$ has been performed, and that heat has been delivered to the coolest bath. Every part of this procedure is reversible, and therefore also the process as a whole. Since the second bath has been returned to its original state, the whole process may be considered a reversible cycle running between the first and the third baths; and its efficiency,

$$\eta = \frac{1}{Q_1} (W_1 + W_2) \equiv \eta(\theta_1, \theta_3), \tag{39}$$

must be determined completely by θ_1 and θ_3 and must be independent of θ_2. On the other hand, the ratio (39) can also be expressed in terms of the efficiencies of the cycles running between the first and the second, and the second and the third baths, respectively. The work W_1 must be

$$W_1 = \eta(\theta_1, \theta_2) \, Q_1, \tag{40}$$

and the heat transferred to the second bath

$$Q_2 = [1 - \eta(\theta_1, \theta_2)] \, Q_1. \tag{41}$$

As a result, the work done in the next cycle, W_2, must be

$$W_2 = \eta(\theta_2, \theta_3)[1 - \eta(\theta_1, \theta_2)] \, Q_1. \tag{42}$$

If we substitute these expressions, we get the relationship

$$\eta(\theta_1, \theta_3) = \eta(\theta_1, \theta_2) + \eta(\theta_2, \theta_3)[1 - \eta(\theta_1, \theta_2)]. \tag{43}$$

If we now replace the efficiencies themselves by new quantities,

$$\eta(\theta_1, \theta_2) = 1 - \epsilon(\theta_1, \theta_2), \quad \text{etc.,} \tag{44}$$

we get for the functions ϵ the simple relationship

$$\epsilon(\theta_1, \theta_3) = \epsilon(\theta_1, \theta_2)\, \epsilon(\theta_2, \theta_3). \tag{45}$$

It can be shown quite easily that this relationship can be satisfied only if ϵ has the form

$$\epsilon(\theta_1, \theta_2) \equiv \frac{T(\theta_2)}{T(\theta_1)}. \tag{46}$$

The result of our derivation is, therefore, that there must exist a universal function of the temperature, $T(\theta)$, determined except for an arbitrary constant coefficient. This function determines the efficiency of a reversible cycle by means of the simple formula

$$\eta(\theta_1, \theta_2) = \frac{T(\theta_1) - T(\theta_2)}{T(\theta_1)}. \tag{47}$$

Quite obviously, T increases monotonically with the temperature, and hence it is suitable as a temperature scale in its own right and is independent in its definition of any specific substance and its equation of state. This new temperature scale is called the *absolute*, the *thermodynamic*, or the *Kelvin scale*. Its arbitrary factor is usually fixed by the requirement that the difference between the temperature of freezing and boiling water under standard pressure is to be 100°K. This thermodynamic definition of the absolute temperature is evidently independent of the concept of a perfect gas. It can, however, be shown to be identical with the temperature of the perfect gas, where the perfect gas is defined in terms of its equation of state and as a substance where U is a function of the temperature only (independent of the volume occupied).

If we go back to our original four-component system consisting of two baths, a machine, and an energy repository, we find that for a reversible process

$$\frac{Q_1}{T_1} = \frac{Q_2}{T_2}, \tag{48}$$

whereas for an irreversible process

$$\frac{Q_1}{T_1} - \frac{Q_2}{T_2} > 0. \tag{49}$$

We shall now go a step further. Suppose we construct a system of arbitrary complexity, consisting of n subsystems held at temperatures $\theta_1, \cdots, \theta_n$, a number of "machines" capable of transferring energy reversibly or irreversibly between these subsystems, and an energy repository. In such a system of great complexity, it is particularly important to choose the "machines" of such diminutive size that very small amounts of heat can be transferred by means of complete cycles of the various machines. Any complicated change in the system can be accomplished by means of a succession of elementary steps involving only two subsystems at one time. If we call the amount of heat transferred to the kth subsystem dQ_k, and if we call the absolute temperature of that subsystem T_k, then a reversible process of the whole system is characterized by the equality

$$\sum_{k=1}^{n} \frac{dQ_k}{T_k} = 0. \tag{50}$$

In an irreversible process, at least one subsystem must have received more heat than in a similar reversible process (so that a transition to the final state produced by the reversible process could be accomplished only in violation of the *perpetuum mobile* law of the second kind), or

$$\sum_{k=1}^{n} \frac{dQ_k}{T_k} > 0. \tag{51}$$

Finally, there is no conceivable process by which the end state can differ from the initial state in the manner

$$\sum_{k=1}^{n} \frac{dQ_k}{T_k} < 0 \tag{52}$$

as long as we restrict ourselves to processes within our closed system.

The last three equations have given us a criterion enabling us to decide whether a given infinitesimal process is reversible, irreversible, or impossible. We shall now show that the expression on the left hand is an exact differential and hence that it defines a variable of state for the whole system, and furthermore that this variable of state cannot decrease for any possible process involving only our system; in brief, that this variable is the *entropy*.

For the argument that follows we must remember that the n subsystems capable of heat exchange are all assumed to be *simple;* that is, each whole subsystem is always at one temperature. Once the temperature and the necessary number of additional macroscopic parameters are known (volume, electric potential, or whatever is required to determine the Hamiltonian in the language of statistical mechanics), there is only one possible state for that subsystem. In other words, we do not permit irreversible internal adjustments within a given subsystem, and if necessary we split up such a subsystem into components.

From what we have said about the entropy, it is clear that for our particular system S increases whenever the differential $\sum_k (dQ_k/T_k)$ is positive and remains constant whenever that differential vanishes. We can, therefore, assert that

$$dS = N \sum_{k=1}^{n} \frac{dQ_k}{T_k}, \qquad (53)$$

where the factor N is some function of all the parameters determining the state of our system as a whole. If we can determine that factor N, our task is solved.

Let us split the big system into two smaller parts, each containing at least one subsystem. Each of these parts is similar in construction to the big system. We could run each part as a closed system, and thus we can assign to each state of either part a partial entropy. We shall call these partial entropies S_I and S_{II}. We shall now show that S, if written as a function of S_I, S_{II}, and a number of additional variables as required to define the exact state of each part, is actually a function of S_I and S_{II} only. Suppose that we carry out a reversible process in which at the end of the process S_I resumes its old value. Then S_{II} must do so as well, for otherwise we could carry out a process in which part I acts merely as a cyclic machine and in which part II goes either through an irreversible or through an impossible process, depending on whether we need to increase or decrease S_{II}. In other words, for any given value of S and S_I, S_{II} is capable of only one value. If we solve this functional relationship with respect to S, we get S as a function of S_I and S_{II} only, without regard to any other variables of state.

Now since the two parts are systems similar in structure to S

itself (though smaller), we can confidently assert that

$$dS_I = N_I \sum_{k=1}^{l} \frac{dQ_k}{T_k},$$

$$dS_{II} = N_{II} \sum_{k=l+1}^{n} \frac{dQ_k}{T_k}, \tag{54}$$

where N_I is an unknown function of the variables of the first part only, while N_{II} depends on the variables of the second part. Since, on the other hand, for any process

$$dS = \frac{\partial S(S_I, S_{II})}{\partial S_I} dS_I + \frac{\partial S(S_I, S_{II})}{\partial S_{II}} dS_{II}, \tag{55}$$

we find, by simple substitution from eqs. (53) and (54), and because the quantities dQ_k are arbitrary (these relations hold for any kind of process, whether impossible, reversible, or irreversible), that

$$\frac{\partial S}{\partial S_I} = \frac{N}{N_I}, \qquad \frac{\partial S}{\partial S_{II}} = \frac{N}{N_{II}}, \tag{56}$$

or

$$\frac{N_I}{N_{II}} = \frac{\partial S/\partial S_{II}}{\partial S/\partial S_I}. \tag{57}$$

On the left-hand side, N_I depends only on variables describing part I, and N_{II} only on variables describing part II. On the right-hand side, we have an expression that depends only on S_I and S_{II} and none of the other variables. Clearly, N_I must be a function of S_I only, and N_{II} a function of S_{II} only. We shall now show that under these circumstances we may set both N_1 and N_{II} equal to 1.

If we had a function S serving appropriately as entropy, then any new function that is a function of S only (and does not depend on any of the other variables of state) and increases with S monotonically would also be suitable as a measure of reversibility. Thus, from what we have said so far, the new function would also serve as entropy. We can use this freedom of choice by introducing, as a new partial entropy, the function $\bar{S}_I$, which is defined by the differential equation

$$d\bar{S}_I = \frac{dS_I}{N_I}, \qquad \bar{S}_I = \int \frac{dS_I}{N_I(S_I)}. \tag{58}$$

In the same manner, we shall introduce the function $\bar{S}_{II}$ as the partial entropy of part II. Since we shall use these normalizations for entropies consistently, we shall drop the bar and set, as a specialization of eqs. (54),

$$dS_I = \sum_{k=1}^{l} \frac{dQ_k}{T_k},$$
$$dS_{II} = \sum_{k=l+1}^{n} \frac{dQ_k}{T_k}. \tag{59}$$

It follows immediately that we can also set the total entropy change equal to .

$$dS = dS_I + dS_{II} = \sum_{k=1}^{n} \frac{dQ_k}{T}, \tag{60}$$

and that is our final result.

Our expression for the entropy is an additive function; that is, the entropy of a composite system equals the sum of the entropies of the individual components. We can also generalize our result for the case that our system is not isolated but is in heat exchange with its surroundings. For a system in thermal contact with the outside world, we call a reversible process one in which any increase or decrease in entropy is offset by a corresponding decrease or increase elsewhere, so that the total entropy of the universe (if this function can be defined) is not affected by the process we are considering.[1] If heat can thus be transferred from the outside, the decrease in entropy of the outside is determined by the amounts of heat transferred to the inside, at the temperatures at which these transfers take place. If we call the amount of heat transferred to the k-th subsystem *from the outside* dQ_k^*, then the increase in entropy of the outside equals $- \sum_k dQ_k^*/T_k$, and our characterizations of reversible and irreversible processes become

$$dS - \sum_k \frac{dQ_k^*}{T_k} \geq 0. \tag{61}$$

---

[1] To obviate the necessity for considering the "entropy of the universe," we can think of our system as part of a greater but finite system that is closed.

These expressions represent the most general mathematical formulation of the second law. They become identical with the expression of eq. (35) of Section 5.3, provided we set

$$\beta = \frac{1}{kT} \tag{62}$$

and multiply the entropy of eq. (35) by the factor k. k is a conversion factor introduced by the historical fact that the original definition of the Kelvin scale was not determined by knowledge of the canonical exponent of statistical mechanics but by close relationship to the centigrade scale. k is called the *Boltzmann constant*. Its numerical value is 1.37×10^{-16} erg/degree.

5.5. Applications

The entropy of a perfect gas. It is well known that the equation of state of a perfect gas is

$$pV = nRT \tag{63}$$

and its internal energy

$$U = nc_vT. \tag{64}$$

In both these equations, n is the number of mols present. R is the gas constant. For the entropy we have the differential equation

$$dS = \frac{dQ}{T} = \frac{1}{T}(dU + p\,dV) = nc_v\frac{dT}{T} + nR\frac{dV}{V}, \tag{65}$$

and its integral is

$$S = n\left(c_v \ln \frac{T}{T_0} + R \ln \frac{V}{V_0}\right). \tag{66}$$

On the other hand, we can also determine the entropy of the gas from its micromodel. Let us assume that each molecule has f degrees of freedom on which its energy depends quadratically. In n mols there are, altogether, nN molecules, where N is Avogadro's number. Thus the total number of degrees of freedom is fnN. By carrying out the integrations indicated in eq. (3.90), we can find the correct expression for the partition function,

$$Z = Z_0 V^{nN} \beta^{-\frac{1}{2}fnN}. \tag{67}$$

The entropy equals F_c, eq. (10), except for the normalization factor k

(the Boltzmann constant), and we have

$$S = k\beta\langle E \rangle + k(\ln Z_0 + nN \ln V - \tfrac{1}{2}fnN \ln \beta)$$
$$= k(\ln Z_0 + \tfrac{1}{2}fnN + nN \ln V - \tfrac{1}{2}fnN \ln \beta) \tag{68}$$

Let us combine all the constant terms into one and designate it by S_0. We find then that the entropy is

$$S = S_0 + nkN(\ln V + \tfrac{1}{2}f \ln T), \tag{69}$$

because of eq. (62). If we compare this result with the thermodynamic expression (66), we come to the conclusion that the Boltzmann constant k is equal to the molar gas constant R, divided through by Avogadro's number; *k is the gas constant per molecule.*

Incidentally, we find that the gas temperature, which we introduced in Chapter 3, eq. (3.78), is identical with the Kelvin scale, and that the constant κ in that equation equals the Boltzmann constant k. There remains, however, an essential conceptual distinction between the gas temperature scale θ_g and the absolute temperature T. The former is a conventional temperature scale, defined with the help of a particular (idealized) equation of state, that of the so-called perfect or ideal gas; the definition of the Kelvin scale, on the other hand, is based on general laws of thermodynamics and quite independent of the equation of state of any particular substance, idealized or otherwise.

Experimental determination of the Kelvin scale. Suppose we wish to determine the Kelvin scale in terms of some conventional temperature scale θ, and assume that we have available for this purpose the complete equation of state of some fluid, as well as knowledge of its internal energy U as a function of its volume V and the (conventional) temperature θ.

We start by rewriting the differential equation for the entropy:

$$dS = \frac{dQ}{T} = \frac{1}{T}(dU + p\,dV)$$
$$= \frac{1}{T}\left[\left(\frac{\partial U}{\partial V}\right)_\theta + p\right]dV + \frac{1}{T}\left(\frac{\partial U}{\partial \theta}\right)_V d\theta. \tag{70}$$

The absolute temperature T is some function of our conventional temperature θ, the unknown function we have set out to determine. Now S is a variable of state, and the differential (70) is therefore an *exact* differential. It follows that the partial derivative of the coefficient of dV with respect to θ must equal the partial derivative of the coefficient of $d\theta$ with respect to V:

$$\frac{\partial}{\partial\theta}\left\{\frac{1}{T}\left[\left(\frac{\partial U}{\partial V}\right)_\theta + p\right]\right\}_V - \frac{\partial}{\partial V}\left[\frac{1}{T}\left(\frac{\partial U}{\partial\theta}\right)_V\right]_\theta$$
$$= \frac{1}{T}\left(\frac{\partial p}{\partial\theta}\right)_V - \left[\left(\frac{\partial U}{\partial V}\right)_\theta + p\right]\frac{dT}{T^2 d\theta} = 0. \quad (71)$$

In this equation, we can now separate T from the other functions, obtaining

$$\frac{d\ln T}{\partial\theta} = \frac{\left(\frac{\partial p}{\partial\theta}\right)_V}{\left(\frac{\partial U}{\partial V}\right)_\theta + p}. \quad (72)$$

The integral of this separated differential equation is

$$T = T_0\exp\left\{\int\frac{\left(\frac{\partial p}{\partial\theta}\right)_V d\theta}{\left(\frac{\partial U}{\partial V}\right)_\theta + p}\right\}, \quad (73)$$

and this formula is the desired result. The integral can be taken over θ for arbitrary reversible processes; in other words, the integrand is independent of V. The factor of integration, here called T_0, is the arbitrary factor that is standardized by the requirement that the step interval between the freezing point and the boiling point of water be the same as in the centigrade scale. The location of the absolute zero, near $-273°C$, is, of course, independent of the disposition over this factor. The absolute zero represents a canonical distribution with β equal to ∞, that is, a distribution where all systems are at the lowest available energy level.

Helmholtz and Gibbs potentials. When a (composite) system undergoes changes in which the total available volume is being kept constant (meaning in more general terms that the Hamiltonian of the statistically interpreted system remains constant), reversible changes are characterized by the equation

$$dS = \frac{dQ}{T} = \frac{dU}{T} \quad (74)$$

while for an irreversible change

$$dS - \frac{dU}{T} > 0. \quad (75)$$

For composite systems it is possible to have changes in which both the temperature and the volume remain constant. Consider, for instance, Joule's paddle wheel. Starting from a state in which the weight is on a high level, we may permit the weight to drop slowly and to heat the viscous liquid. If at the same time we permit the liquid to transfer heat to a constant-temperature bath, our system will carry out a change in which only the total energy changes (that is, the energy of liquid, weight, and paddle wheel), with the volume and the temperature remaining constant. For such an isochoric-isothermal process, eqs. (74) and (75) are equivalent to

$$dF \leq 0, \qquad F = U - ST. \tag{76}$$

The expression F, called the *Helmholtz potential*, will always decrease for this type of process. In terms of the partition function, the Helmholtz potential is

$$F = F_0 - \frac{1}{\beta} \ln Z = \frac{1}{\beta} \ln \frac{Z_0}{Z}. \tag{77}$$

A similar function exists for isobaric-isothermal processes. If the pressure remains constant during a process, we have

$$dS \geq \frac{dQ}{T} = \frac{1}{T} d(U + pV) = \frac{d\Psi}{T}. \tag{78}$$

If the temperature remains constant as well, it follows that

$$dG \leq 0, \qquad G = U + pV - ST = \Psi - ST. \tag{79}$$

The function G is called the *Gibbs potential*. Some authors call F and others call G the *free energy*, and among physical chemists the Gibbs potential is frequently denoted by F. In the face of such confusion, it is advisable in reading both texts and research papers to make sure what significance the author attaches to the term "free energy" and to the symbol F. Only the terms *Helmholtz potential* and *Gibbs potential* are completely free of ambiguity in this respect but have the disadvantage of being rather nondescriptive.

Isobaric-isothermal processes are frequent in physical chemistry. If we compress a gas slowly and isothermally at its condensation point, it will gradually liquefy in a reversible manner. In this process the Gibbs potential of the substance remains unchanged, and from this information, the change in volume, and the heat of condensation, we can determine both the change in U and the change in entropy.

Clausius-Clapeyron equation. In transitions of a substance from one phase to another, the equilibrium pressure is a function of the temperature, and vice versa, the transition temperature a function of the pressure. We can determine the dependence of one on the other by carrying out a cycle on the substance: We take the substance along one side of the dividing curve in the phase diagram,

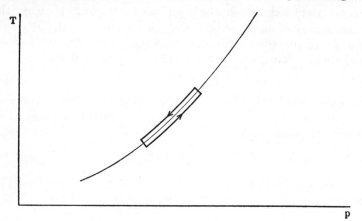

Fig. 5. Cycle along transition curve in phase diagram.

then carry out the transition, go back on the other side of the dividing line, and finally carry out the phase transition leading to the initial state (Fig. 5).

The total change in the entropy S, which must vanish because the process is both cyclic and reversible, consists of four terms,

$$\Delta S = -\frac{\Delta \Psi_2}{T_2} - \int_1^2 \frac{d\Psi' - V'\, dp}{T} + \frac{\Delta \Psi_1}{T_1} + \int_1^2 \frac{d\Psi'' - V''\, dp}{T} = 0, \tag{80}$$

which can be combined as follows:

$$0 = \int_1^2 \left[\frac{1}{T} d\Delta\Psi - \frac{1}{T} \Delta V\, dp - d\left(\frac{\Delta\Psi}{T}\right) \right]$$

$$= \int_1^2 \left(\frac{\Delta\Psi}{T^2} dT - \frac{\Delta V}{T} dp \right) \tag{81}$$

$$(\Delta\Psi = \Psi'' - \Psi', \qquad \Delta V = V'' - V').$$

The last integral must vanish no matter how the two end points are chosen along the phase boundary curve, and the integral can be zero regardless of the limits only if the integrand itself vanishes:

$$\frac{dT}{dp} = \frac{T \, \Delta V}{\Delta \Psi}. \qquad (82)$$

This last equation, which determines the slope of the boundary curve at every point as a function of the temperature, the change in volume, and the heat of formation, is our result; it is known as the *Clausius-Clapeyron equation*. In most changes of phase, the increase in volume and the heat of formation have the same sign, and as a result the temperature at which the change of phase occurs increases with increasing pressure. An exception is provided by the example of the fusion of ice, which was mentioned previously. The heat of fusion is positive, but the volume decreases on melting. As a result, the melting point is lowered by an increase in pressure, and this circumstance is responsible for the skidding of automobile tires on ice at temperatures slightly below freezing. At extremely low temperatures, traction is much better.

Problems

1. Consider a liquid in equilibrium with its vapor, but so that the liquid phase is dispersed and suspended in the form of many small droplets. Consider vapor phase plus droplets as a single system and attempt to formulate a theory of equilibrium distribution of the droplets, including both their number and size distribution, on the assumption that you know both pressure and temperature of the whole system and the following pertinent data: the density of the vapor and the density of the liquid phase, the saturation pressure of the vapor in equilibrium with the liquid having a plane surface (that is, being present in a single drop of infinite size), and the (positive) surface energy per unit area of the liquid-vapor interface.

2. In the usual theory of a van der Waals gas it is shown that the isotherms in a pressure-volume phase diagram have two extremes and a point of inflection for all values of the temperature below the critical temperature. Show that the phase transition that cuts across the region of positive slope of the isotherm will be reversible only if the area under the actual transition curve equals the area under the curve that would be followed if there were no discontinuous phase transition.

3. What information is required to determine the loss in free energy of a chemical reaction that proceeds at ordinary pressure and temperature essentially in one direction only?

Chapter 6

Thermodynamics, Statistical Mechanics,

and Heat-Death

Frequently we hear that the history of natural science had its inception with the giants of the sixteenth and seventeenth centuries; that the first ones to resurrect the spirit of scientific inquiry after the Dark Ages were Galileo, Kepler, and Newton; and further, that from Newton's time onward appeal to tradition or to scholastic authority has been ruled out as an argument in scientific discussions. While there is some substance in these assertions, the whole truth is a good deal more involved than would appear from such categorical statements. There have been recurrent periods of "scholasticism" long after Newton, though often disguised, and true scientific inquiry existed before Galileo.

If we trace the development of the natural sciences after Newton, we find considerable insistence on established theory, even though evidence against it was available or could have been obtained without great difficulty. Newton himself was apparently wavering concerning the nature of light, feeling that the evidence then known did not decisively favor either a corpuscular or a wave hypothesis. But in view of the fact that a noncorpuscular light would be hard to fit into the framework of mechanics, Newton's successors insisted for a long time on the corpuscular hypothesis. Finally, the greatest physicists of the nineteenth century attempted to interpret the by then undeniable wave nature of light, and electromagnetic effects in general, as states of mechanical stress of a hypothetical medium, the ether. It was not until well after the discovery of the special theory of relativity that these attempts ceased.

Likewise, the theory of heat was destined to shatter Newton's theoretical foundation of the natural sciences. The first discovery required was, of course, the realization of the statistical nature of heat. Originally, and well into the nineteenth century, the prevalent belief had been that heat was a substance somewhat like the ether, present in varying amounts in other chemical substances, and capable of being liberated by chemical reactions (burning, for instance) and by phase transitions.   That heat is a form of energy rather than a substance was discovered in the middle of the nineteenth century independently by Robert Mayer and by Helmholtz. Even then it was another thirty years or so before the nature of this energy was clearly grasped: that it was not an entirely new form of energy but, rather, mechanical or electromagnetic energy present in atomistic-statistical distribution.

Thus the "classical" theory of heat was developed along two separate lines. On the one hand, we have so-called "phenomenological thermodynamics," based essentially on the two laws of thermodynamics and developed as a macroscopic theory without regard to any implications of the essentially atomistic nature of heat.   Thermodynamics can be developed deductively from the two "principles of impotence"; that no cyclic machine can create or destroy energy, and that no cyclic machine can convert heat energy wholly into other (macroscopic) forms of energy. Its power permits far-reaching conclusions concerning the general nature of thermodynamic (including chemical) processes; an example of its power is the derivation of the Clausius-Clapeyron equation.   But thermodynamics is incapable of predicting the form of an equation of state; the discussion of random phenomena such as Brownian motion is also outside its realm.

Statistical mechanics, the other development of heat theory, is based on the atomistic-statistical nature of heat.   Not only does statistical mechanics include the laws of thermodynamics; with its methods we can treat fluctuations, and we can derive equations of state from hypothesized force laws between the smallest particles— molecules for some considerations, atoms or even subatomic particles for others.   In fact, the power of statistical mechanics is so far-reaching that there is every reason to believe that we have not nearly exhausted its possibilities. Because of its power, we can make predictions that permit the comparison between hypothesized micromodels and macroscopic observations.   And here we run into a number of difficulties that cannot be resolved along classical lines: we do get expressions for the specific heats of gases and solids that are borne out by experimental evidence, but these results are based on micromodels we know to be much too crude; and we can make predictions about the radiation spectra of "black" bodies and of gases that are completely contrary to the facts.

Most of these facts were known by 1880. Nevertheless, it was not until 1925 that modern quantum mechanics was put into such a form that it could replace Newtonian mechanics in the theoretical treatment of atomic phenomena. There are several explanations of how scientists could be so stubborn or so dull. First of all, the discovery of chinks in the armor of an old theory does not automatically lead to a new theory. To formulate a new theory takes positive construction, creative thought that tells the investigator where to look for new experimental evidence and how to proceed theoretically. Second, it is not even possible for a scientific investigator to be unprejudiced. Almost all our theoretical concepts are molded by our experience and by the experience of those who went before us and taught us; but this experience is "educated experience." The intuitive concept of force that everybody develops when as a child he fights with his peers or his elders is very different from the Newtonian concept of force that is useful in mechanics, even though the latter is historically the outgrowth of the former. Modern concepts, such as that of a field or of a canonical ensemble, are even further removed from primitive experience, although they all are related to the real world about us. The creation of new concepts or the constructive modification of old ones is an extremely difficult activity of the educated human mind if this creation is to be more than idle speculation and if the new concepts are to be a real step forward in our understanding of nature. It is only natural for us to be conservative—at every stage, including the present, to try to put new wine into old bottles.

Logically, a theory is discredited when a single observed fact contradicts the theory. In actual investigations of nature, we are frequently not at all certain that a given contradiction is crucial. A physical theory is usually logically complex. Any prediction of statistical mechanics concerning an actual substance, for instance, will stem from a combination of the general principles with very specific assumptions concerning the underlying micromodel. An observed discrepancy may possibly be held to discredit the general conceptual approach, but it may also mean merely that we must assume a more complex micromodel. Thus, it is not only defensible but eminently reasonable for us to interpret newly observed facts in terms of established concepts as long as such attempts seem to have any chance of success.   To decide when these attempts have become fruitless, to judge the need for a completely new approach, and to find the new elements called for has been the accomplishment of the very great scientists of all times.

The theory of heat occupies a peculiar position within the body of classical physics.   On the one hand, it was through statistical mechanics that physicists discovered the key to modern quantum mechanics.   On the other, the concepts of statistical mechanics in their application lead beyond the customary confines of physics in a manner that is not yet completely understood.   Since the second part of this book deals with quantum physics at length, we shall devote the remainder of this chapter to a review of the role of statistics in physics.

Inasmuch as the theory of heat is concerned with systems too complex for detailed treatment, it is absolutely essential to introduce methods enabling us to treat systems whose initial states are incompletely described.   To do so, we introduce the concept of an ensemble, that is, a collection of systems that are similar in some respects but not completely identical.   In our treatment we have considered ensembles of a particular type: all systems of the ensemble possess the same Hamiltonian, but they differ in their initial configurations and momenta.   It is perfectly possible to construct different kinds of ensembles, and this has been done.   One might consider ensembles of systems that have only approximately the same number of molecules ("grand canonical ensembles," for instance).   It is possible to consider systems of which the Hamiltonian functions are not identical but are themselves subject to a statistical distribution, and so on.   However, in one essential respect all these constructs are similar: ensembles as such do not occur in nature; they are merely constructs that enable us to make predictions about an imperfectly known single system.

And thus, whereas predictions about ensemble averages are perfectly definite, the predictions about the system actually present in nature (the subject of our inquiry) are not.   The energy of a system at a known temperature is not perfectly known; we know only a distribution of values we should measure if we were to carry out a long series of measurements on the same system while it remains in contact with a temperature bath. For macroscopic systems, this distribution is so highly peaked that we can be practically certain that the first measurement we make (or any other definite measurement) will deviate only slightly from the predicted mean; what is more, we can predict the rms deviation as well.

As a result, certain thermodynamic quantities are defined only because our information about the actual system is incomplete. Among these quantities are the temperature and the entropy. The temperature of a closed system whose energy we know perfectly is meaningless. At best, we could talk about the temperature of an ensemble of systems having the same Hamiltonian as our one actual system and having a canonical distribution such that the mean energy of the ensemble equals the actual energy of our system. Even with a quasi-ergodic system, we cannot replace canonical ensemble averages by time averages if the system is closed, but only if it is loosely coupled to a temperature bath. The same is true of entropy. Entropy is a quantity defined for an ensemble, not for an individual system. Any consistent formulation of entropy for an ensemble of closed systems leads to the result that the entropy of the ensemble is constant in time. The nearest thing to the second law of phenomenological thermodynamics is the law that the entropy of an ensemble will not decrease; usually it will increase if we bring an originally closed system in contact with a temperature bath at such a temperature that the mean energy transferred is zero.[1]

A great deal has been written about the eventual demise of our universe as a result of the gradual approach of its entropy to the maximum value. From what has been said, there are several logical flaws in the application of the second law to the universe as a whole. First of all, it is difficult to see how one can define an entropy for the universe. As far as we are aware, only one version of the universe exists, and the construction of an ensemble of universes is somewhat dubious. Occasionally, we have defined ensembles as representative of the lack of knowledge we possess about our particular system, and in this manner we could construct an ensemble of universes. The ensemble would not be canonical, since the universe

---

[1] An equivalent formulation is that contact of an ensemble of originally closed systems with temperature baths at any one temperature will lead to an increase of entropy not less than the mean energy transferred to the systems, divided through by the absolute temperature of the baths.

does not possess a uniform temperature, but we can also define an entropy for ensembles that are not canonical.   Unfortunately, as long as the system remains closed, the entropy of the representative ensemble would not change, because of Liouville's theorem, unless, of course, we should receive additional information about the system as we go along.   Such additional information would modify the representative ensemble in that more or better information enables us to reduce the spread of the distribution.   But such a reduction in spread is more likely to lead to an entropy decrease than to an increase.   For instance, it is easy to show that precise knowledge of any one dynamic variable, such as the energy of the system, leads to a negative infinite entropy.   An increase in entropy will result if we can bring our system in contact with a temperature bath (that must be large compared to the system itself) at the right temperature.   This procedure could hardly be given any meaning, even as a conceptual experiment, if our system is the universe.

For ordinary closed systems, it is a matter of common laboratory experience that they "run down."   A liquid initially engaged in some flow pattern in a vessel will eventually come to rest, with a consequent increase in temperature.   However, in the laboratory it is the experimenter who first produces a nonequilibrium situation and then cuts off outside contacts to the extent necessary to observe the running down.   For the universe, our present knowledge gives us no hint how a similar process might have taken place, and consequently the pronouncement of a law of "devaluation of energy" appears to be based on an unwarranted analogy.

There appears to be some evidence that the universe has a history; that the present over-all situation in the universe—distribution of star types, typical distances, and so on—does not represent an eternal state of affairs but has developed more or less steadily during the past 3×10^9 years.   Nobody has even the vaguest notion what the the universe looked like previous to this period, nor do we know where we are headed.   Statistical mechanics, applied to systems of stars, combined with cosmological hypotheses, may give us some ideas, but nothing in this respect can fairly be considered established knowledge of the past of the universe or of its future.

PART II
QUANTA

Summary of Classical Statistical Mechanics

At the beginning of Part II of this book, devoted to quantum physics, we shall summarize in declaratory fashion those results of classical statistical mechanics which are required for an understanding of the early history of quantum mechanics. These results may be arranged under the heading of the *Maxwell-Boltzmann statistics*, the *equipartition law*, and the *theory of specific heats*.

Classical statistical mechanics is the theoretical development of Newtonian mechanics along lines that are specially suitable for a treatment of mechanical systems with exceedingly large numbers of degrees of freedom, numbers of the order of Avogadro's number. In such systems, a tabulation of all the equations of motion together with the initial situation (configuration and velocities of all the component mass points), and their subsequent integration, is out of the question. Nevertheless, such systems as "one mol of oxygen gas" are known empirically to obey certain gross laws of behavior, called the *thermodynamic properties* of the substance. Statistical mechanics succeeds in deriving these gross laws by making a number of assumptions concerning the nature of thermodynamic systems.

The most important of these assumptions is the introduction of the *concept of probability*, with the underlying idea that the thermodynamic laws are not rigorous laws of nature in the same fashion as Newton's laws of mechanics, but rather predictions concerning the "average" behavior of very complex systems. Thus the treatment of an individual system with exactly specified initial conditions is replaced by the treatment of an *ensemble* of systems, that is, a set of similar systems, but started with varying initial conditions. The object of our theoretical treatment, then, is not so much to follow the development of each individual system in the course of time but rather to obtain laws for the behavior of *ensemble averages*, values of interesting physical quantities that have been averaged over all member systems of the ensemble. This approach leads to manageable results only if we apply it to appropriately constructed ensembles. Actually, most of the laws of statistical mechanics are derived for a very restricted class of ensembles.

The first restriction is that we consider primarily *stationary ensembles*, that is, ensembles so constructed that in the course of time the ensemble as a whole does not change its structure, though the individual member systems change. This restriction is justified because in (macroscopic) thermodynamics we ordinarily consider only systems in thermodynamic equilibrium or so close to it that all macroscopic changes take place with unlimited slowness. We find, then, that as a matter of mathematical convenience we can treat stationary ensembles best in phase space, where each individual system appears as a single representative point, the ensemble as a whole as a cloud of points, and the stationary character of an ensemble implies that the density of the cloud at any fixed point in phase space does not change with time. But as a result of the so-called *Liouville's theorem*, we find that for a large class of systems (*quasi-ergodic systems*) the density of the cloud in phase space for a stationary ensemble must be a function of the energy only.

Among all the stationary ensembles, we focus our attention further on an even more restricted class, ensembles that have the density distribution in phase space that would result if the systems were to be permitted to interact thermally (that is, to exchange energy through random processes) with a very much larger system, a *temperature bath*. This interaction is restricted only by the requirement that the combination system-bath is isolated from the remainder of the universe. Strangely enough, it turns out that the resulting distribution-in-phase (density in phase space) is always exponential, regardless of the detailed structure of the temperature bath, and that the only adjustable parameter depends on the total energy available to the system-plus-bath. This remaining parameter is the *temperature;* once we adopt the Kelvin scale of temperature, the density of the cloud in phase space turns out to be

$$\mu = \frac{1}{Z} e^{-\frac{E}{kT}}, \qquad \int \mu \, dX = 1, \qquad (1)$$

where dX is a volume element in phase space,

$$dX = dq_1 \cdots dq_f \, dp_1 \cdots dp_f, \qquad (2)$$

k is a universal constant, known as the *Boltzmann constant*, and Z

is a normalizing factor,

$$Z = \int_X e^{-\frac{E}{kT}} \, dX,$$ (3)

called the *partition function*. Equations (1) to (3) describe the standard or *canonical* ensemble of classical statistical mechanics, also known as *Maxwell-Boltzmann* (or just Boltzmann) *statistics*. All ensemble averages are taken with this density distribution.

In particular, the mean energy of a canonical ensemble is the expression

$$\langle E \rangle = \int_X E \, \mu \, dX,$$ (4)

which more simply can be put into the form

$$\langle E \rangle = k \, T^2 \frac{\partial \ln Z}{\partial T}.$$ (5)

From this expression we can obtain the specific heat of the substance in question by once more differentiating with respect to the Kelvin temperature T. We get

$$C_v = k \frac{\partial}{\partial T} \left(T^2 \frac{\partial \ln Z}{\partial T} \right).$$ (6)

Quite generally, Eqs. (5) and (6) can be used to predict the most important thermal properties of a substance on the basis of the hypothesized forces between its constituent ultimate particles.

In many cases the partition function that follows from some assumed force law between the molecules is very hard to compute, involving, as it does, the integral (3) to be extended over all of phase space. However, a number of general relations can be obtained fairly easily. For instance, if a system is composed of several subsystems that interact with each other only weakly, then the partition function of the composite is the product of the partition functions of the components, and the mean energy (5) of the composite is therefore the sum of the mean energies of the components.

Of special importance, because of the ease of integration and because of the wide applicability of the result, is the case that some of the canonical coordinates of the system appear in the expression for the energy E (the Hamiltonian of the system) *purely quadrati-*

cally. Among such coordinates are the components of the linear momentum of the center of mass of a free molecule (as in a gas), the components of the angular momentum of a rigid body, and both the coordinates and momenta of a harmonic oscillator.

Call such a canonical coordinate that enters the Hamiltonian quadratically x. Then the total Hamiltonian of the system is

$$H = ax^2 + H', \tag{7}$$

where H' is independent of the coordinate x. The partition function under these circumstances is

$$Z = Z' \int_{-\infty}^{\infty} e^{-\frac{a}{kT}x^2} dx = \sqrt{\frac{\pi k T}{a}} Z', \tag{8}$$

where Z' is the partition function belonging to H'. Applying eqs. (5) and (6), we find for $\langle E \rangle$ and for C_v the expressions

$$\langle E \rangle = \langle E' \rangle + \tfrac{1}{2}k T \tag{9}$$

and

$$C_v = C_v' + \tfrac{1}{2}k. \tag{10}$$

In other words, every quadratic coordinate contributes to the specific heat the constant amount $\tfrac{1}{2}k$. This law is known as the *equipartition law* of classical statistical mechanics.

The equipartition law is remarkable in that the value of the coefficient a of Eq. (7) does not enter into the result. This means, for instance, that there is an essential difference, and a discontinuous one, between a rigid molecule and one that has large restoring forces with respect to distortions of its shape. By definition, a perfectly rigid body has no internal degrees of freedom, and there can be no contribution to the heat capacity from internal energy storage. But a body with very strong shape-preserving internal forces will carry out internal vibrations of sufficient amplitude that their contribution to the total energy is, on the average, equal to $\tfrac{1}{2}k T$. Intuitively, this result of the theory appears paradoxical, because the rigid body in physics is nothing but an idealization of a very resilient body.

Nevertheless, in classical physics at any rate, the equipartition law is inescapable. Its qualitative meaning may be appreciated by envisaging what happens if a very stiff harmonic oscillator (normally approximated by a rigid dumbbell) is subjected to random excitation. Suppose the oscillator is initially in its equilibrium position. A random impact will then transfer to it an amount of kinetic energy that is independent of the binding-force constant and depends only on the mass of the vibrating particle. This amount of energy will be the total energy of the oscillator until its next impact, because in an atomic system there is no such thing as continuous damping. Because of the stiffness of the binding force, the amplitude of oscillation will be very small and the frequency high. On the average throughout this oscillation, the kinetic energy will be one half of the total energy imparted, the other half being potential energy. In the event of another random collision, the amount of energy transferred (either accepted or relinquished) will depend only on the average kinetic energy, not on the potential energy. Thus, in the course of many random collisions with other molecules, the mean kinetic energy of vibration will equal the mean kinetic energy of translatory motion of a free (gas) molecule in a particular direction, $\frac{1}{2}k\,T$, and the total energy of vibration, kinetic plus potential energy, will be twice that amount. That is precisely the result obtained by means of the equipartition law.

The equipartition law leads to a number of predictions concerning specific heats that are in close agreement with experimental values, and others that are completely wrong. As for monatomic gases, each molecule has three translatory degrees of freedom, and the specific heat per molecule (atom) should therefore equal $\frac{3}{2}k$ or, per mol, $\frac{3}{2}R$, where R (the gas constant) is the product of the Boltzmann constant k and Avogadro's number N. At normal temperatures, the internal (electronic) degrees of freedom of the atoms do not contribute noticeably to the heat capacity. Likewise, a diatomic gas possesses three translatory and two rotatory degrees of freedom and should therefore have a molar heat of $\frac{5}{2}R$. Finally, a polyatomic gas has one additional degree of freedom and should have a specific heat of $3R$. All specific heats of gases satisfy these predictions fairly well, except at temperatures where there is appreciable chemical decomposition. Although these results indicate the power of the statistical approach to thermodynamic problems, there is a disturbing failure to contribute on the part of the internal vibrations of molecules containing more than one atom. A diatomic molecule possessing one vibratory degree of freedom in addition to the translatory and rotational motions should have a molar heat of $\frac{1}{2}R$, which it does not. Similar discrepancies are to be noted in the case of solids, where the Dulong-Petit law of specific heats can be obtained only if we are willing to disregard the contributions of electronic motion. But the worst disaster befalls the physicist who determines specific heats with the help of the equipartition law when he approaches the problem of radiative equilibrium in a heated cavity. These problems will be dealt with extensively in Chapter 7.

Chapter 7

Early Quantum Theories

7.1. Specific heats. Black-body radiation

Early quantum theories have two origins: the investigation of specific heats and the theory of atomic spectra. To the student of today it would appear that the evidence of spectroscopy is more conspicuous and more clear-cut than that from specific heats. Somewhat surprisingly, it was the investigation of specific heats and in particular the examination of the thermodynamic properties of an empty space filled with electromagnetic radiation that led to constructive results, thirteen years earlier than the theory of spectra. Planck's decisive paper on black-body radiation appeared in 1900,[1] that of Bohr on the hydrogen spectrum in 1913.[2]

Actually, black-body radiation became the starting point for the development of quantum physics because in black-body or cavity radiation there can be no doubt concerning the laws obeyed by the system, and any breakdown of the classical theory must touch the foundations directly.

In Chapter 3 we saw how the specific heats of gases and solids can be explained only by a theory that disregards the contributions of certain internal degrees of freedom. These difficulties are emphasized even more strongly when we examine the equilibrium distribution of electromagnetic radiation in the interior of a cavity. We shall discuss this problem now.

When a solid body is heated to any appreciable degree, it gives off electromagnetic radiation. The hotter the body, the more copious the radiation and the more prevalent the shorter wave lengths. If we compare with each other the frequency characteristics of radiations given off by different substances, we find that the differences between these substances are outweighed by the differences at differ-

---

[1] M. Planck, *Verhand. Deutsch. phys. Ges.*, **2**, 237 (1900); *Ann. Physik*, **4**, 553 (1901).

[2] N. Bohr, *Phil. Mag.*, **26**, 1, 476 (1913).

ent temperatures. This qualitative observation can be put on a firm foundation when we consider equilibrium situations.

Suppose that we enclose a number of different bodies in an enclosing jacket and that this jacket is heated to some particular temperature. We can call the jacket an oven. If the oven is thermostatically controlled, conditions in the interior will gradually settle down to some equilibrium situation in which all the substances in the interior will receive on the average the same types of radiation and in the same amounts as they radiate, so that no one substance in the oven disturbs the equilibrium corresponding to the oven temperature. For each substance the incident radiation within a certain range of wave lengths will be partially reflected, partially absorbed into the interior; the latter amount must equal the amount radiated. Thus the intensity of radiation inside our substance must have a definite ratio to that outside, equal to the absorptivity (1 minus the reflectivity) of that substance at the oven temperature and for the range of wave lengths under consideration. This law, known as *Kirchhoff's law*, enables us to predict the radiation spectrum of every substance at every temperature if we know the equilibrium distribution of electromagnetic radiation for empty space for that same temperature and if we know the absorptivity of the particular substance in question. Consequently, all problems of radiation can be reduced in principle to that of finding the equilibrium distribution of radiation inside an evacuated cavity whose walls are at a particular temperature. It is quite certain that such an equilibrium distribution exists, for otherwise no heated body with cavities inside could ever assume a stationary condition.

We shall now attempt to find the equilibrium distribution by assuming that the walls of the oven are very good reflectors. In crudest approximation, the field in the interior is simply some electromagnetic field in a cavity, bounded on all sides by a perfect conductor (a zero-potential surface). Only as a correction do the walls absorb and reradiate a small fraction of the electromagnetic waves incident on them. In other words, we can consider the electromagnetic fields of the cavity as a nearly closed system that is loosely coupled to a temperature bath, the walls. From what we have said in Chapter 3, the time average of the radiation field inside will be the same as the ensemble average of a canonical distribution. Our task, then, is to find the canonical distribution for a system that consists of electromagnetic radiation inside a cavity with conducting walls.

When we proceed to obtain the canonical distribution, we have the advantage that the laws governing our system are perfectly known (classically speaking): these are the laws of Maxwell as they apply to the vacuum. On the other hand, we have not attempted to formulate statistical mechanics for a *field*, only for *mechanical systems*. However, we shall find that in our special case the generalization is straightforward.

In order to formulate Maxwell's field equations with the necessary boundary conditions, we shall introduce[1] a special set of potentials so that the electric potential vanishes everywhere and the components of the vector potential **A** are related to the components of the electromagnetic field by the equations

$$\mathbf{E} = -\frac{1}{c}\frac{\partial \mathbf{A}}{\partial t}, \qquad \mathbf{B} = \operatorname{curl} \mathbf{A}. \tag{1}$$

The vector potential **A** itself satisfies the differential equations

$$\nabla^2 \mathbf{A} - \frac{1}{c^2}\frac{\partial^2 \mathbf{A}}{\partial t^2} = 0, \qquad \operatorname{div} \mathbf{A} = 0. \tag{2}$$

The boundary condition that the walls are perfect conductors leads to the requirement that the tangential components of the vector potential field at each boundary vanish.

In order to be able to apply the concepts of mechanics to our field-theoretical problem, we shall attempt to replace the partial differential equations typical of a field theory by ordinary differential equations governing the behavior of functions of one coordinate (the time) only. We can carry out this conversion of the field equations by introducing, instead of the field variables themselves, their Fourier components. In other words, we first express each component of the field (in our case, the vector-potential field) as a series in trigonometric functions at each instant of time. The dependence of the field on the spatial coordinates is then expressed completely by the instantaneous values of the (infinitely many) Fourier coefficients. But the dependence on time is reflected in the time-dependence of the Fourier coefficients. It is true that there will be an infinite number of time-dependent variables; and

---

[1] M&E, p. 223, eq. (8.75).

equally, there will be infinitely many ordinary differential equations. But this seemingly impossible problem can be treated because the equations, as we shall find, separate into small groups. Each group of equations corresponds to one normal mode of vibration of the cavity.

Let us choose as our cavity a rectilinear parallelepiped, with edges of length α, β, and γ. The shape of the cavity does not matter too much if we do not care in terms of what functions we expand. For a hollow circular cylinder, for instance, we should need Bessel functions; for a sphere, spherical harmonics. But the calculations are easiest in a parallelepiped, and there are proofs available that all our final results are independent of the shape of the cavity.[1] In our particular cavity, any function of the three coordinates x, y, and z can be expanded into a series of triple products of trigonometric functions of these three coordinates. Ordinarily, Fourier series are used to represent *periodic* functions, and our problem does not call for those. However, it is quite easy to show that any reasonable function of x defined for a domain of x from 0 to α (the function must be bounded, piecewise continuous, and so on) can be expanded into a series of trigonometric functions having a period 2α and chosen so that they are mutually orthogonal in the domain $0 \leq x \leq \alpha$, but are otherwise a complete series of either sines or cosines. An expansion in cosines of the form $\cos (h \pi x/\alpha)$ will represent functions whose first derivatives vanish at 0 and at α, and series expansions in $\sin (h \pi x/\alpha)$ vanish at these two points. We can avoid both of these restrictions and can represent functions of arbitrary behavior even at the end points by adding, if necessary, a linear function of the form $(Ax + B)$ to an expansion in sines, so as to provide for the correct values at the end points; to an expansion in cosines we should have to add a function of the form $(Ax + \frac{1}{2}Bx^2)$.

In our problem these additions are unnecessary. For those components of the field which are required to vanish at the end points, we shall choose an expansion in terms of sines and thus auto-

---

[1] For an elementary discussion, cf. Margenau and Murphy, *The Mathematics of Physics and Chemistry*, Van Nostrand, New York, 1943. A more general discussion is given in Courant and Hilbert, *Methoden der mathematischen Physik*, Vol. 1, Springer, Berlin, 1924; reprinted by Interscience Publishers, New York.

matically satisfy the boundary conditions without restricting as
yet the behavior of the function in the interior. We shall expand
the remaining components in terms of cosines. Thus for the
three vector components A_x, A_y, and A_z we shall get the Fourier
representations

$$A_x = \sum_{h,k,l=0}^{\infty} u_{hkl} \cos \frac{h\pi x}{\alpha} \sin \frac{k\pi y}{\beta} \sin \frac{l\pi z}{\gamma},$$

$$A_y = \sum_{h,k,l=0}^{\infty} v_{hkl} \sin \frac{h\pi x}{\alpha} \cos \frac{k\pi y}{\beta} \sin \frac{l\pi z}{\gamma}, \qquad (3)$$

$$A_z = \sum_{h,k,l=0}^{\infty} w_{hkl} \sin \frac{h\pi x}{\alpha} \sin \frac{k\pi y}{\beta} \cos \frac{l\pi z}{\gamma}.$$

The only additions to these expansions that might be necessary to
ensure generality would be linear and quadratic terms to the
cosine factors. However, such additions are excluded by the
necessity of satisfying the divergence requirement of eq. (2). Hence
the terms indicated in eqs. (3) are the only ones compatible with
eqs. (2). In the triple summations, those integral indices h, k, and l
occurring in a sine factor start with 1, and those occurring in a
cosine factor with 0.

If we substitute the expressions (3) into eqs. (2), we find first
that the divergence requirement imposes a number of algebraic
conditions on the coefficients u_{hkl}, v_{hkl}, and w_{hkl}. These conditions
are

$$\frac{h}{\alpha} u_{hkl} + \frac{k}{\beta} v_{hkl} + \frac{l}{\gamma} w_{hkl} = 0, \qquad (4)$$

and they must be satisfied separately for each combination of three
non-negative integers (h, k, l). As far as the wave equations are
concerned, we get for the time-dependence of the same coefficients
the conditions

$$\pi^2 c^2 \left[\left(\frac{h}{\alpha}\right)^2 + \left(\frac{k}{\beta}\right)^2 + \left(\frac{l}{\gamma}\right)^2 \right] u_{hkl} + \ddot{u}_{hkl} = 0,$$

$$\pi^2 c^2 \left[\left(\frac{h}{\alpha}\right)^2 + \left(\frac{k}{\beta}\right)^2 + \left(\frac{l}{\gamma}\right)^2 \right] v_{hkl} + \ddot{v}_{hkl} = 0, \qquad (5)$$

$$\pi^2 c^2 \left[\left(\frac{h}{\alpha}\right)^2 + \left(\frac{k}{\beta}\right)^2 + \left(\frac{l}{\gamma}\right)^2 \right] w_{hkl} + \ddot{w}_{hkl} = 0.$$

When we look at equations (4) and (5), which are the only restrictions on the coefficients of our expansions, we notice first of all that in any set of conditions only coefficients with the same set of (h, k, l)-values are tied together.   In other words, the whole problem separates into an infinite though discrete set of partial problems, but each one of the partial problems has only a finite, and indeed very small, number of degrees of freedom.

The partial problems can now be attacked and solved in short order.   If we introduce, for the sake of brevity, the "wave propagation vector" $\mathbf{k}_{hkl}$ with the components $\left(\dfrac{\pi}{\alpha} h, \dfrac{\pi}{\beta} k, \dfrac{\pi}{\gamma} l\right)$, and the "amplitude vector" $\mathbf{A}_{hkl}$ with the components $(u_{hkl}, v_{hkl}, w_{hkl})$, eqs. (4) and (5) reduce to

$$\mathbf{k}_{hkl} \cdot \mathbf{A}_{hkl} = 0,$$

$$c^2 \left|\mathbf{k}_{hkl}\right|^2 \mathbf{A}_{hkl} + \ddot{\mathbf{A}}_{hkl} = 0. \tag{6}$$

Taking up the second set of equations first, we can immediately obtain the time dependence of the amplitude vector, since each component separately behaves like a harmonic oscillator; the solution of these equations is then

$$\mathbf{A}_{hkl} = \mathbf{C}_{hkl} \cos \omega_{hkl}(t - t^0_{hkl}), \qquad \omega_{hkl} = c \left|\mathbf{k}_{hkl}\right|. \tag{7}$$

As for the first equation (6), the amplitude vector $\mathbf{A}_{hkl}$, and therefore also the constant coefficient vector $\mathbf{C}_{hkl}$, must be perpendicular to the wave-propagation vector $\mathbf{k}_{hkl}$.   In other words, our expansion shows that for each triplet of integers (h, k, l) there are possible two linearly independent directions for the amplitude vector (determining together the plane at right angles to $\mathbf{k}_{hkl}$), and that these two independent directions of polarization satisfy the same equations as harmonic oscillators do in mechanics.

Herewith the first stage of the theory is completed: we have shown that the electromagnetic field inside a cavity of the assumed shape with perfectly conducting walls is mathematically equivalent to an infinite series of harmonic oscillators with specific resonant frequencies.   The analogy can be carried further; if we wish, we can construct expressions for the Lagrangian or the Hamiltonian of the system, and these expressions will turn out to be identical with the Lagrangian and the Hamiltonian functions of the electromagnetic field, expressed in terms of Fourier coefficients.   These derivations, of great significance in quantum electrodynamics, would serve no particular purpose here except to confirm the validity of our analogy. Therefore we shall proceed directly to obtain the statistical theory of this collection of harmonic oscillators.

In our situation as we have assumed it, these infinitely many oscillators vibrate completely independently of each other and of the remainder of the universe. As a result, each one of them will retain the total energy of vibration with which it is initially endowed. There are, however, means by which we can couple some or all of our oscillators with a temperature bath. Any oscillator thus coupled will tend to assume the average (time-average) energy determined by the equipartition law, and that is

$$\epsilon = k\,T, \tag{8}$$

where k is the Boltzmann constant and T is the Kelvin temperature. How can we achieve such a coupling? For once, we can place small particles of dust inside the cavity. The dust is capable of absorbing electromagnetic energy in certain frequency bands and of re-emitting in those same bands. Walls that are not perfect electric conductors will have the same effect as dust. Depending on the choice of materials, we can produce slight interaction and consequent exchange of energy between the various modes of vibration of the cavity (so-called normal modes) either in selected frequency ranges or throughout the complete range of frequencies from zero to infinity.

If complete equilibrium is reached by means of some mechanism of coupling, then the average distribution of energy, according to the classical theory, will be given by eq. (8). If we count the number of Fourier coefficients belonging to frequencies within some finite range (say from 0 to ω_0), we shall always find a finite number of normal modes and, as a result, a finite radiative energy per unit of frequency range. But the total number of modes or of equivalent oscillators is infinite, and the classical theory predicts, therefore, that the radiative field is capable of soaking up an infinite amount of energy before assuming thermal equilibrium. This result, known as the *ultraviolet catastrophe*, is, of course, at variance with all observations. In reality, at room temperature the energy contained in a radiation-filled cavity is negligible compared with the energy required to keep the walls at the same temperature. At higher temperatures, for instance in the interior of stars, the energy of the radiation field is no longer negligible, but it remains finite.

Before we attempt to find a way out of the classical ultraviolet catastrophe, let us determine the spectral distribution of energy. For this purpose, we must count the independent oscillators with frequencies between 0 and ω_0. The frequency of a given oscillator is determined by the last eq. (7), so that a given oscillator will have a frequency $\leq \omega_0$ if its triplet (h, k, l) satisfies the inequality

$$c^2 |\mathbf{k}_{hkl}|^2 \equiv \pi^2 c^2 \left(\frac{h^2}{\alpha^2} + \frac{k^2}{\beta^2} + \frac{l^2}{\gamma^2}\right) \leq \omega_0^2. \tag{9}$$

The number of oscillators satisfying this condition can now be estimated easily and accurately, at least for fairly large frequencies ω_0. Let us consider a symbolical space in which the quantities h, k, and l are to be considered as the coordinates of a symbolical point. The triplets of integers (h, k, l) form in that space a lattice of points so that one point of the set is contained in each cubelike unit of volume. The inequality (9) now characterizes all those lattice points which are contained in the interior of the positive octant of an ellipsoid whose three semiaxes are $\frac{\omega_0}{\pi c} \alpha$, $\frac{\omega_0}{\pi c} \beta$, and $\frac{\omega_0}{\pi c} \gamma$. The volume of such an ellipsoid, according to an elementary formula, is

$$w(\omega_0) = \frac{4}{3} V \frac{\omega_0^3}{\pi^2 c^3} \qquad (V = \alpha\beta\gamma), \tag{10}$$

and the volume of the positive octant is one-eighth that value. That is also the number of lattice points satisfying the inequality (9). Our estimate is inaccurate only because the surface of the ellipsoid cuts through the interior of some of the cubes. If we increase the dimensions of the volume V, and with it those of the ellipsoid belonging to a particular value of ω_0, the value of $w(\omega_0)$ will increase proportionally to V, but the number of unit cubes intersected by the surface of the ellipsoid only with the two-thirds power of V. Thus the percentage error of expression (10) will approach zero if we make our volume V sufficiently large, for any fixed value of ω_0; for a fixed value of the volume V, the percentage error of (10) will go to zero for sufficiently high values of the frequency ω_0. Altogether, the expression (10) will be very accurate for ordinary laboratory dimensions of the cavity V and for light in the visible range of frequencies. Since two independent oscillators belong to each triplet of integers (h, k, l), the total number of oscillators with frequencies $\leq \omega_0$ will be in good approximation:

$$N(\omega_0) = \frac{1}{3} V \frac{\omega_0^3}{\pi^2 c^3}. \tag{11}$$

The mean energy contained in this band of frequencies will be kT times this value. Since V is the volume of the cavity, we can introduce the *energy density* of all frequencies below ω_0. It is

$$\tau(\omega_0) = \frac{1}{3} kT \frac{\omega_0^3}{\pi^2 c^3}. \tag{12}$$

If we differentiate this expression with respect to ω_0, we get the energy density per unit band width of angular frequency,

$$u(\omega) = kT \frac{\omega^2}{\pi^2 c^3}. \tag{13}$$

This expression shows that the intensity of thermal equilibrium radiation increases with increasing frequency without limit and that an integral taken over all frequencies would diverge. The infinite contribution comes from the high-frequency end of the spectrum; this breakdown of the classical theory is known by the picturesque expression *ultraviolet catastrophe*.

Let us examine once more the assumptions that lead to this self-contradictory result. These assumptions are of three different types: general assumptions concerning the nature of statistical equilibrium, assumptions concerning the laws of the electromagnetic field, and assumptions concerning the role of absorbing and radiating matter. As for the general nature of a statistical equilibrium, we have assumed that for each normal mode separately, the remainder of the system acts as a large temperature bath. The justification for this assumption hinges on our ability to provide "loose coupling" between this normal mode and the remainder of the system. Otherwise, only the general arguments of statistical mechanics need to be used, that is, the general characterization of a stationary ensemble and the more detailed calculation that leads to the distribution-in-time of a small system interacting with a large system in the absence of interaction with the rest of the universe.

As for the role of the material of which the walls are made and of the dust particles that provide for interaction, we must satisfy two requirements. In order to decompose the field into normal modes, in the manner we have done it, we require definite *boundary conditions* to be satisfied by the electromagnetic field on the surface of the domain in which we wish to study it.   These boundary conditions are provided by perfectly conducting walls.   It is true that the perfect conductor is an idealization, not to be achieved with ordinary materials.   Suppose we had merely a *good conductor*, one in which small potential gradients lead to large but not infinite current densities.   Then, if we make the walls sufficiently thick, we find that energy will seep across the interface and that a normal mode, once excited, will die out in time, obeying an exponential law of decay.   However, if the walls are kept at any finite temperature, they will also act as (random) emitters of electromagnetic energy, and thus feed energy back to the individual normal modes.

If we wish to study the role of such a wall in greater detail, we must assume some sort of a molecular structure because otherwise we cannot describe properly the fact that it is being kept at a particular temperature. We may, for instance, think of the wall as having embedded in it a large number of electrons that are bound elastically to certain equilibrium positions.   If we make the density of these electrons infinite, the wall will act as a perfect conductor.   Otherwise the electrons will permit part of the electromagnetic waves to penetrate into the wall and be absorbed there. Again, these electrically charged oscillators will give rise to electromagnetic waves, and we can determine the average intensity of radiation that will leave the surface of such a wall.   In all calculations of this sort, we obtain the same result (13) because of the operation of the equipartition law.

The other role attributed to matter is the *coupling* between individual normal modes.   To couple several modes, a particle of dust must be capable of absorbing and emitting at all these frequencies and directions of propagation and polarization.   No material is completely diaphanous (nonabsorbing) at *any* frequency.   But if there were some gap in the emissive powers of one speck of dust, we could introduce additional specks, made of different materials, to close that gap.

Would it be possible to avoid the ultraviolet catastrophe by modifying Maxwell's equations slightly?   Unfortunately, a careful analysis of the steps leading to eq. (13) shows that minor modifications will not change the essential characteristics of the result.   Actually, all that is necessary to obtain the ultraviolet catastrophe is the assumption that the equations are *linear* and *homogeneous* and that the normal modes at high frequencies are *infinitely many*.   First, as to linearity, we need to assume linear homogeneous field equations as long as we wish to maintain the general property of the electromagnetic field that solutions can be linearly superimposed on each other; in other words, and very crudely speaking, we accept the fact that two searchlight beams intersecting in empty space do not interfere with each other, that electromagnetic waves do not scatter each other.   Although no experimental evidence exists that would contradict that assumption, of course it is conceivable that such interaction effects would be encountered at very high radiation intensities.   But such a weak deviation of Maxwell's laws from linearity would presumably lead to a build-up of intensities in thermal radiation to the level where the nonlinearity of the equations becomes important.   Actually, at temperatures convenient for the measurement of radiation intensities, these intensities remain appreciably below the level of intensities that we can produce by other means—intensities at which no trace of radiation-radiation inter-action has ever been observed.

If the assumption of nonlinearity does not help us, what about the number of normal modes possible in a theory that is linear but deviates from the precise Maxwellian form? For instance, the velocity of propaga-tion of electromagnetic waves in empty space might depend slightly on wave length. Such an attempt is also bound to end in failure. In order to help us, the hypothetical modification of the laws of the electromagnetic field would need to have the effect of spacing the higher normal modes (corresponding to greater values for the magnitude of the vector $\mathbf{k}_{hkl}$) farther apart with respect to frequency and even of preventing values of $|\mathbf{k}_{hkl}|$ above a certain cutoff value. At the cutoff value the frequency would have to be infinite. For such a wave field, the phase velocity of the wave in free space would have to drop for high frequencies and approach zero for the cutoff value. The group velocity, on the other hand, would tend to infinity. All these effects would have to become noticeable at frequen-cies at which the experimentally known curve of energy distribution in thermal radiation deviates clearly from the theoretical distribution (13). For normal high laboratory temperatures of between 1000 and 3000°C, the actual energy density passes through a maximum in the region of visible light, and it is common knowledge that empty space is not dispersive for electromagnetic radiation even at frequencies a thousand times higher. Thus we have no reason to believe that a modification of the Maxwell equations consistent with the known facts at moderate frequencies and moderate intensities will get around the ultraviolet catastrophe.

Planck finally changed the line of attack of theoretical physicists on this problem. Starting with the fact that at the low-frequency end the experimental curve and the one given by eq. (13) coincide but that at higher frequencies the experimental curve reaches a maximum and then drops rapidly to very low intensities, and realiz-ing that a sufficiently severe change in Maxwell's laws to explain this maximum would fly in the face of everything else known about electromagnetic waves, he attempted a modification of the founda-tions of statistical mechanics that would explain the "freezing" of the high-frequency degrees of freedom of the electromagnetic radiation inside a cavity.

His original formulation was successful for cavity radiation but could not have been applied to the theory of specific heats of poly-atomic gases and similar systems, where we also have seen that the high-frequency degrees of freedom contribute less than the amount required by the classical equipartition law. Instead of reproducing Planck's hypothesis, we shall introduce that formulated many years later by A. Sommerfeld. Sommerfeld's hypothesis yields Planck's formula for cavity radiation; it can also be applied successfully to atomic and molecular mechanical systems.

7.2. Quantization in phase space. Closed orbits

Planck's principal idea was the hypothesis that a mechanical system is not capable of assuming all the states permitted by the laws of classical physics, but that for some reason as yet not understood a system can exist only in certain discrete states. In consequence, the energy cannot assume all conceivable values, only certain ones permitted by the *quantum laws* that must be added as restrictions to the laws of classical physics.

How can we expect the quantum hypothesis to help us avoid the ultraviolet catastrophe and all the other difficulties encountered in the applications of the equipartition law? The answer lies in the fact that the derivation of the equipartition law depends rather critically on the assumption that the energy states of all mechanical systems are distributed continuously. In eq. (3.27), we found that the characteristic volume of a harmonic oscillator (in three dimensions) equals $\frac{1}{6}(E/\nu)^3$. Thus for an oscillator of high resonant frequency ν, the volume in phase space bounded by the energy surface $E = E_0$ is much smaller than for an oscillator of lower frequency. At a given temperature both oscillators possess the same *mean* value of the energy, $3kT$, because the Boltzmann factor $e^{-\epsilon/kT}$ confines the high-frequency oscillator to a smaller portion of phase space. Now if we assume that the distribution of possible states in phase space is discrete, evidently a wide spacing of the permissible energy levels, if the Boltzmann factor remains unchanged, will make it more difficult for the system to be at any level other than its lowest; thus its mean energy will be *less* than the value predicted by classical theory.

To Planck's contemporaries and to Planck himself, the quantum hypothesis must have appeared as a desperate remedy of a desperate situation, justifiable only by some subsequent rational development. Such a development has indeed taken place, but the birth of the new self-consistent theory did not take place for another twenty-five years. In the meantime, quantum physics developed as the juxtaposition of two mutually contradictory sets of concepts, classical physics on the one side, and the "quantization rules" (that is, the recipes on how to select among all the classical states the permissible ones) on the other. That such a monstrosity could live at all must be credited to its striking success in explaining almost all the principal facts of atomic and molecular physics.

We shall now attempt to explain how one might set up a rule of quantization so that the successful features of classical statistical mechanics are preserved but that, at the same time, deviations from the classical theory appear just where we need them. Classical statistical mechanics is based principally on Liouville's theorem, which, coupled with the quasi-ergodic hypothesis, leads to the conclusion that the density of a stationary ensemble is constant on each energy surface. To this principle we must add the derivation of the asymptotic formula known as the Boltzmann factor, which we obtained by studying the energy distribution of a subsystem forming part of a sufficiently complex closed system.

Apparently we shall be able to save most of the results of classical statistical mechanics only if we can retain the notion of constant density in phase space on each energy surface. Then most of the other conclusions of classical mechanics can be retained, and in particular the Boltzmann factor. The most natural rule of quantization is, therefore, to assume that *the discrete quantum states of a system are distributed with constant density in phase space.*

This rule obviously does not determine the quantum states completely. As a matter of fact, we shall see later that it is not possible to strengthen this rule sufficiently to make the quantum states completely unique. For different phase spaces, the spacing (that is, the volume containing a single quantum state) cannot be the same, because the volume in phase space has a dimension, and this dimension is (energy · time)^f, with f being the number of degrees of freedom of the system. In order to formulate a rule that will be applicable equally to all phase spaces, we shall require that the size of the unit cell in phase space equal h^f, where h is a universal constant—to be determined later—having the dimension of a product of energy and time (usually called *action*). This simple requirement will make it possible to apply the quantum rule simultaneously to a complex system and to its component subsystems, since a cell in the big phase space of size h^f can be considered the geometric intersection (and therefore its volume the product of the corresponding volumes) of the cells in the various subspaces.

Our quantization rule has the further merit that it is conserved in time. Suppose we divide phase space into cells of equal volume h^f in some fashion and place inside each cell just one permitted quantum state. If we let each representative point in phase space travel along its mechanical trajectory, then the cells will be transformed continuously, but because of Liouville's theorem, their volumes will remain constant, and thus each quantum state will permanently have one cell of volume h^f for its residence.

Obviously, the quantity h must be sufficiently small that for large bodies the discrete distribution in phase space called for by our new rule shall be indistinguishable from the classical continuous distribution. But for systems of atomic dimensions we should be able to observe deviations from classical behavior. These deviations can be twofold. For small, isolated systems such as individual atoms, it might be possible to observe the individual quantized states or, at any rate, their energy levels, and thus the new quantum rule might lead to a theory of atomic spectra (as in fact it does). For complex systems composed of components of atomic dimensions, we might find that the statistical distribution of energy states is affected, primarily at the lower temperatures at which even classically the complex system is most likely to be near the energy zero in phase space. We must follow up both of these possible consequences, but we shall take the statistical consequences first.

Two of the most important mechanical systems in physics, the harmonic oscillator and the particle subject to an attractive inverse-square law, have for their trajectories *closed, periodic orbits.* All the trajectories of the harmonic oscillator are closed, whereas, for the inverse-square law at least, all the trajectories corresponding to bound, negative-energy states are closed. We shall now study our conjectured quantization rule particularly for such periodic motions in order to apply it first to the problem of cavity radiation.

Consider a one-dimensional harmonic oscillator and its trajectories in phase space (Fig. 6). All the trajectories appear as concentric ellipses. The center of the figure corresponds to absolute rest. The dashed lines in the figure represent a possible equal-volume grating in phase space. If we let all the points of this phase space move in accordance with the canonical laws of motion, each point will start sliding along its particular ellipse. In fact, had we chosen a scale so that the ellipses appeared as circles (and this can be done readily), then the motion of the phase space would be a simple constant-speed rigid rotation about the center of the figure. In the scale of Fig. 6 the rotation will not be rigid, but the transformation will at least be collinear; that is, straight lines will remain

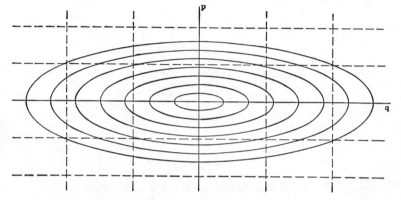

Fig. 6.   Harmonic oscillator in phase space.

straight lines, though right angles will become oblique. Thus throughout the motion the grating will be a parallelogram grating, and twice during each period it will return to its original shape.

Whenever we have periodic motion we can introduce a grating whose cells are transformed into themselves throughout the motion; in other words, we can introduce a grating that remains *conserved* throughout the motion. All we have to do is to choose as the boundaries between cells dynamic orbits, spaced so that each cell has the same volume h. This grating is shown in Fig. 7. The ratios between the axes of consecutive ellipses in this figure are as $1 : \sqrt{2} : \sqrt{3} : \sqrt{4} : \sqrt{5} : \cdots$. Clearly, each point of the phase space will stay permanently in the cell in which it finds itself initially. A similar arrangement of cells can be found whenever we have a periodic system. These time-independent gratings have the advantage that they enable us to study the permanent distribution of energy levels in such periodic systems.

Regardless of the detailed nature of our periodic motion, it is clear that the volume enclosed by the boundary of the first cell must equal h (assuming that we have a single degree of freedom).

Since the outside boundary of the second cell encloses altogether two cells, it must enclose a total volume equal to $2h$. By the same argument, the outside boundary of the nth cell, enclosing a total of n cells, must be the edge of a volume nh. On the other hand, there

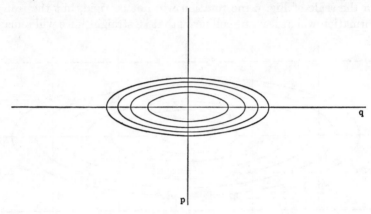

Fig. 7.   Stationary grating for the harmonic oscillator.

is a simple formula for the volume enclosed by a curve, the integral $\oint p \, dq$. Thus, the condition for the outside boundary of the nth cell is

$$\oint p \, dq = nh. \tag{14}$$

Without further ado, we can safely assume that for the nth quantized orbit we have

$$(n-1)\,h \leq \oint p \, dq \leq nh. \tag{15}$$

Naturally, for any quantitative calculations, the quantized orbits must be fixed more completely. Experience has shown that for most situations it is correct to assume that the lowest quantized state is that of rest, provided that this state exists and has a finite energy (for the inverse-square law, the lowest energy is negative infinite), and that all the following states are evenly spaced; so we have as a general rule for the quantized states of periodic systems

$$\oint p \, dq = nh \qquad (n = 0, 1, 2, \cdots). \tag{16}$$

For the contingency that the state $n = 0$ is not reasonable, the lowest state is usually the one for which $n = 1$. Only rarely has it been found necessary to assume that the quantized states are in the center of their respective cells, so that the number n passes through all half-odd values ($\frac{1}{2}$, $\frac{3}{2}$, $\frac{5}{2}$, $\cdots$). Incidentally, these uncertainties do not arise in modern quantum mechanics; the current theory predicts in each instance just what values n must assume.

Rule (16) was first formulated by Wilson[1] and by Sommerfeld[2] and is known as the method of *phase-integral quantization*. For about ten years the quantization of phase integrals [the type of integral appearing on the left-hand side of eq. (16)] was the only reliable method available for ascertaining the position of quantized orbits in phase space. The corresponding energy levels depend on the detailed model being quantized. For the harmonic oscillator we shall find that the energy levels are spaced evenly as well, but for most other systems the spacing of energy levels is more involved.

If a system has several degrees of freedom, we shall always attempt to reduce the problem to the one-dimensional type by the introduction of a coordinate system in which the problem *separates*. If this procedure is feasible, the n-dimensional problem becomes equivalent to n one-dimensional problems, each of which is quantized according to rule (16). As a result, the quantized states of a system with n degrees of freedom will be characterized by n different quantum numbers. In particular, for the radiation in a cavity we shall have to introduce an infinite number of quantum numbers, each belonging to a different normal mode of the cavity. Only if all these quantum numbers are specified will the state of radiation inside the cavity be completely determined.

7.3. Statistics

Before we can tackle the case of cavity radiation conclusively, we must also consider the statistical behavior of a quantized system. Just as in classical physics, we can construct ensembles of quantized systems that are similar, except that they start out with different initial conditions. We shall call an ensemble *stationary* if the distribution of the representative points in phase space does not change

---

[1] *Phil. Mag.* **29**, 795 (1915).
[2] *Ann. d. Physik*, **51**, 1 (1916).

in the course of time. In general the points in phase space that may be occupied are discrete, and they will be spaced evenly in the sense explained in Section 7.2. Instead of introducing a continuous density function μ in phase space, we must introduce occupation probabilities, that is, fractions of all the systems found in each particular quantized state. Naturally, the sum of all the occupation probabilities must equal unity.

In a closed system each representative point remains confined to its energy surface, but if the system is quasi-ergodic it will cover that surface. Hence in a stationary ensemble we must assume that the occupation probabilities of all the quantized states on the same energy surface will be the same, in close analogy to the classical situation. In other words, we must assume that the occupation probability for a given state will depend on its energy level but will be independent of all other parameters. If we want to discover the analogue to the canonical ensemble, we must now consider systems loosely coupled with a temperature bath.

Let us consider a *quantized temperature bath*. Such a bath can be constructed as before, except that the numerous component systems are each capable only of certain discrete quantum states. We must discover the distribution of energy levels for the composite system, and that irrespective of the detailed energy level distribution for the component systems. Fortunately, our problem can be reduced mathematically to the classical problem. Instead of the "characteristic volume" of Chapter 3, we can now introduce as the *characteristic function* the number of quantized states with an energy below E. This function is a so-called step function; that is, it increases only by discrete jumps. But it increases monotonically, and if multiplied by a suitable exponential factor it possesses a Fourier transform. If we compose a system of several quantized components, the characteristic function of the composite can be obtained by the same integrations as before. Finally, a careful analysis shows that the asymptotic distribution of energy levels for a very large composite obeys an exponential law such that the number of energy levels of the temperature bath between two energies $E + \epsilon_1$ and $E + \epsilon_2$ (with E proportional to the heat capacity of the bath and ϵ_1 and ϵ_2 of atomic order of magnitude) is

$$N(E, \epsilon_1, \epsilon_2) = N_0(E)[e^{\beta(E)\epsilon_2} - e^{\beta(E)\epsilon_1}] \qquad (\epsilon_1 < \epsilon_2). \qquad (17)$$

There is an obvious similarity between this expression for the distribution of energy levels of a temperature bath and the corresponding classical expression (3.62).

The number of energy levels of the temperature bath within a given energy bracket is, of course, proportional to the volume in phase space bounded by two energy surfaces corresponding to $(E + \epsilon_1)$ and $(E + \epsilon_2)$, because of our assumption that the quantized states are evenly distributed in phase space. That is why for a system of sufficient complexity the quantum formula for the energy-level density is the same as the classical formula for the characteristic volume derivative. This sameness is of restricted validity, however. Apart from the requirement that the temperature bath be large (which must be met even in classical physics if the asymptotic expression known as the Boltzmann factor is to hold), it is also necessary that the temperature be sufficiently high that almost all the component systems are in "excited" states, not in their respective lowest energy states. For if they are in the latter, then the distribution of energy levels depends critically on the first energy step, the one that leads from the lowest level to the next one. Even if eq. (17) is applicable, the distribution of energy levels will not be completely smooth, but the validity of eq. (17) will depend on our choosing an energy range $(\epsilon_2 - \epsilon_1)$ of sufficient width. The larger the capacity of the temperature bath, the narrower may we choose this width before expression (17) becomes inaccurate.

Now we shall couple to our temperature bath an atomic system that possesses a sequence of energy levels ϵ_k, $k = 0, 1, 2, \cdots$. If the total energy available for the combined system is called E, the energy possessed by the bath alone will be $(E - \epsilon_k)$. Let us now construct an ensemble so that each member is the combination of an atomic system and a temperature bath, and let the total energies vary from E to $(E + \Delta E)$, where ΔE is sufficiently large that eq. (16) is valid for the temperature bath but small compared with the energy differences between the various levels ϵ_k of the atomic system. We shall now ask for the number of states of the combined system when the atomic system by itself is in its kth state. Very obviously this number depends only on the density of levels of the temperature bath and equals

$$N_k = N_0(E)[e^{\beta(E)(\Delta E - \epsilon_k)} - e^{-\beta(E)\epsilon_k}]$$
$$\sim N_0(E)\,\beta(E)\,e^{-\beta(E)\epsilon_k}\,\Delta E. \tag{18}$$

If our whole ensemble is stationary, the occupation probabilities for all quantized states of the combined system in the very narrow energy shell considered must be equal, and the ratio of the probabilities of finding the atomic system in the kth or the lth states, respectively, must equal the ratio of the numbers of energy levels of the combined system, or

$$\frac{P_k}{P_l} = e^{\beta(E)(\epsilon_l - \epsilon_k)},$$

$$P_k = P_0\, e^{-\beta\epsilon_k}. \tag{19}$$

With this expression, we have reached a state of the argument where again we can introduce the concept of the partition function. For if we know the approximate total energy available to the combined system, the coefficient P_0 in eq. (19) can be evaluated. All we have to do is to take into account the fact that the sum of all the probabilities P_k must equal unity. We have then

$$P_0 \sum_{k=0}^{\infty} e^{-\beta\epsilon_k} = 1,$$

$$P_0 = Z^{-1}, \qquad Z = \sum_{k=0}^{\infty} e^{-\beta\epsilon_k}. \tag{20}$$

The *sum Z* is called the *partition function*. It plays the same role in a quantized system that the *integral Z* does in classical physics. Our former expressions for the mean energy, for the rms spread of the energy, and for the specific heat remain unchanged. In other words, the thermodynamic properties of a quantized system differ from its classical analogue only insofar as the partition function (20) as a function of the parameter β is in general different from its classical counterpart. But the validity of the *general* laws of thermodynamics, the first and the second law, remains unaffected by quantization.

With this completed theory, we are now ready to tackle the problem of cavity radiation.

7.4. The quantized harmonic oscillator. Planck's law of heat radiation

In Section 7.1 we determined the number of normal modes within a given frequency range. By multiplying this number by the mean energy kT of the classical harmonic oscillator, we obtained an expression for the energy spectrum that diverged at the high-frequency end of the spectrum. Will the course of the argument be changed if we apply our new quantum hypothesis? The number of normal modes in a given frequency bracket will, of course, remain unaffected. What we can hope for is that the mean energy of an individual oscillator may come out differently. To find that mean energy we shall have to obtain the expression for the partition function. And to get that expression, we must first find the energy levels of the quantized harmonic oscillator. If we introduce in the differential equations for the harmonic oscillator the canonically conjugate variables q and p, the Hamiltonian H always assumes the form

$$H = \frac{1}{2} a \left(p^2 + \frac{\omega^2}{a^2} q^2 \right), \tag{21}$$

regardless of the physical significance of that oscillator. ω denotes the (angular) resonance frequency of the oscillator, and a is a constant coefficient which in the case of a mechanical oscillator has the significance of the reciprocal mass, but for our purposes it is of no consequence. The energy of the oscillator is, of course, equal to H. If we wish to evaluate the phase integral $\oint p \, dq$, we can refer advantageously to the formula for the area of an ellipse, because the trajectories in phase space are ellipses. Obviously, the semiaxes of the ellipse are the maximum values of q and p, respectively,

$$q_{max} = \frac{1}{\omega} \sqrt{2aH},$$

$$p_{max} = \sqrt{\frac{2H}{a}}, \tag{22}$$

and therefore the value of the phase integral is

$$\oint p \, dq = \frac{2\pi H}{\omega} = nh. \tag{23}$$

It follows that the energy levels of the harmonic oscillator are given by the expressions

$$\epsilon_n = \frac{\omega}{2\pi} nh \qquad (n = 0, 1, \cdots), \tag{24}$$

which depend only on the resonant frequency.

The partition function is the sum

$$Z = \sum_{n=0}^{\infty} e^{-\beta \frac{\omega}{2\pi} n h}, \tag{25}$$

which can be evaluated simply by means of the summation formula for geometrical series. We have

$$Z = \frac{1}{1 - e^{-\beta \frac{\omega}{2\pi} h}}. \tag{26}$$

The mean energy of the oscillator is therefore given by the logarithmic derivative

$$\langle \epsilon \rangle = -\frac{\partial \ln Z}{\partial \beta} = \frac{\hbar \omega}{e^{\frac{\hbar \omega}{kT}} - 1} \qquad \left(\beta = \frac{1}{kT}, \qquad \hbar = \frac{h}{2\pi} \right). \tag{27}$$

In this expression, we have introduced the absolute temperature T and the Boltzmann constant k, and we have used the abbreviating symbol $\hbar$, which is now in more common use than the original symbol h, from which it differs by the factor $(1/2\pi)$.

Expression (27) for the mean energy of the harmonic oscillator looks very different from the classical expression kT. The two expressions become equal, however, if the frequency is sufficiently low or the temperature sufficiently high, if, in other words, the classical mean energy kT is large compared with the energy-level spacing of quantum theory, $\hbar \omega$. In that case, we can expand the expression (27) into a power series with respect to the *small* quantity $(\hbar \omega / kT)$,

$$\langle \epsilon \rangle = \hbar \omega \frac{kT}{\hbar \omega} \left(1 - \frac{1}{2} \frac{\hbar \omega}{kT} + \cdots \right)$$
$$= kT - \tfrac{1}{2} \hbar \omega + \cdots. \tag{28}$$

If, on the other hand, the level spacing $\hbar \omega$ is large compared with kT, then $\langle \epsilon \rangle$ can be approximated by the expression

$$\langle \epsilon \rangle = \hbar \omega \, e^{-\frac{\hbar \omega}{kT}} \left(1 + e^{-\frac{\hbar \omega}{kT}} + \cdots \right). \tag{29}$$

If we have a collection of oscillators at different frequencies, as we do in cavity radiation, then the low-frequency oscillators will have a mean energy approximately equal to the value given by the classical equipartition law, but the oscillators vibrating at higher frequencies will have smaller and smaller mean energies, and for very high frequencies the mean energies tend exponentially to zero. The calculation just completed bears out the qualitative remarks made at the end of the previous section: If the energy levels of a quantized system are spaced closely, then our new quantization rule leads to statistical results not far different from those of the classical theory; but if the energy levels are spaced widely, then it is so difficult for the system to reach the higher levels that the mean energy is given in first approximation just by the percentage of systems in the canonical ensemble that are raised one step above the ground level. That is the import of the two expansions (28) and (29).

Now we can introduce the rigorous expression (27) into the equations of Section 7.1. If we replace kT in eq. (13) by the new expression (27), we find for the energy density per unit volume of space and per unit band width of frequency

$$u(\omega) = \frac{1}{\pi^2 c^3} \frac{\hbar\omega^3}{e^{\hbar\omega/kT} - 1}. \qquad (30)$$

This formula is Planck's law for equilibrium thermal radiation. At the low-frequency end it agrees with the classical expression (13), but at the high-frequency end, instead of increasing without limit, it drops off exponentially, thus leading to a converging integral over all frequencies. Planck's formula agrees within the limits of experimental accuracy with the empirical curves.

Planck's work of 1900 is historically the birth of quantum physics. That the quantum was discovered in the field of radiation theory rather than in the theory of atomic spectra can be explained by the fact that only in the theory of cavity radiation could the classical laws of the "atomic system" be considered well known. Only in cavity radiation do we have sufficient confidence in the validity of the physical model and its laws of behavior that we cannot attempt to explain the failure of the equipartition law by the crudeness of the model used. Once the decisive step had been taken, it turned out that the other failures of classical statistics were in most part not due to faulty models but to the lack of quantization.

Returning to our new theory of radiation, we can now focus our attention on its nonstatistical features. We have assumed that each normal mode of a cavity can carry only an integral multiple of the "energy quantum" $\hbar\omega$. What happens if we gradually increase the size of the cavity to the point where we can disregard the walls and deal with progressive waves in free space? Apparently the basic energy quantum of a given normal mode depends only on its frequency, not on its orientation with respect to the walls or any other local characteristic. We must conclude that radiative energy in general will occur only in quanta $\hbar\omega$.

This same conclusion can be reached by another conceptual experiment. Let a cavity with perfect walls have a small hole through which the enclosed radiation can leak out and through which radiative energy can enter the cavity. We can say that our system "cavity" is "loosely coupled" to the system "free space." Of course this loose coupling destroys the rigorous periodicity of the cavity system, but if the hole is small enough the cavity system will be very nearly periodic, and our previous quantization can be maintained with any desired degree of accuracy. While the two systems interact with each other through the connecting small hole, the state of the cavity is subject to changes, but at any given instant the state of the cavity must resemble one of its quantized states.

Any one particular normal mode can change its energy only by integral multiples of $\hbar\omega$, where ω is its resonant frequency. Now in any interaction between a particular normal mode of the cavity and the radiation field present in free space, only those frequencies which are very nearly equal can affect each other. In this situation we can think of all the normal modes of the cavity and of all the conceivable plane waves in free space as separate harmonic oscillators. If we provide for small coupling forces between these oscillators, actual exchanges of energy will take place only between oscillators of very nearly the same frequency. The permissible difference in frequency is of the order of the detuning produced by the coupling forces. If the law of conservation of energy continues to hold in our new physics (and we have assumed that all the classical laws remain valid), then the quantum of energy $\hbar\omega$ that disappears inside the cavity as a result of the interaction must appear at very nearly the same frequency in free space, and vice versa. Our cavity will emit and absorb radiative energy only in quanta $\hbar\omega$.

Any other emitters and absorbers of electromagnetic radiation can be coupled to a cavity. Unless nature is to burst at the seams, all quantized systems must emit and absorb according to the same law, and we shall postulate the general principle that electromagnetic radiation can be produced or absorbed and, in fact, can exist only in quanta of magnitude $\hbar\omega$.   Very obviously, this assumption, which is a necessary consequence of our method of quantizing cavity radiation, will lead to new results in all parts of physics where radiative energy plays a role.

7.5. Specific heats

The general scheme of quantization developed so far is sufficient to explain the specific heats of polyatomic gases.   We can also understand why the Dulong-Petit law for solids remains valid in the presence of additional degrees of freedom represented by very tight bonds inside certain ionic groups (such as the sulfate ion $SO_4^=$).   We cannot offer at this time any explanation why in metals the translatory energy of the free electrons in a metal (the so-called conduction electrons) makes no appreciable contribution, though modern quantum mechanics has cleared up that point as well.   As an example of the power of the hypotheses advanced so far, we shall discuss the specific heat of a diatomic gas, such as O_2.

A diatomic gas molecule has three translatory degrees of freedom, permitting free motion of the molecular center of mass; it has two rotatory degrees of freedom, enabling the molecule to carry out rotations about its center of mass in two different directions (the rotation about its own longitudinal axis makes no contribution to the energy); finally, it has one vibratory degree of freedom (so that the distance between the two atomic nuclei can oscillate about its equilibrium value).   If the two atoms have the same mass m and if the potential energy between them is given by some function $V(r)$, r being the distance between the two nuclei, then the total energy of the molecule is given by the expression

$$E = V(r) + m\,(\dot{X}^2 + \dot{Y}^2 + \dot{Z}^2) + \frac{m}{4}\,(\dot{x}^2 + \dot{y}^2 + \dot{z}^2). \quad (31)$$

X, Y, and Z are the coordinates of the center of mass, x, y, and z the coordinates of one atomic nucleus with respect to the other. The system separates as a matter of course into the motion of the center of mass on the one hand and the internal motion on the other.

We have for the Hamiltonian of the system the expression

$$H = H_{ext} + H_{int},$$

$$H_{ext} = \frac{1}{4\,m} (P_x^2 + P_y^2 + P_z^2), \tag{32}$$

$$H_{int} = V(r) + \frac{1}{m} (p_x^2 + p_y^2 + p_z^2).$$

These two partial systems separate further. The center-of-mass motions in the X-, Y-, and Z-directions are independent of each other and must be quantized separately. The internal motion will be dealt with later.

The motion of the center of mass is, of course, unaccelerated. If we apply our uniform principle of quantization separately to the motion in the X-direction, the Y-direction, and finally the Z-direction, we must first divide the phase space consisting of the two coordinates X and P_x into cells of equal size. If the gas molecules are really free to move, the number of such cells corresponding to any energy shell whatsoever is infinite, because of the infinite range of values of X irrespective of energy. As a result, the energy levels of the X-component of the motion are continuous rather than discrete, and quantum statistics must give the same result as classical statistics. The three translatory degrees of motion will give a mean contribution to the energy determined by the equipartition law,

$$\langle \epsilon_{ext} \rangle = \tfrac{3}{2} kT. \tag{33}$$

Now we shall determine the properties of the internal motion. Except for very special types of potentials $V(r)$, it is not possible to separate H_{int} in rectilinear coordinates, and hence we shall go over to spherical coordinates r, θ, and ϕ. In terms of such coordinates, the Hamiltonian of the internal motion takes the form

$$H_{int} = V(r) + \frac{1}{m} \left[p_r^2 + \frac{1}{r^2} (p_\theta^2 + \sec^2 \theta \cdot p_\phi^2) \right]$$

$$\left(0 \leq \phi \leq 2\pi, \; -\frac{\pi}{2} \leq \theta \leq \frac{\pi}{2} \right). \tag{34}$$

If the molecule is to be stable, the potential energy $V(r)$ must have a strong minimum for some particular value of r, say r_0.

The Hamiltonian (34) is separable with respect to its three degrees of freedom, at least to the extent that the angular motion can be dealt with before we tackle the radial motion. Inasmuch as the angle ϕ does not appear explicitly, the momentum component p_ϕ is an integral of the motion. The azimuthal angle ϕ itself passes through all the values from 0 to 2π; in fact, the motion is periodic with respect to all three variables, though the radial period need not coincide with the joint period of the two angles. As far as the angle ϕ is concerned, the phase integral and our standard quantum condition for periodic motion reduce to

$$\oint p_\phi \, d\phi = 2\pi \, p_\phi = n_1 h,$$

$$p_\phi = n_1 \hbar. \tag{35}$$

According to quantum physics, the angular momentum about the z-axis of any spherically symmetric system satisfies the quantum condition that it is an integral multiple of the universal constant $\hbar$.

We can now proceed to the motion with respect to the angle θ. From the canonical equations of motion, it can be shown easily that the total angular momentum,

$$I^2 = p_\theta^2 + \sec^2 \theta \cdot p_\phi^2, \tag{36}$$

is also an integral of the motion. We have, therefore, for the second phase integral and for the quantum condition for θ-motion,

$$\oint p_\theta \, d\theta = \oint \sqrt{I^2 - \sec^2 \theta \cdot n_1^2 \, \hbar^2} \, d\theta$$
$$= 4 \int_0^{\theta_0} \sqrt{I^2 - \sec^2 \theta \cdot n_1^2 \, \hbar^2} \, d\theta = n_2 \, h. \tag{37}$$

For any choice of the quantum number n_1, this second quantum condition imposes some restriction on the possible values of the total angular momentum I, the only undetermined constant in the expression (37). This restriction we now have to obtain more explicitly.

For any real motion, p_θ must be real; we conclude that

$$I^2 \geq n_1^2 \, \hbar^2 \tag{38}$$

and that the limit of integration θ_0 is given by the condition

$$\theta_0 = \arc\cos \left| \frac{n_1 \, \hbar}{I} \right|. \tag{39}$$

With these two conditions, the integral can be evaluated either by straightforward integration or by contour integration in the complex plane, the choice of method depending chiefly on the mathematical background of the reader. Either way, the result is that the integral (37) equals $2\pi(|I| - |n_1|\hbar)$. We find, thus, that I itself is subject to the quantum condition

$$I = (|n_1| + |n_2|)\hbar. \tag{40}$$

Just like the angular momentum about the z-axis, the total intrinsic angular momentum of the molecule is an integral multiple of the universal constant $\hbar$. This result is universal and may be generalized into the statement that in any central-force problem which may occur in atomic physics and, in fact, in any system not subject to external torques, the total angular momentum is quantized and must equal an integral multiple of $\hbar$.

The sum of the two integers $|n_1|$ and $|n_2|$ is known as the *azimuthal quantum number* and in the older literature was always designated by the symbol k. Depending on the value of k, the value of n_1, more usually designated by m (the "magnetic" quantum number) is restricted. If k equals zero, m also must be zero. If k equals 1, then m may be -1, 0, or 1, and so on. Generally, m is capable of assuming $(2k + 1)$ different values. In spectroscopic literature, the different values of the azimuthal quantum number bear names that antedate the systematic and numerical organization of the possible states of a molecule or atom. For $k = 0$ it is customary to speak of an s-state. The next value, $k = 1$, is called a p-state, the next a d-state, then f-state; from then on the names are alphabetical (g, h, and so forth). These letter designations are abbreviations of former descriptive designations of spectral line series as "sharp," "principal," "diffuse," and "fundamental."

Let us return to eq. (34). The intrinsic energy and the intrinsic Hamiltonian of our symmetric diatomic molecule are now given by the expression

$$H_{int} = V(r) + \frac{1}{m}\left(p_r^2 + \frac{1}{r^2}k^2\hbar^2\right) \qquad (k = 0, 1, 2, \cdots). \tag{41}$$

Everything now depends on the shape of the potential energy $V(r)$. If the binding energy is sufficiently strong, we may assume that r differs from the equilibrium value r_0 only by small amounts throughout the motion of the molecule.   In that case it will be all right to expand V into a power series about r_0:

$$V(r) = V_0 + \frac{K}{2}(r - r_0)^2 + \cdots. \qquad (42)$$

V_0 is the minimum potential energy of the bond and is negative for a stable molecule (that is, we must add energy to dissociate the molecule).   The first power of the expansion must vanish if r_0 is to be a minimum.   The coefficient of the second power is the binding force per unit displacement.   Except for the effect of the rotation and the resulting centrifugal force, $\sqrt{2K/m}$ is the resonant angular frequency of the vibrating molecule.   The further course of the calculation depends on the relative magnitude of the centrifugal force and the elastic binding force.   We shall make the usually justified assumption that the binding force is greater by far, so that the centrifugal force distends the molecule but slightly.   In that case the principal effect of the rotational motion is to displace the equilibrium radius.   In other words, we must treat the last term of eq. (41) as if it were a contribution to the potential energy,

$$V(r) + \frac{k^2 \hbar^2}{m\, r^2} = V'(r), \qquad (43)$$

leading to a new equilibrium radius r_0' and a new power expansion about that value:

$$V'(r) = V_0' + \frac{K'}{2}(r - r_0')^2 + \cdots. \qquad (44)$$

As long as r_0' does not differ very much from r_0, the new binding constant K' will also be only slightly different from K.

In the power expansion for the internal Hamiltonian,

$$H_{\text{int}} = \frac{1}{m} p_r^2 + V_0' + \frac{1}{2} K'(r - r_0)^2 + \cdots = E_{\text{int}}, \qquad (45)$$

we shall suppress all the higher terms (which would make for anharmonic motion) and retain only those written down.   Our quantum condition will then be

$$\oint p_r\, dr = \oint \sqrt{m[\epsilon_{\text{int}} - V_0' - \tfrac{1}{2}K'(r - r_0)^2]}\, dr = n_3\, h. \qquad (46)$$

In this condition the only remaining adjustable constant is the energy

ϵ_{int}, and it is from this last condition that the quantum energy levels will be determined.

The integral (46) can be carried out even more easily than the previous integral (37). Its value turns out to be

$$n_3 h = 2\pi \frac{\epsilon_{\text{int}} - V_0'}{\omega'} \qquad \left(\omega' = \sqrt{\frac{2K'}{m}}\right), \qquad (47)$$

and the energy levels are therefore

$$\begin{aligned} \epsilon_{\text{int}} &= n_3 \hbar \omega' + V_0' \\ &\sim n_3 \hbar \omega + V_0'. \end{aligned} \qquad (48)$$

This formula is incomplete only in one respect. Although the binding constant K' equals K with great accuracy and deviations need to be taken into account only in a detailed consideration of molecular spectra, the value of the adjusted potential energy $V'(r_0')$ differs from V_0 in a manner that we can easily take into acount. If we expand V', eq. (44), into a power series, considering only terms up to quadratic terms, we have

$$V'(r) = V_0 + \frac{1}{2} K (r - r_0)^2$$
$$+ \frac{k^2 \hbar^2}{m r_0^2} \left[1 - 2 \frac{r - r_0}{r_0} + 3 \left(\frac{r - r_0}{r_0}\right)^2 - \cdots \right]. \qquad (49)$$

Obviously, the new equilibrium radius r_0' is, in this approximation,

$$r_0' = r_0 + \frac{2k^2 \hbar^2}{m \left(K + 6 \frac{k^2 \hbar^2}{r_0^4/m}\right) r_0^3} \sim r_0 + \frac{2k^2 \hbar^2}{mK r_0^3}, \qquad (50)$$

and V_0' is

$$V_0' \sim V_0 + \frac{k^2 \hbar^2}{m r_0^2}. \qquad (51)$$

If we substitute this result into expression (48), we find finally, in fairly crude approximation, that the internal-energy levels are determined by the two quantum numbers k and n_3, but that these two quantum numbers enter differently:

$$\epsilon_{\text{int}} = V_0 + n_3 \hbar \omega + k^2 \frac{\hbar^2}{m r_0^2}. \qquad (52)$$

The total internal energy of our molecule is composed additively of the rotational and the vibrational contributions. The vibrational levels are spaced evenly, whereas the rotational levels are separated by ever-widening steps.

For our calculation we have assumed throughout that the centrifugal force is small compared with the average elastic force. Indeed, for most molecules it has been found that the vibrational steps, which have the width $\hbar\omega$, are very large compared even with fairly high rotational steps, which are multiples of $\hbar^2/(mr_0^2)$. Thus our assumption of relative order of magnitude is fully justified in the great majority of molecular spectra.

In order to evaluate the contributions of the various degrees of freedom to the mean energy and to the specific heat of our gas, we must attempt to decide mainly whether at a given temperature the step leading to the first excited level is small or large compared to the denominator in the Boltzmann exponent, kT. At typical laboratory temperatures it turns out that the rotational degrees of freedom will behave classically, the vibrational levels not.

Let us arrive at some idea of the orders of magnitude involved. First of all, Boltzmann's constant k equals 1.38×10^{-16} erg degree^{-1}. Thus, at room temperatures ($\sim 300°$K), kT equals 4.15×10^{-14} erg. In terms of electron volts, kT at the same temperature is about 0.026 eV. Next we can determine the order of magnitude of the energy steps involved in rotational motion, the quantity $\hbar^2/(mr_0^2)$. Assuming a distance of 1 Å and the mass of oxygen atoms, we find that this quantity is of the order of 3.3×10^{-4} eV, or one-hundredth of kT. Thus at room temperature the rotational energy steps of such a molecule are really very small compared with the average energy possessed by a single degree of freedom obeying the classical equipartition law, and therefore this law should hold with great accuracy.

As for the vibratory motion, we should have to estimate the value of the step interval $\hbar\omega$. Although $\hbar$ is, of course, known, ω would have to be estimated from vibrational spectral lines or from chemical heats of dissociation. For the oxygen molecule, O_2, this energy step interval is, for instance, 0.19 eV, or about five times the value of kT. As a result, the contribution of the vibrational energy to the internal energy of the oxygen molecule is only roughly one-thirtieth of the classical value (at room temperature), and its contribution to the specific heat about one-sixth. Naturally, at higher temperatures these contributions increase rapidly.

Problems

1. A particle has one degree of freedom and moves within a box of length L with rigid walls. (a) Determine its quantum energy levels. (b) Compute its partition function and compare that function with the classical partition function of the same mechanical model. (c) Compare the mean energy of this model as a function of the Kelvin temperature T in quantum theory and in classical physics.

2. Consider a three-dimensional harmonic oscillator with slightly different restoring forces along the three perpendicular axes. Consider the distribution of its energy levels both for very small and for very large quantum numbers, comparing the resulting characteristic function with the corresponding classical characteristic volume in phase space.

3. Discuss the quantum theory of a free particle enclosed in the interior of a spherical shell with perfectly rigid and perfectly reflecting walls.

4. Consider a one-dimensional problem with a Hamiltonian H_0, in which the quantum levels have been determined completely and are designated by ϵ_k^0. How will the quantum levels be displaced if we add to the original Hamiltonian a minute *perturbation* H_1?

Chapter 8
Atomic Spectra

8.1. The hydrogen atom

So far, the quantum hypothesis has enabled us to account for the equilibrium distribution of the energy in cavity radiation, and we have also shown, at least in outline, how some degrees of freedom in a gas might contribute less than their classical share to the internal energy of the gas. In this chapter we shall consider the more detailed consequences of the theory. We have seen that electromagnetic radiation will carry energy only in integral multiples of $\hbar\omega$, where ω is the angular frequency of the radiation. Conversely, if a radiating system goes over from one energy level to another, the frequency of the radiation emitted or absorbed must be given by the same rule,

$$\Delta\epsilon = \hbar\omega, \tag{1}$$

except in those rare cases where a single transition gives rise to the emission of two or more separate "photons." Equation (1) enables us to correlate the frequencies found in atomic and molecular spectra with the differences in the possible quantized states of the atoms and molecules responsible for the radiations.

Our present interpretation of spectral lines accounts for the fact that all spectra of gaseous substances, that is, of free molecules, appear to consist of lines rather than of a continuous sequence of frequencies. Previously, J. J. Thomson had attempted to explain the nature of atomic spectra by the assumption that the electrons were bound elastically to equilibrium positions inside a very extended atomic nucleus with uniformly distributed electric charge. Although this model of the atom would account qualitatively for the line character of atomic spectra, it does not lead to correct quantitative results concerning the frequencies that will occur in these spectra. Thomson's model of the atom was discredited entirely when Rutherford and his students, beginning in 1909, showed by means of scattering experiments of alpha particles that the atomic nucleus consists of a very small concentration of charge inside the atom and that the electrons, therefore, cannot be bound to their equilibrium positions elastically, but must obey the inverse-square law of Coulomb. Thus Rutherford's experiments ruled out the only classical explanation of line spectra that was ever proposed.

On the other hand, our present quantum-theoretical interpretation of spectral line frequencies, which implies that the line frequencies are proportional to energy-level differences, immediately leads to a sequence that can be tested: the large number of frequencies in a typical atomic spectrum must be representable in the form of differences between a much smaller set of numbers, each number representing a possible energy level. This consequence can be confirmed by the analysis of any gas spectrum, and this regularity was well known even before Bohr proposed its interpretation in terms of quantum jumps of the atom. A detailed calculation of atomic energy levels will, therefore, enable us to predict accurately the system of lines forming an atomic spectrum. We shall carry out these calculations for the hydrogen atom, the simplest atom for which the results can be tested in terms of a readily available line spectrum.

Just as in the preceding section, we can split the total energy of the hydrogen atom (a two-body system consisting of a heavy nucleus and a light electron) into two terms, the *external* energy resulting from the motion of the joint center of mass, and the *internal* energy consisting of the potential and the remaining kinetic energy. Our interest, of course, lies in the internal energy. A rather trivial transformation of coordinates shows that the two-body problem can be reduced to a one-body problem, one whose arithmetic proceeds as if the hydrogen nucleus, the proton, were nailed to a fixed position and only the electron were free to move under the influence of the proton's inverse-square attraction. The only effect of the motion of the proton is to require that we reduce the mass of the electron by a minute amount. In other words, in the work that follows, m is the so-called reduced mass of the electron, $1/1800$ less than its true mass.

The internal part of the Hamiltonian of the hydrogen atom in spherical coordinates will have the form

$$H = \frac{1}{2\,m} \left[p_r^2 + \frac{1}{r^2} \left(p_\theta^2 + \sec^2 \theta \; p_\phi^2 \right) \right] - \frac{e^2}{r}. \tag{2}$$

This expression is very much like (7.34), which we set up for the diatomic symmetric molecule. The chief difference lies in the fact that the potential energy, which is now a definite known function, has no minimum but is negative throughout the range of the variable r, the more negative the closer we get to the center. However, the quantization of the angular motion is not affected by the particular properties of the potential energy, as long as we have a central-force field (that is, as long as the potential energy depends on the distance from the center only). We adopt the results of Chapter 7 and set

$$p_\theta^2 + \sec^2 \theta \, p_\phi^2 = k^2 \, \hbar^2. \tag{3}$$

This intermediate result must be carried into eq. (2). If we call the energy ϵ, as before, setting it equal to the Hamiltonian H, we find that

$$\epsilon = \frac{1}{2m} \left(p_r^2 + \frac{1}{r^2} k^2 \, \hbar^2 \right) - \frac{e^2}{r}. \tag{4}$$

There remains the question whether the radial motion is periodic. Physically, we shall have closed orbits only if the negative potential energy exceeds the kinetic energy of the systems, if, in other words, the total internal energy of the system, ϵ, is negative. In that case, we know from elementary mechanics and from the theory of planetary motion (M&E—Chap. 1), that the orbits are closed and elliptic. If, on the other hand, the kinetic energy is large enough to make ϵ positive, then the orbits are hyperbolic, and the radial part of the motion extends to infinite values of r. In the latter case, our general quantum hypothesis does not lead to the possibility of a time-independent grating in phase space, and the permissible states may have any positive energy whatsoever. Thus we must expect that in the hydrogen atom negative-energy states are quantized but positive-energy states are not. This conclusion is borne out by spectroscopic evidence.

Let us focus our attention on the bound states, in which ϵ is negative. For these trajectories, the motion is going to be periodic in r, and we can set up and quantize a phase integral. Our quantum condition will be

$$\oint p_r \, dr = \oint \sqrt{2m \, \epsilon + \frac{2m \, e^2}{r} - \frac{k^2 \, \hbar^2}{r^2}} \, dr = n_3 \, h, \tag{5}$$

with ϵ the only adjustable parameter to satisfy this equation. The periodic motion will take place between the two extreme possible values of r, which are the two zeros of the square root. Outside this domain, the square root, and with it the radial momentum p_r, is purely imaginary. Had we chosen ϵ positive, the root would have only one zero, and all larger values of r would lead to real values of p_r.

The integral (5) can be evaluated by the same methods applicable in the cases of the two integrals in Section 7.5. The result of the calculation is

$$n_3 h = -kh - \pi e^2 \left| \sqrt{\frac{2m}{\epsilon}} \right| \tag{6}$$

or

$$\epsilon = -\frac{m e^4}{2\hbar^2} \frac{1}{n^2} \qquad (n = k + n_3, \qquad n_3 \geq 0). \tag{7}$$

The binding energies of the various states of the hydrogen atom are proportional to n^{-2}, $n = 1, 2, \cdots$. This result, known as the *Rydberg formula*, was found empirically long before the development of the quantum theory of atomic spectra.

In the hydrogen atom, there is no reasonable configuration that might be described as static equilibrium. The state of lowest potential energy is the one in which the electron coincides with the proton, and the potential energy of that configuration is $-\infty$. Obviously, this state cannot be achieved by any reasonable process. Hence the lowest state of which the hydrogen atom is capable is that for which $n = 1$. In consequence, this state is considered the ground state of the hydrogen atom, even though it is not a state of rest. Our theory might lead to the conclusion that this state can be realized in two ways. In the first the motion is purely radial, and we should have $n_3 = 1$; this state would be an s-state. Or the motion is purely tangential, with $k = 1$, $n_3 = 0$, and with three possible values for the magnetic quantum number m. Thus there would appear to exist four distinct states with the same negative binding energy $-m e^4/2\hbar^2$. Spectroscopic experience, however, has shown that this conclusion of the theory is erroneous. Actually, the ground state is an s-state, and p-states are encountered only in the excited states. Modern quantum mechanics explains this discrepancy and furnishes the correct results.

In other respects, however, the predictions of the early quantum theory were quite correct. The possible energy levels of the hydrogen atom are given correctly by eq. (7), which incidentally leads to an accurate experimental determination of Planck's constant. They are widely spaced for small values of the quantum number n but move together more and more closely for large n's, so that there is an infinite number of bound states in the immediate vicinity of the energy zero (the energy at which the atom becomes ionized). The complete atomic spectrum of hydrogen contains lines corresponding to transitions between all energy levels. Depending on the lower of the two levels (the final level in the case of an emission process), the hydrogen lines form systematic series of lines, conspicuous even in a casual inspection of the complete spectrum. Transitions to the ground state occur most frequently and form a series of lines known as the *Lyman series*. The first few lines of this series lie in the ultraviolet. Transitions from the higher excited states to the first excited state ($n = 2$) lead to a series lying wholly in the visible range and known as the *Balmer series*. For details concerning further series designations, the reader is referred to any text on atomic spectra.

There are a number of elements whose atomic spectra resemble the hydrogen spectrum to some extent. First of all, there are the spectra of elements that have been partly *ionized* so that they retain but a single electron, such as singly ionized helium, doubly ionized lithium, and so forth. The spectra of these elements differ from the hydrogen spectrum only insofar as the term representing Coulomb's law in the Hamiltonian must be replaced by $-Ze^2/r$, where Z is the multiplicity of the nuclear charge—2 for He, 3 for Li, and so on. As a result, expression (7) must be multiplied by Z^2 to remain correct for these elements.

Then there are neutral elements in which all but one electron cluster closely about the nucleus, and essentially only one electron is ordinarily involved in radiative processes. These elements are known as the alkali metals and include Li, Na, K, Rb, and Cs. As long as the single active electron is well outside the cloud of the remaining electrons, this cloud "screens" the nucleus electrically, and as a result the energy levels are given in fair approximation by eq. (7), with Z only slightly greater than 1. But for eccentric orbits, the active electron dips deeply into the cloud of the remaining electrons, where the "screening" is less complete, and as a result the effective nuclear charge, averaged over the whole orbit, is somewhat greater. For example, in the alkali spectra the different states belonging to the same "principal" quantum number n do not possess the same binding energy, but their binding energy (the distance these levels lie below the energy of ionization) for a given n increases with the eccentricity of the orbit.

How is the eccentricity related to the "azimuthal" quantum number k? If, for a given n, k is small, then n_3, the "radial" quantum number, must be large, the radial motion is appreciable, and the orbit must be rather elongated and eccentric. If, on the other hand, k approaches n, then the orbits begin to resemble circles more and more, they stay well outside the electron screen, and the corresponding levels are only slightly below the hydrogen level with the same value of n. And this state of affairs is borne out by the alkali spectra. For any particular value of n, the s-state is always lowest, followed in order by the p-level, the d-level, and so on.

In quantum physics, we call states *degenerate* when more than one combination of quantum numbers lead to the same energy level. The hydrogen atom is a highly degenerate system in that only the sum n,

$$n = n_3 + k,$$
$$k = |m| + |n_2|, \tag{8}$$

determines the energy levels, but neither m nor k separately has any effect. In the alkali metals, this degeneracy is partly removed. The principal quantum number determines the energy level only very approximately, and actually the s- and the p-levels belonging to the same value of n are often widely separated. However, the degeneracy with respect to the magnetic quantum number m remains unchanged, and this degeneracy is unavoidable as long as we do not modify the spherical symmetry of the system. The only manner in which we can destroy the spherical symmetry is by applying an external field; a strong magnetic field, for instance, will affect the motion of the electrons differently when the plane of the orbit is at different angles relative to the lines of force of the magnetic field. As a matter of fact, in a strong magnetic field, originally single lines of atomic spectra are split up into complicated systems, called *multiplets*, because the states belonging to different values of m now have slightly different values. The *Zeeman effect* is historically the first instance in which it was possible to modify an atomic spectrum under laboratory conditions. Because of the importance of the quantum number m for the Zeeman multiplets, m is called the *magnetic quantum number*.

8.2. Space quantization. The oscillator in three dimensions

Our presentation of early quantum physics has been incomplete. We have failed to discuss Pauli's *exclusion principle*, according to which no two electrons can ever be in the same state (possess the same set of identical quantum numbers) and which explains the arrangement of the chemical elements in the periodic table. Nor have we gone into the important question of the probability with which a transition from one atomic state to another takes place, a question that leads to the famous selection rules, according to which a transition cannot take place unless the angular quantum numbers between the old and the new state satisfy certain relationships. Most important, we have failed to introduce the intrinsic angular momentum possessed by individual elementary particles, both electrons and nucleons (protons and neutrons), whose magnitude as well as component in any particular direction is always $\frac{1}{2}\hbar$. Historically, all these problems were attacked during the period of early quantum physics, but their solution was tentative and in many cases incorrect, according to our present deeper understanding. For our purposes, their discussion here would not be very useful, because better explanations are now available. In Chapter 11 we shall give a brief introduction to the theory of quantum transitions accompanied by the absorption and emission of radiation. As for the exclusion principle and the particle spin, we shall leave their discussion to more advanced texts of quantum mechanics.

There is one aspect of early quantum physics whose discussion belongs here, and that is the question of *space quantization*. We shall discuss the orientation of the electronic orbits with respect to the chosen coordinate axes here because this question sheds some light on the physical significance of the Sommerfeld-Wilson rules of quantization. Previously, we found that we can quantize the angular momentum about the z-axis and that this angular momentum component turns out to be an integral multiple of $\hbar$. Obviously, there is no intrinsic criterion for choosing any particular direction for the z-axis in spherically symmetric atomic systems, and it would appear reasonable that the angular momentum about any axis, chosen at random, is subject to the same rule of quantization. As a matter of fact, our rule of quantization is somewhat arbitrary. All we need to do is to find *some* system in which the problem will separate. With respect to that system, we can formally carry out our scheme of quantization, leading to results that can be compared with experiment. If a system can be separated in more coordinate systems than one, then our rule of quantization is intrinsically arbitrary. Expressed in different terms, there will then be more than one method of cutting up phase space into stationary cells of equal volumes.

Remarkably enough, a system will separate in more ways than one only if its quantum states are degenerate. In such a case, it is possible to obtain the several states belonging to a given energy level in different ways and, in fact, the states obtained in one way need not coincide with the states obtained in another. However, in any case, the total number of states belonging to a particular energy level and the numerical value of the energy always come out the same; that is, both the energy levels and their multiplicities are independent of the coordinate system in which we accomplish the quantization. These facts are so remarkable that we shall illustrate them with the help of an example of high degeneracy that requires comparatively little effort to carry through. This example is the spherically symmetric harmonic oscillator in three dimensions.

We consider a mass point of mass M which is tied to a fixed equilibrium point with an elastic force having the force constant K. The resonant angular frequency of that oscillator is, of course,

$$\omega = \sqrt{\frac{K}{M}}. \tag{9}$$

In Section 7.4 we dealt with the harmonic oscillator in one dimension. A somewhat similar three-dimensional problem was dealt with in Section 7.5, with the difference that there the potential energy had a minimum on a whole spherical surface of the non-vanishing radius r_0. Now we shall consider the case in which the equilibrium configuration is at rest at a single point. Naturally, we shall adopt this point as the origin of our coordinate system.

In Cartesian coordinates the Hamiltonian of our system takes the form

$$H = \left(\frac{p_x^2}{2M} + \frac{K}{2}\,x^2\right) + \left(\frac{p_y^2}{2M} + \frac{K}{2}\,y^2\right) + \left(\frac{p_z^2}{2M} + \frac{K}{2}\,z^2\right), \quad (10)$$

and in spherical coordinates it becomes

$$H = \left(\frac{p_r^2}{2M} + \frac{K}{2}\,r^2\right) + \frac{1}{2Mr^2}\,(p_\theta^2 + \sec^2\theta \cdot p_\phi^2). \quad (11)$$

The remarkable fact is that we can carry out the complete quantization in either coordinate system.

In Cartesian coordinates the course of the calculation follows the one-dimensional case. The energy consists additively of the contributions of the three parentheses, each of which is the Hamiltonian of a complete one-dimensional oscillator. Hence each of these three additive contributions must be quantized according to the results of Section 7.4. If we call the three appropriate quantum numbers n_x, n_y, and n_z, respectively, the total energy, according to the quantization procedure suggested by eq. (10), comes out as

$$\epsilon = n\,\hbar\,\omega,$$

$$n = n_x + n_y + n_z \qquad (n_x \geq 0,\, n_y \geq 0,\, n_z \geq 0). \quad (12)$$

The result indicates a high degree of degeneracy. Specifically, we can produce a principal quantum number $n = 0$ in only one way. There are three different combinations belonging to $n = 1$, six that belong to $n = 3$, and generally $\frac{1}{2}n(n+1)$ different states for which the total energy of the three-dimensional oscillator equals $n\,\hbar\,\omega$.

Let us now turn to the Hamiltonian (11). As for the angular part of the motion, we can insert our previous result, eq. (3), noting parenthetically that each quantum number k represents $(2k+1)$ different states. Only the radial motion remains to be quantized. For the phase integral for the radial motion, eq. (11) together with (3) furnishes us with the expression

$$\oint p_r\,dr = \oint \sqrt{2M\,\epsilon - M\,K\,r^2 - \frac{k^2\,\hbar^2}{r^2}}\,dr = n_3\,h, \quad (13)$$

which can again be evaluated by one of several standard methods.

The result is that

$$n_3 h = \pi \left(\frac{\epsilon}{\omega} - k\,\hbar \right) \qquad (14)$$

or $\epsilon = n\,\hbar\,\omega,$

$$n = k + 2n_3 \qquad (k \geq 0,\ n_3 \geq 0). \qquad (15)$$

The energy levels turn out to be the same as before, and so does the multiplicity of each level.

Gratifying as this result may be, we shall now demonstrate that except for the actual energy levels, the quantized trajectories obtained by the two methods are quite different. First of all, our quantization procedures do not completely determine the shape of a mechanical trajectory. In Cartesian coordinates, for instance, the three quantum numbers n_x, n_y, and n_z merely determine the amplitudes of the motion in the three directions but say nothing about the phase relations. If all three vibrations are in phase, the motion will actually take place along a straight line through the center, and the angular momentum will be zero. By changing the phase relations continuously (and without changing our quantum numbers), we can also change the angular momentum of the trajectory continuously, in apparent violation of our results from the form (11). Likewise, any ellipse determined by a particular choice of the three quantum numbers m, k, and n can be turned continuously about the z-axis, with the result that the amplitudes in the x- and y-directions change continuously, without any change in our original quantum conditions.

At first sight it might appear that we must require that of all the possible orientations of the ellipse and of all the possible phase relationships in Cartesian coordinates, only those are realized which permit us to satisfy all the quantum conditions at once. But such a hypothesis cannot be maintained. We must remember that an infinity of Cartesian coordinate systems is possible, with all possible orientations in space, and likewise an infinity of spherical coordinate systems. None of these coordinate systems is intrinsically preferable to the others. But obviously, we could not find harmonic orbits that have quantized amplitudes in all conceivable directions, nor can we find elliptical paths whose angular momentum about any conceivable axis is an integral multiple of $\hbar$ (with only the trivial exception of the straight-line trajectories, whose angular momentum vanishes).

As an alternative hypothesis, we might suppose that of all the conceivable coordinate systems in which our quantization rule can be formulated, actually one is preferred, and that it is merely our insufficient knowledge of the laws of nature that prevents us from deciding which one. But that hypothesis can be refuted, too. We shall find that minute modifications of the force law lead to the adoption of a particular coordinate system as a matter of necessity, not of choice, and that different modifications lead to different coordinate systems.

First we shall consider a minute modification of the force law that destroys the harmonic character of the system but not its spherical symmetry. For instance, we might suppose that the force law includes a small fourth-degree term in addition to the principal quadratic term $\frac{1}{2}K r^2$. Or we might think of a system in which the equilibrium is not reached at the center but on some concentric spherical surface r_0. Any such modification will lead to a partial splitting up of the energy levels, so that each combination of k and n leads to a different energy. However, the degeneracy with respect to the quantum number m remains intact, because we have not dropped our assumption of spherical symmetry.

With any such modification of the force law, the spherical coordinate systems are the only ones in which separation and quantization remain possible. If we follow the motion of any classical system that is slightly "anharmonic," we find that the trajectory is still approximately an ellipse. But the ellipse is not closed. Slowly, the whole ellipse precesses in its orbital plane, in such a manner that the dimensions of its major and minor axes remain unchanged. Thus the angular momentum of the modified problem remains constant in magnitude and in direction and so, of course, does the total energy. Consequently, m, k, and n are "good" quantum numbers, because they refer to elements of the trajectory that remain preserved in time. But as the ellipse precesses, the amplitudes in three mutually perpendicular directions change slowly and continuously. In the language of the quantum physicist, n_x, n_y, and n_z are no longer "good" quantum numbers.

Let us now consider another modification of the force law, one which does not destroy the harmonicity but which destroys the spherical symmetry. All we need to assume is that the binding-force constants in the three Cartesian coordinate directions are slightly different:

$$H = \left(\frac{p_x^2}{2M} + \frac{K_x}{2}\,x^2\right) + \left(\frac{p_y^2}{2M} + \frac{K_y}{2}\,y^2\right) + \left(\frac{p_z^2}{2M} + \frac{K_z}{2}\,z^2\right). \quad (16)$$

This problem will still separate in Cartesian coordinates, with the result that the energy levels are given by the expression

$$\epsilon = n_x\,\hbar\,\omega_x + n_y\,\hbar\,\omega_y + n_z\,\hbar\,\omega_z. \quad (17)$$

The trajectory of a particle moving under the force law described by the Hamiltonian (16) is a Lissajou figure that will gradually fill out a rectangular parallelepipedon. Because of the slightly different frequencies in the x-, y-, and z-directions, the phase relations between the three components of the motion will change continuously, with the result that the angular momentum will change both its magnitude and its direction. Therefore m and k are no longer "good" quantum numbers, but the amplitudes in the three coordinate directions remain unchanged in time. Hence n_x, n_y, and n_z are the appropriate "good" quantum numbers for this system.

That our conclusions are valid is borne out by spectroscopic evidence. In the case of a diatomic molecule, we find invariably that m and k are appropriate quantum numbers. The case of the anisotropic oscillator is approximated in triatomic molecules of sufficient asymmetry that there are three distinct normal modes of vibration with three different characteristic frequencies. And really, with such molecules we find spectral lines corresponding to transitions of these distinct and different one-dimensional harmonic oscillators.

These considerations lead to the conclusion that our quantum rule is still too "classical," that the particle trajectory probably possesses much less reality than was assumed in early quantum physics. In the case of degenerate systems, alternative procedures of quantization lead to the same results as far as readily observable facts are concerned, namely, primarily the locations and the multiplicities of the energy levels (these multiplicities count in all statistical considerations and can be tested by measurements of specific heats). As far as the details of the trajectories are concerned, the alternative procedures lead to contradictory results, but strangely enough each procedure can be justified by means of experiments which involve slight changes in the force laws and which remove some of the degeneracies. In modern experiments such modifications can be turned on and off at will (by passing a molecular beam through external magnetic or electric fields), and in every instance the theoretical choice of quantum numbers is confirmed by the experimental findings. Evidently the early quantum rules, superimposed on the laws of classical mechanics, represented a highly successful "cookbook recipe," but eventually they had to be supplemented by a deeper understanding of the laws of atomic physics.

Problems

1. For any electronic orbit, the angular momentum and the Amperian magnetic dipole moment are connected by the formula

$$M_{\text{magn}} = -\frac{e}{2\,m\,c}\,p_\theta$$

(M&E, pp. 156, 157). If an atom is exposed to an external magnetic field of uniform field strength H along the z-axis, determine the corrections that must be added to the unperturbed atomic energy levels because of the interaction between the field and the electronic orbit.

2. In a later chapter, it will be explained that ordinarily the quantum number m changes only by ± 1 in an electronic transition. How will the external magnetic field of Problem 1 modify the appearance of a spectral line? (The answer to this question depends on the angle that the magnetic lines of force form with the line of view. Consider the two angles of $0°$ and $90°$.)

3. Determine the energy levels of the hydrogen atom in so-called parabolic coordinates, in which the three coordinates used are the angle ϕ (same significance as in spherical coordinates) and two coordinates u and v corresponding to rotational paraboloids whose joint axis is the z-axis and whose joint focus is the origin of the spherical coordinate system.

4. Determine the energy levels of an anisotropic harmonic oscillator whose potential energy is a positive definite, homogeneous quadratic function of the Cartesian coordinates x, y, z, but otherwise arbitrary.

5. Consider a spherically symmetric harmonic oscillator and add to the potential energy a fourth-order term of very small amplitude. Determine the corrections to be added to the energy levels.

Chapter 9

Probability Waves

9.1. De Broglie's hypothesis

Quantization proved its power both in statistical mechanics and in the analysis of atomic and molecular spectra. But the imposition of a quantization prescription on top of an unmodified classical structure could not lead by itself to a logically connected theory. As a matter of fact, in the case of degenerate systems, alternative executions of the basic rule lead to mutually contradictory results. Also, as the analysis of spectra proceeded, the original simple rules needed to be modified in a number of cases. For instance, it was found that the rotational energy levels of polyatomic molecules corresponded to half-odd quantization rather than to ordinary integral quantum numbers. Also, there was no consistent theory that would furnish spectral line *intensities* (that is, transition probabilities). Finally, the jumps necessary in radiative processes if a system was to go over from one quantum state to another were hard to visualize or to comprehend with an essentially classical view of the trajectory as such. For all these reasons, a more fundamental approach to the nature of quantum processes was called for if any further progress was to be made. As happens so frequently in the history of theoretical physics, the new departure was begun in close analogy to well-known facts of classical physics.

De Broglie[1] asked himself whether something like quantization occurs in any field of physics, as it was known in the early 1920's. Discrete situations do, in fact, occur in classical physics. Whenever a wave is permitted to interfere multiply with itself, the only states capable of existence are those in which the interfering waves are all in phase with each other, and there are (and were known in 1923) two such situations of considerable importance.

The first instance of discrete phenomena concerns the diffraction

---

[1] *Phil. Mag.*, **47**, 446 (1924); *Ann. de physique*, **3**, 22 (1925).

of electromagnetic waves by periodic gratings. If a collimated monochromatic beam strikes an optical grating in which scratches or lines have been engraved by machine at regular intervals somewhat longer than the wave length of the light employed, electromagnetic energy will be transmitted only in a finite number of discrete directions. Each of these directions is characterized by the requirement that the difference in optical path length between light paths passing through corresponding neighboring points of the grating shall be an integral multiple of the wave length of that light. Optical gratings form, of course, a standard device for separating light of different wave length and for determining the wave length of each fraction in terms of a macroscopic laboratory standard, the period of the grating.

Another instance of quantized wave fields is provided by the normal mode of any isolated piece of elastic material capable of transmitting elastic waves. A very simple example is provided by an elastic string capable of transverse vibrations. If its two ends are tied to rigid supports, the only vibrations possible are those at which both ends of the string are permanently at rest. If the mass of the string per unit length is m' and if its tension is designated by T, then its transverse motion at any point along its length is determined by the law that the local acceleration tends to shorten the string and hence is proportional to and directed toward the direction of concave curvature. The quantitative law of its motion is

$$m' \frac{\partial^2 y}{\partial t^2} - T \frac{\partial^2 y}{\partial x^2} = 0, \tag{1}$$

where x is the coordinate parallel to the string and y a coordinate at right angles to the string. If the string were of infinite length, the simplest solutions would be of the form

$$y = e^{-i\omega\left(t \pm \frac{x}{c}\right)} \qquad \left(c = \sqrt{\frac{T}{m'}}, \ -\infty < \omega < \infty\right), \tag{2}$$

or progressive waves. Because of the linear homogeneous character of the equation of motion (1), the sum of two solutions is again a solution, and the most general solution for the infinite string would be a linear superposition of the particular solutions (2), or

$$y = \int_{\omega = -\infty}^{\infty} \left[\phi(\omega)e^{-i\omega\left(t - \frac{x}{c}\right)} + \psi(\omega)e^{-i\omega\left(t + \frac{x}{c}\right)}\right] d\omega. \tag{3}$$

By means of the Fourier integral theorem, we may also represent the most general solution of the partial differential equation (1) by means of the two arbitrary real functions f and g, thus:

$$y = f\left(t - \frac{x}{c}\right) + g\left(t + \frac{x}{c}\right). \tag{4}$$

This last form of the solution lends itself most easily to an intuitive interpretation. In a string of infinite length, the most general solution is composed linearly of two waves traveling in opposite directions at the velocity c and having entirely arbitrary profiles.

If we consider the string of finite length L with the end points fixed, only those solutions (3) or (4) remain possible which have permanent zeros at $x = 0$ and $x = L$. A single traveling wave cannot possibly have such permanent zeros, but two such waves together may, if their profiles have such a relationship to each other that their contributions at these two specified points always cancel. For the point $x = 0$, this condition will be satisfied provided the function g equals $-f$ for all values of the argument t,

$$f(t) + g(t) = 0 \qquad (-\infty < t < \infty) \tag{5}$$

For the point $x = L$, the necessary and sufficient condition is that

$$f\left(t - \frac{L}{c}\right) + g\left(t + \frac{L}{c}\right) = 0 \tag{6}$$

or
$$f(t') + g\left(t' + 2\frac{L}{c}\right) = 0 \qquad \left(t' = t - \frac{L}{c}\right). \tag{7}$$

Conditions (5) and (7) must hold for all positive and negative values of the parameters t and t'. Combining them we find, then, that

$$g\left(t + \frac{2}{c}L\right) = g(t),$$

$$f\left(t + \frac{2}{c}L\right) = f(t) \qquad (g = -f). \tag{8}$$

Hence the most general motion of the string of finite length is represented by the expression

$$y(x, t) = f\left(t - \frac{x}{c}\right) - f\left(t + \frac{x}{c}\right) \qquad \left[f\left(t + \frac{2}{c}L\right) = f(t)\right], \tag{9}$$

where f is a periodic but otherwise arbitrary function of its argument, the period being $2L/c$.

The "quantization" enters our problem in the following manner. Fourier-series theory (M&E, pp. 214 ff.) teaches us that periodic functions can be represented conveniently as infinite sums of trigonometric functions. Since the right-hand side of eq. (9) for $t = 0$ is an odd function of the argument x, the Fourier series can be set up in terms of sine functions only, without the benefit of cosine terms. The proper Fourier representation is, therefore,

$$y(x, t) = \sum_{n=1}^{\infty} a_n \sin \frac{\pi n x}{L} \cos \left(\frac{\pi n c}{L} t - \delta_n \right), \qquad (10)$$

where the a_n are the arbitrary real Fourier coefficients of the expansions, and the δ_n are arbitrary phase constants. We can say that the most general solution is the linear superposition of an infinite but discrete number of particular solutions, each one of which depends on the time "harmonically" (sine function, cosine function, or exponential with imaginary exponent). Another interpretation of result (9) is that both ends of the string will reflect any traveling wave reaching them, thus causing multiple reflections. Of all the trigonometric waves (2), only those will persist which interfere with themselves constructively no matter how often reflected back and forth by the end points of the string.

We can easily increase the complexity of our problem, for instance by endowing our string with an uneven mass distribution $m'(x)$. In that case, the problem cannot be solved in closed form such as eq. (9). Nevertheless, the most general solution, for both the infinite and for the finite string, can still be represented by integrals or series resembling eqs. (3) or (10), because the time-dependence in eq. (1) can be separated off. For the string of finite length, for instance, the most general solution can be given the form

$$y(x, t) = \sum_{n=1}^{\infty} a_n f_n(x) \cos (\omega_n t - \delta_n), \qquad (11)$$

where each function $f_n(x)$ satisfies the equation

$$f_n''(x) + \frac{T \omega_n^2}{m'(x)} f_n(x) = 0 \qquad (12)$$

and the *boundary conditions*

$$f_n(0) = f_n(L) = 0, \tag{13}$$

and where the number of zeros (nodes) of f_n between the end points equals $(n - 1)$. The characteristic frequencies ω_n are determined by the boundary conditions (13) and are in general different from the values $(\pi n c/L)$ of eq. (10). The general solution (11) is again composed linearly of a discrete set of particular solutions, each of which has a simple periodic dependence on time. Unless the different frequencies ω_n are commensurable (have rational ratios), the general solution is not periodic in time but is "almost periodic." The only strictly periodic functions are the individual terms in expression (11).

Even the nonuniform string is a very simple example of vibrating bodies. Membranes (elastic two-dimensional domains) and vibrating solids of various shapes all have one feature in common: As long as the conditions on the edges or surfaces, the *boundary conditions*, are well defined, their only periodic motions form a discrete set of vibration patterns, each possessing its own characteristic frequency, and the most general motion possible is an arbitrary linear superposition of the periodic solutions, the so-called "normal modes of vibration." In the case of a membrane, two different integers are needed to identify the individual normal modes, because for each normal mode the membrane is intersected by a network of node lines, and we need to know the number of lengthwise and crosswise node lines to identify a particular normal mode. For a vibrating solid, there are three sets of mutually intersecting nodal surfaces, and each normal mode must be characterized by a set of three integers. Incidentally, the treatment of the vibrating solid is closely analogous to the solution of Maxwell's equations inside a cavity, a problem we have tackled in Chapter 7. The reader can easily verify that we then encountered triplets of integers, (h, k, l).

In view of all these facts, which were well known by 1923, de Broglie proposed to explain the rules of quantization on the basis of wave interference. Without constructing a complete field theory, with partial differential equations like Maxwell's, he assumed that each elementary particle is accompanied on its trajectory by some wave of definite wave length. If the particle is free, coming from infinity and departing into infinity, the waves are essentially progressive, and there will be no more interference and quantum restrictions than there are in a traveling light wave in classical physics. But if the particle moves in a bound orbit, the orbit will turn back on itself again and again, and the waves will interfere with themselves. The only stationary patterns will be those in which the trajectory of the particle permits an integral number of wave lengths to be placed alongside before it returns to the starting point. This self-interference of the waves then would explain why only certain types of paths will be stationary whenever a particle moves in a bound trajectory.

If this hypothesis is to prove useful, we must assume some general principle by which we can ascertain the wave length of the *de Broglie waves;* only then can we make quantitative predictions and compare with experience. In arriving at his results, de Broglie assumed that the law to be postulated would be Lorentz-covariant. That is, the relationship between the mechanical properties of the particle and the wave properties of the accompanying de Broglie wave would have to be the same in all frames of reference, assuming the validity of the Lorentz equations of the special theory of relativity (M&E, p. 234). De Broglie started, therefore, by assuming some relationship in that frame in which the particle is at rest.

If a particle of mass m is at rest and if we wish to associate with it a particular wave motion, then there is no criterion by which we could assign to the waves some direction of propagation; and if we cannot, the most natural assumption would be to make the wave purely time-dependent. The frequency still must be set, and to do this de Broglie adopted the original proposal of Planck, made for the purpose of quantizing the normal modes of the electromagnetic cavity radiation: he assumed that the frequency of the wave is proportional to the (relativistic) energy of the particle, which for a free particle at rest equals $m c^2$. Thus the fundamental assumption of de Broglie's in the rest system is

$$m c^2 = h \nu' = \hbar \omega'. \tag{14}$$

At this stage of the theory, there is no need to speculate on the physical nature of the wave. We shall call anything that "waves" the *wave function* and designate it by the symbol ψ. Thus, in the rest system, the de Broglie wave is to be described by the expression

$$\psi = \psi_0 e^{-i\frac{m c^2}{\hbar}t'}. \tag{15}$$

Now we can carry out a Lorentz transformation, treating the wave function as a scalar field. Because of the transformation equations

$$x' = \frac{x - vt}{\sqrt{1 - v^2/c^2}}, \qquad t' = \frac{t - \dfrac{v}{c^2} x}{\sqrt{1 - v^2/c^2}}, \qquad (16)$$

$$y' = y, \qquad\qquad z' = z$$

(M&E, p. 234), expression (15) turns into

$$\psi = \psi_0 \, e^{-i\frac{m\,c^2}{\hbar}\frac{t - v\frac{x}{c^2}}{\sqrt{1 - v^2/c^2}}}. \qquad (17)$$

In a system in which the particle moves in the x-direction,

$$u_x = v, \qquad u_y = u_z = 0, \qquad (18)$$

the frequency and the wave length of the de Broglie wave become, respectively,

$$\omega = \frac{1}{\hbar} \frac{m\,c^2}{\sqrt{1 - v^2/c^2}}, \qquad \lambda = \frac{h \sqrt{1 - v^2/c^2}}{m\,v}. \qquad (19)$$

These expressions happen to be related closely to the relativistic expressions for the total energy and for the linear momentum of a free particle. We can reformulate the relationships (19) by stating that

$$\hbar \, \omega = E, \qquad \hbar \, \mathbf{k} = \mathbf{p}. \qquad (20)$$

$\mathbf{k}$ is the so-called *wave propagation vector*, defined for any plane wave as the vector pointing in this positive direction of propagation and having the magnitude of 2π times the inverse wave length. Because of eqs. (20), eq. (17) can also be written in the form

$$\psi(\mathbf{x}, \, t) = \psi_0 \, e^{\frac{i}{\hbar}(\mathbf{p}\cdot\mathbf{x} - E\,t)} \qquad (21)$$

This last exponent is an invariant four-dimensional scalar product with respect to all Lorentz transformations, and thus has greater generality than expression (17).

Before we can apply eq. (21) successfully, we must go over to the nonrelativistic limit, which, as we know, is represented by velocities $\mathbf{u}$ that are small compared with c. In nonrelativistic physics, the "energy" of a system is merely the deviation of E in eq. (21) from the rest energy, and thus, for a free particle, the excess of the total energy over $m\,c^2$. To allow for a similar split-off in the de Broglie frequency, we must separate the total angular frequency ω into a "rest frequency" (equal to $m\,c^2/\hbar$) and the leftover, the "beat frequency" as it were, between the de Broglie waves corresponding to the same particle at rest and in motion. Thus in the relationship between propagation vector and linear momentum we must merely replace the relativistic momentum by its nonrelativistic approximation, but in the expression for the frequency we must set

$$\bar{\omega} = \omega - \omega_0 = \frac{1}{\hbar}\,(E - E_0) = \frac{\bar{E}}{\hbar}. \tag{22}$$

As a result, we find that relationship (20) requires no modification in notation, but the significance of the various symbols has been shifted from the relativistic quantities to their nonrelativistic counterparts.

It remains to assign a wave train to an arbitrary moving particle and to examine the possibilities of self-interference. If we wish to ascertain the number of wave lengths along a certain trajectory in accordance with eq. (20), we find for the number of wave lengths per unit length of path

$$\frac{dn}{dl} = \frac{1}{\lambda} = \frac{1}{2\pi}\,|\mathbf{k}| = \frac{1}{h}\,|\mathbf{p}|; \tag{23}$$

therefore

$$n = \frac{1}{h}\int |\mathbf{p}|\,dl = \frac{1}{h}\int \mathbf{p}\cdot d\mathbf{l}. \tag{24}$$

If the orbit of a particle is closed, the condition for constructive interference is that the number of wave lengths once around the complete orbit be an integer, or

$$\oint \mathbf{p}\cdot d\mathbf{l} = n\,h, \tag{25}$$

our original condition for quantizing periodic motion. Thus, de Broglie's hypothesis of a wave that is closely associated with the mechanical trajectory was a help to an intuitive understanding of the nature of the original quantization rule, but it did not lead to new relationships. However, de Broglie's work was of the greatest importance for the further development of the quantum theory.

9.2. Wave fields

De Broglie's original hypothesis suffered from two principal faults: it did not accomplish any more than was accomplished in the earlier period of quantum physics under the rules formulated by Sommerfeld and Wilson; and it failed to give a clear accounting why in systems with several degrees of freedom each degree carried a separate quantum condition. Also, the introduction of a new wave field without any specific physical properties gave the hypothesis the appearance of an interim proposal, not that of a complete physical theory.

Wherever waves appear in physics, they will always pervade the whole domain available, and they will not be confined to narrow ray trajectories or narrow beams. It seemed reasonable to assume that de Broglie's waves, too, were probably not confined or confinable to the immediate vicinity of the path of the particle, though the classical trajectory of the particle might coincide with the region of greatest wave intensity. Without sticking too closely to the actual historical unfolding of the new departure, we may now ask ourselves just what is the domain of definition for the de Broglie waves. For an answer, let us turn once more to the known facts of spectroscopy. In Chapter 8 we indicated the course of the theory of the hydrogen and the alkali spectra, but of course there is a large class of spectra in which the spectral lines give evidence of the involvement of two or even more electrons. In He the two electrons present are of equal importance, and in the Be, Mg, Ca, Sr, Ba, and Ra spectra, two electrons are equally active throughout the optical region. Each of these two electrons possesses a complete set of quantum numbers, and the same is true of the infinitely many degrees of freedom of a radiation cavity, as evidenced by the success of Planck's theory. Thus all the evidence points to the fact that the quantum rules must be formulated in the phase space of the mechanical system, no matter what the number of dimensions of that phase space, and that the number of separate quantum numbers characterizing a system equals the number of degrees of freedom of the system, or the number of dimensions of the configuration space. That is, of course, what we had assumed in Chapters 7 and 8, but it is worth while to point out that in this respect, at any rate, our assumptions appear to be confirmed by the facts.

Whenever multiple reflection and interference leads to the emergence of discrete stationary states in classical wave problems, the number of integers characterizing the individual stationary states or normal modes equals the number of dimensions of the domain in which the waves propagate. Hence we are led inescapably to the conclusion that *the de Broglie waves must be multidimensional wave fields in configuration space.* For a single particle the configuration space and the physical space coincide. But for a system of any complexity they do not, and then it is of decisive importance that we cannot expect to have de Broglie waves in *physical space.* Any hypothesis concerning the physical nature of the de Broglie wave field will have to be consistent with this fact.

If de Broglie waves are capable of spreading throughout the configuration space of a mechanical system, how is it that they ever are reflected on themselves, that somehow they are confined? In classical physics, waves may be confined to a certain domain by impenetrable walls, but they may also be confined in another manner. When a plane wave is traveling toward a medium in which its speed of propagation exceeds the speed in the medium it is about to leave, it may happen that no energy is transferred across the interface because the normal component of the wave-propagation vector in the new medium would become imaginary. In that case, we speak of *total reflection.* If it should happen that the propagation vector is imaginary outside a region no matter what its direction, then the wave pattern will be confined essentially to that region through total reflection, in spite of the absence of perfectly rigid walls. If the wave propagation vector is proportional to the linear momentum of a particle, then wherever the potential energy of a configuration exceeds the total energy available, neither the classical particle nor a plane (or nearly plane) de Broglie wave can get to that part of configuration space, and we have established the existence of a "prison for waves." Thus we should expect quantum conditions in any situation in which a system is bound together. Even the extended wave pattern will then be confined mostly to that part of configuration space in which the classical motion takes place. But no matter what the detailed laws of propagation of these waves, we can expect that the number of quantum numbers determining "normal modes" will equal the number of degrees of freedom.

In the next section, we shall formulate the hypothetical law to be satisfied by the de Broglie waves, and thus we shall be in a position to derive quantitative results on atomic energy levels. But before doing so, we shall attempt to find out whether we can construct "wave packets" for the *free* particle, where without the formulation of a comprehensive wave law, we may adopt eq. (20). In a free particle, moving without any external forces, plane de Broglie waves are certainly a possible solution. But most wave fields in physics obey the *law of linear superposition:* the linear combination of two or more wave fields is again a possible wave field.[1] We can, therefore, attempt to construct wave packets as linear superpositions of plane waves. Again, the theory of the Fourier integral comes to our help. It assures us that at any particular time t_0 any square-integrable function $f(x, y, z)$ can be represented as a linear superposition of trigonometric functions, and eq. (20) will then tell us what happens to each one of these trigonometric functions in the course of time. If, at the time $t = 0$, ψ can be represented by an expression having the form

$$\psi(\mathbf{x}, 0) = \left(\frac{1}{2\pi\hbar}\right)^{3/2} \int\int\int_{\mathbf{p}} \alpha(\mathbf{p}) \, e^{\frac{i}{\hbar}\mathbf{p}\cdot\mathbf{x}} \, d\mathbf{p}, \tag{26}$$

then the time dependence of ψ must be given completely by the expression

$$\psi(\mathbf{x}, t) = \left(\frac{1}{2\pi\hbar}\right)^{3/2} \int\int\int_{\mathbf{p}} \alpha(\mathbf{p}) \, e^{\frac{i}{\hbar}[\mathbf{p}\cdot\mathbf{x} - E(\mathbf{p})t]} \, d\mathbf{p}. \tag{27}$$

In particular, the rate of change of ψ at the time zero is given by the expression

$$\frac{\partial\psi}{\partial t}\bigg|_{t=0} = -\frac{\hbar}{i}\left(\frac{1}{2\pi\hbar}\right)^{3/2} \int\int\int_{\mathbf{p}} E(\mathbf{p}) \, \alpha(\mathbf{p}) \, e^{\frac{i}{\hbar}\mathbf{p}\cdot\mathbf{x}} \, d\mathbf{p}. \tag{28}$$

The choice of α determines, of course, the relative contribution of the various plane de Broglie waves to the total wave function ψ. Conversely, we may require that at the time zero ψ shall be a specified function, and in that case α is given, according to Fourier

---

[1] If a wave field fails to satisfy the law of linear superposition, then two plane-wave beams meeting each other will produce mutual scattering. The principle of linear superposition rules out such mutual scattering but not, of course, interference.

theory, by the integral

$$\alpha(\mathbf{p}) = \left(\frac{1}{2\pi\hbar}\right)^{3/2} \int \int \int_{\mathbf{x}} \psi(\mathbf{x},\, 0)\, e^{-\frac{i}{\hbar}\mathbf{p}\cdot\mathbf{x}}\, d\mathbf{x}. \tag{29}$$

Without adopting as yet any particular interpretation concerning the significance of ψ, we may assume that whenever we succeed in localizing the bulk of the wave function in a small domain, that domain will probably contain the particle. Hence it is natural to introduce the average position of the particle as the centroid of the wave distribution. We shall denote this average position by $\bar{\mathbf{x}}$, which we might consider introducing by the definition

$$\bar{\mathbf{x}} \int \psi\, d\mathbf{x} = \int \mathbf{x}\, \psi\, d\mathbf{x}. \tag{30}$$

But this definition would have the disadvantage that regions in which the wave variable ψ is negative would make a negative contribution to the averaging process. Actually, all of wave physics teaches us that whenever questions of intensity are involved, it is the *square* of the wave variable rather than the wave variable itself that determines intensity, energy density, and so forth. Inasmuch as we are even admitting complex values of ψ, we shall use the *absolute square of ψ* for weighting, and define $\bar{\mathbf{x}}$ by the relationship

$$\bar{\mathbf{x}} \int |\psi(\mathbf{x})|^2\, d\mathbf{x} = \int \mathbf{x}|\psi(\mathbf{x})|^2\, dx. \tag{31}$$

Now we may ask how with a given initial distribution $\psi(\mathbf{x}, 0)$ the center of mass of the wave pattern will change its location. We shall determine $d\bar{\mathbf{x}}/dt$, from the obvious relationship

$$\frac{d\bar{\mathbf{x}}}{dt} \int |\psi|^2\, d\mathbf{x} + \bar{\mathbf{x}} \int \left(\psi^* \frac{\partial\psi}{\partial t} + \psi \frac{\partial\psi^*}{\partial t}\right) d\mathbf{x}$$
$$= \int \mathbf{x} \left(\psi^* \frac{\partial\psi}{\partial t} + \psi \frac{\partial\psi^*}{\partial t}\right) d\mathbf{x}. \tag{32}$$

In this formula the time derivatives of ψ are determined by eq. (28). Substituting these expressions, we find

$$\int \left(\psi^* \frac{\partial\psi}{\partial t} + \psi \frac{\partial\psi^*}{\partial t}\right) d\mathbf{x} = 0. \tag{33}$$

The evaluation of the right-hand side of eq. (32) takes a little more work. We have first

$$\int_{\mathbf{x}} x_k \left(\psi^* \frac{\partial \psi}{\partial t} + \psi \frac{\partial \psi^*}{\partial t} \right) d\mathbf{x} = \frac{\hbar}{i} \left(\frac{1}{2\pi\hbar} \right)^3 \int_{\mathbf{x}} \int_{\mathbf{p}} \int_{\mathbf{p}'} [E(\mathbf{p}') - E(\mathbf{p})] x_k$$

$$\cdot \alpha(\mathbf{p}) \, \alpha^*(\mathbf{p}') \, e^{\frac{i}{\hbar}(\mathbf{p} - \mathbf{p}') \cdot \mathbf{x}} \, d\mathbf{p}' \, d\mathbf{p} \, d\mathbf{x}. \qquad (k = 1, 2, 3) \quad (34)$$

This expression can be converted from a ninefold integral to a
triple integral. As a first step, we shall carry out an integration by
parts with respect to the three variables $\mathbf{p}$. The result of this
transformation is

$$\int_{\mathbf{x}} x_k \left(\psi^* \frac{\partial \psi}{\partial t} + \psi \frac{\partial \psi^*}{\partial t} \right) d\mathbf{x} = \left(\frac{1}{2\pi\hbar} \right)^3 \int_{\mathbf{x}} \int_{\mathbf{p}} \int_{\mathbf{p}'} (E' - E) \, \alpha(\mathbf{p}) \, \alpha^*(\mathbf{p}')$$

$$\cdot \frac{\partial}{\partial p_k} [e^{\frac{i}{\hbar}(\mathbf{p} - \mathbf{p}') \cdot \mathbf{x}}] \, d\mathbf{p}' \, d\mathbf{p} \, d\mathbf{x}$$

$$= - \left(\frac{1}{2\pi\hbar} \right)^3 \int_{\mathbf{x}} \int_{\mathbf{p}} \int_{\mathbf{p}'} \frac{\partial}{\partial p_k} [(E' - E) \, \alpha(\mathbf{p})] \, \alpha^*(\mathbf{p}') \, e^{\frac{i}{\hbar}(\mathbf{p} - \mathbf{p}') \cdot \mathbf{x}} \, d\mathbf{p}' \, d\mathbf{p} \, d\mathbf{x}.$$
$$(35)$$

Now we must first carry out the differentiation indicated, and then
we may integrate over the variables $\mathbf{x}$. Because of the fundamental
theorem for Fourier integrals, we get, with

$$\frac{\partial}{\partial p_k} [(E' - E) \, \alpha(\mathbf{p})] = (E' - E) \frac{\partial \alpha}{\partial p_k} - \alpha(\mathbf{p}) \frac{\partial E(\mathbf{p})}{\partial p_k}, \qquad (36)$$

the final form of the integral:

$$\int_{\mathbf{x}} x_k \left(\psi^* \frac{\partial \psi}{\partial t} + \psi \frac{\partial \psi^*}{\partial t} \right) d\mathbf{x}$$

$$= - \int_{\mathbf{p}} \int_{\mathbf{p}'} \delta_3(\mathbf{p} - \mathbf{p}') \frac{\partial}{\partial p_k} [(E' - E) \, \alpha(\mathbf{p})] \, \alpha^*(\mathbf{p}') \, d\mathbf{p} \, d\mathbf{p}'$$
$$(37)$$

$$= \int_{\mathbf{p}} \frac{\partial E}{\partial p_k} |\alpha|^2 \, d\mathbf{p}.$$

By means of a very similar but simpler calculation, we can find that

$$\int_{\mathbf{x}} |\psi|^2 \, d\mathbf{x} = \int_{\mathbf{p}} |\alpha|^2 \, d\mathbf{p}. \qquad (38)$$

Thus we find, as our final result, that

$$\frac{d\bar{x}_k}{dt} \int_{\mathbf{p}} |\alpha|^2 \, d\mathbf{p} = \int_{\mathbf{p}} \frac{\partial E}{\partial p_k} |\alpha|^2 \, d\mathbf{p}. \qquad (39)$$

Hence the motion of the center of mass is determined as the average of the contributions of all the component plane de Broglie waves, with the absolute square of α as the weighting factor. Each plane wave contributes a share that is determined by the value of the partial derivative $(\partial E/\partial p_k)$. In the relativistic theory, we have

$$E = \sqrt{m^2 c^4 + c^2 \mathbf{p}^2}; \tag{40}$$

therefore

$$\frac{\partial E}{\partial p_k} = \frac{cp_k}{\sqrt{m c^2 + \mathbf{p}^2}}. \tag{41}$$

This last expression, however, is just the ordinary particle velocity, since

$$\mathbf{p} = \frac{\dot{\mathbf{x}}}{\sqrt{1 - \frac{1}{c^2}\dot{\mathbf{x}}^2}} \tag{42}$$

Naturally, in the nonrelativistic approximation, $(\partial E/\partial p_k)$ is also the velocity. In other words, each plane de Broglie wave, representing, as it does, a particle with definite momentum and definite energy, contributes to the rate of displacement an amount just equal to the ordinary velocity!

This result might indicate that the de Broglie wave packet behaves just like a classical (that is, nonquantum) particle, and that all we need do to make the analogy perfect is to choose a wave packet that is very narrow, something we can always do by an appropriate choice of the function $\alpha(p)$. But this conclusion would be unwarranted. A closer examination shows that the more narrow the initial wave function $\psi(x, 0)$ is chosen, the broader the bracket of linear momenta p that enters into the representation (26). The broader the bracket of momentum components, the quicker the component plane waves get out of step and the initially sharply peaked wave packet disintegrates. These qualitative remarks can be backed up by a quantitative evaluation of the relationship between the initial rms width of the $|\psi|^2$ peak and the rate of its increase, but the calculations are a little involved at this stage, and later we can achieve these results in greater generality with much less work. At any rate, for a free particle the distribution of $|\psi|^2$ in time behaves very much like a classical ensemble of representative points that initially fills a volume of the order of magnitude h in phase space.

If the distribution of configurations is very narrow and highly peaked, the distribution in momentum space must be correspondingly broader (to make up a total volume h). In the course of time this cell filled with representative points will retain its volume (Liouville's theorem assures us of that), but it will become distorted so that its projection into configuration space will increase as time goes on, and at a rate that is proportional to its original extension in momentum space.

In view of the fact that the de Broglie wave function is defined on the purely symbolical configuration space, not on the space of our direct physical experience, it cannot have a very robust physical significance itself. Originally it was thought (for instance by Schrödinger) that the particle, the mass point of classical mechanics, was actually a "cloud" of matter, spread out over space in a density determined by the local value of $|\psi|^2$, but this view could not be maintained. If we have a system of, say, two free electrons, then the wave function is a function of six arguments. What would be the meaning of matter spread out over the six-dimensional configuration space of that system? Also, whenever we carry out any physical experiment designed to determine the whereabouts of matter, we find every electron in one piece! This result occurs in spite of the theoretically required spreading of any $|\psi|^2$ distribution well localized originally. On the other hand, we possess very direct evidence of the correctness of de Broglie's approach in the diffraction of particle beams (electrons as well as neutrons) by crystal lattices; these patterns obey Bragg's law and all other laws of diffraction by spatial gratings that are also observed in X-ray diffraction, and with the exact wave lengths required by de Broglie's law (20).

Our present view is that de Broglie's wave function, or rather its square, represents the *probability density* of finding a particular configuration (for a single particle, a particular location) if we make an experiment determining configuration. By the same token, the square of the function $\alpha(\mathbf{p})$, which we introduced in eq. (26), represents the probability of finding our particles with certain momenta if we carry out an experiment measuring linear momenta. This interpretation of the de Broglie waves implies that it is impossible to determine at the same time, and with complete accuracy, all the $2n$ canonical coordinates of a mechanical system. If we determine the location of a free particle, for instance, then this particle must be represented by a wave function that is highly peaked for that instant; the outcome of a momentum measurement for this particle will be highly indeterminate.   If, conversely, we should carry out a very precise determination of the linear momentum, then any previous information we might possess concerning location will be partially invalidated.   These ideas appear very strange from the classical viewpoint.   But Bohr and his students in particular have carefully analyzed possible experiments designed to refute this conclusion of de Broglie's theory.   They found that the atomic structure of the measuring equipment, including the quantized character of light waves, if assumed to be a universal law, defeats any attempt to break down the complementary uncertainty in the determination of canonically conjugate coordinates.   In other words, though of course, we cannot *prove* that the description of nature by *probability waves* represents the final truth, we are at least assured that this assumption is free of *internal* contradictions.   And it is true that free particles exhibit typical diffraction effects, whereas bound particles have the discrete states typical for waves in bounded domains.

9.3. Wave Equations

We are now ready to set up the equation to be satisfied by the de Broglie waves.   This equation will have a general structure similar to the Maxwell equations in empty space.   It will be a partial differential equation, relating the change in time to the spatial derivatives.   Dealing with a scalar wave function, it will be a single equation rather than a system of equations.   Finally, if the principle of linear superposition is to hold, as we have assumed, then the wave equation must be both linear and homogeneous.

Classical mechanics possesses one instance of a partial differential equation defined on configuration space.   That equation is the Hamilton-Jacobi equation,[1]

$$H\left(q_k, \frac{\partial S}{\partial q_k}, t\right) + \frac{\partial S}{\partial t} = 0. \tag{43}$$

Now we may formulate the Hamilton-Jacobi equation in configura-

---

[1] M&E, pp. 37 ff.

tion space (the space of the q_k), no matter what the physical significance of the q_k. But in canonical transformations of phase space, the q_k introduced by the transformation will often be mixed functions of the original q_k's *and* p_k's. For instance, it is possible to interchange the role of the q_k's and p_k's completely by means of the canonical transformation

$$q_k' = p_k, \qquad p_k' = -q_k, \qquad H' = H. \tag{44}$$

The transformation (44) is called the *transition to momentum space.* If we formulate the Hamilton-Jacobi equation with respect to these particular coordinates, we get

$$H\left(-\frac{\partial S}{\partial q_k'}, \, q_k', \, t\right) + \frac{\partial S}{\partial t} = 0, \tag{45}$$

or, if we substitute,

$$H\left(-\frac{\partial S}{\partial p_k}, \, p_k, \, t\right) + \frac{\partial S}{\partial t} = 0. \tag{46}$$

Thus we may formulate the Hamilton-Jacobi equation in momentum space if we prefer, and this transition leads to a complete interchange of the role of the configuration and momentum coordinates. We may hope that the proper equation for de Broglie waves may also be formulated at will either in the configuration space [and then be an equation for $\psi(\mathbf{x}, \, t)$] or in momentum space [and then be an equation for $\alpha(\mathbf{p}, \, t)$].

The reason for this remark is that for the free particle, at least, the Hamilton-Jacobi equation in momentum space is much simpler than the equation in configuration space. In nonrelativistic mechanics, these two equations are, respectively,

$$\frac{1}{2m}(\nabla S)^2 + \frac{\partial S}{\partial t} = 0 \qquad [S = S(\mathbf{x}, \, t)] \tag{47}$$

and

$$\frac{1}{2m}\mathbf{p}^2 + \frac{\partial S}{\partial t} = 0 \qquad [S = S(\mathbf{p}, \, t)]. \tag{48}$$

The advantages of the latter equation are obvious. Its most general solution can be obtained in closed form and is

$$S(\mathbf{p}, \, t) = S_0(\mathbf{p}) - \frac{1}{2m}\mathbf{p}^2 \, t, \tag{49}$$

where S_0 is an arbitrary function of $\mathbf{p}$. The location $\mathbf{x}$ as a function of $\mathbf{p}$ and t can be obtained by differentiation and comes out as

$$\mathbf{x} = -\nabla_p S = -\nabla_p S_0 + \frac{\mathbf{p}}{m} t. \qquad (50)$$

That is not the main point, however. What we want to get is a differential equation for the de Broglie waves, both in configuration space and in momentum space. Although the equation in configuration space is the one found in all standard introductory texts, the equation in momentum space is simpler, and we shall obtain it first.

The probability wave in momentum space is defined as the Fourier transform of the probability wave $\psi(\mathbf{x}, t)$ in configuration space. At the time $t = 0$, that function is $\alpha(\mathbf{p})$ of eq. (26). At all other times, we have

$$A(\mathbf{p}, t) = \alpha(\mathbf{p})e^{-\frac{i}{\hbar}E(\mathbf{p})t}, \qquad (51)$$

according to eq. (27). The partial differential equation obeyed by the function $A(\mathbf{p}, t)$ can be obtained by inspection. It is

$$\frac{\hbar}{i} \frac{\partial A}{\partial t} + E(\mathbf{p}) A = 0, \qquad (52)$$

and that is, indeed, *the wave equation for the case of the free particle in momentum space.* In the form (52), the equation holds formally both in relativistic and in nonrelativistic physics, depending on the insertion of the appropriate function $E(\mathbf{p})$. But since the relativistic energy is not a single-valued function of the momentum (because of the square root), it has been found necessary to go beyond the rather naive formulation of eq. (52). In the non-relativistic case, E *is* a single-valued function of the momentum,

$$E = \frac{1}{2m} \mathbf{p}^2, \qquad (53)$$

and equation (52), besides being adequate for obtaining the corresponding wave equation in configuration space, is suitable for transition to the case of the particle moving under the influence of external forces.

Let us complete the force-free case first. If the function A satisfies the differential equation (52), then its Fourier transform

$\psi(\mathbf{x}, t)$ must satisfy an equation uniquely determined. Inasmuch as

$$\psi(\mathbf{x}, t) = \left(\frac{1}{2\pi\hbar}\right)^{3/2} \int_{\mathbf{p}} A(\mathbf{p}, t) \, e^{\frac{i}{\hbar}\mathbf{p}\cdot\mathbf{x}} \, d\mathbf{p}, \tag{54}$$

we must have

$$\frac{\hbar}{i} \frac{\partial \psi}{\partial t} = \frac{\hbar}{i} \left(\frac{1}{2p\hbar}\right)^{3/2} \int \frac{\partial A}{\partial t} \, e^{\frac{i}{\hbar}\mathbf{p}\cdot\mathbf{x}} \, d\mathbf{p}$$

$$= - \left(\frac{1}{2\pi\hbar}\right)^{3/2} \int \frac{1}{2m} \, \mathbf{p}^2 \, A(\mathbf{p}, t) \, e^{\frac{i}{\hbar}\mathbf{p}\cdot\mathbf{x}} \, d\mathbf{p} \tag{55}$$

$$= - \frac{1}{2m} \left(\frac{\hbar}{i}\right)^2 \left(\frac{1}{2\pi\hbar}\right)^{3/2} \int A \, \nabla_{\mathbf{x}}^2 (e^{\frac{i}{\hbar}\mathbf{p}\cdot\mathbf{x}}) \, d\mathbf{p}.$$

In this expression, the Laplacian may be shifted in front of the integral sign and by applying eq. (54) in reverse, we get finally

$$\frac{\hbar}{i} \frac{\partial \psi}{\partial t} = - \frac{1}{2m} \left(\frac{\hbar}{i}\right)^2 \left(\frac{1}{2\pi\hbar}\right)^{3/2} \nabla^2 \left\{ \int_{\mathbf{p}} A \, e^{\frac{i}{\hbar}\mathbf{p}\cdot\mathbf{x}} \, d\mathbf{p} \right\}$$

$$= - \frac{1}{2m} \left(\frac{\hbar}{i}\right)^2 \nabla^2 \psi = \frac{\hbar^2}{2m} \nabla^2 \psi. \tag{56}$$

This equation, a linear homogeneous partial differential equation for the de Broglie wave function $\psi(\mathbf{x}, t)$, is known as *Schrödinger's wave equation for the force-free particle*. Derivation of a similar equation for the relativistic case would have led to an equation with a second-order time derivative, and such an equation would possess not only solutions of the form (26) with positive energy but also contributions with negative energy. This result appeared so undesirable that the further treatment of this second-order equation (known as the *Klein-Gordon equation*) was not undertaken until recently.

Consideration of the two wave equations (52) and (56) leads to the following conclusions, valid for the case of the force-free particle at any rate. To construct a wave equation for de Broglie waves, we may proceed either in configuration or in momentum space. In either case, we must ascertain the relationship between the energy on the one hand and the canonical coordinates on the other hand. In other words, we must first find the classical Hamiltonian of the system. Then, in either momentum space or coordinate space, we construct the wave equation by first replacing the energy itself by the differential operator $-\dfrac{\hbar}{i}\dfrac{\partial}{\partial t}$, applying to the wave function. Furthermore, in momentum space each linear momentum is to be replaced by the multiplication of the wave function by that momentum component; in configuration space, on the other hand, each momentum component is to be replaced by the differential operation $\dfrac{\hbar}{i}\dfrac{\partial}{\partial q_k}$, to be carried out on the wave function. To extend the range of our results, we may conjecture that, by virtue of the same mechanism of "translation," if the classical Hamiltonian contains references to coordinates q_k, then in configuration space the wave function is to be multiplied by q_k, where in momentum space it is to be subjected to the operation $-\dfrac{\hbar}{i}\dfrac{\partial}{\partial p_k}$. Those, at any rate, are the operations suggested by the relationships between the two explicitly determined wave equations (52) and (56) and the corresponding Hamilton-Jacobi equations (48) and (47), taken together with the general Hamilton-Jacobi equations (43) in configuration space and (46) in momentum space.

If we adopt this "dictionary" leading us from prequantum mechanics to *wave mechanics*, we may immediately conjecture what the form of the wave equation ought to be if we consider the presence of forces. In configuration space we should expect the wave function to obey the differential equation

$$H\left(q_k, \frac{\hbar}{i}\frac{\partial}{\partial q_k}, t\right)\psi(q_k, t) + \frac{\hbar}{i}\frac{\partial\psi}{\partial t} = 0, \tag{57}$$

while in momentum space it would be

$$H\left(-\frac{\hbar}{i}\frac{\partial}{\partial p_k}, p_k, t\right)A(p_k, t) + \frac{\hbar}{i}\frac{\partial A}{\partial t} = 0. \tag{58}$$

Equation (57) in particular is known as *Schrödinger's time-dependent wave equation.* Although there is no strict "derivation" of that equation, it is the most natural linear homogeneous equation we can conjecture that contains the essential physical interpretation of quantum phenomena proposed by de Broglie but otherwise retains as much as possible of prequantum classical mechanics. In Chapter

11 we shall find that classical mechanics may, in a certain sense, be considered as the short-wave limit of wave mechanics. But before continuing with the general theoretical examination of the Schrödinger equation, we shall first apply it to see whether we can recover some of the basic results of the earlier theory that were so brilliantly confirmed by spectroscopic evidence.

Problems

1. For a free particle construct a wave packet that at the time zero has a Gaussian shape. Determine its subsequent behavior for an arbitrarily chosen initial half-width.

2. Construct an integral expression for $\bar{x}$, but in momentum space. Likewise construct what you would consider reasonable expressions for $\bar{p}$, both in momentum and in configuration space.

3. Construct expressions for the mean square spread of both x and p, in both configuration and momentum space.

4. Using Schwarz's inequality, use the results of Problem 3 to show that the product of the mean square spread of a particular coordinate x_k and its conjugate momentum component p_k has a lower bound.

5. Consider a de Broglie wave which is enclosed in a rectangular box and which is subject to the boundary condition that at the walls the wave must vanish. Determine all the possible stationary states and the corresponding possible values for E, p_x, p_y, and p_z. Compare your results with those obtained by the quantization of phase integrals of a particle that is free inside the box but is reflected without loss of kinetic energy by each wall.

6. Discuss the normal modes of vibration of a uniform circular membrane that is clamped fast all about its circumference.

7. Determine all the possible modes of elastic vibration

    (a) Of a rectangular membrane with free edges.

    (b) Of an elastic rod with a rectangular cross section, having infinite length.

    (c) Of a similar rod of finite length, assuming that both ends are free, that one end is clamped fast, and that both ends are fixed.

In (b) and (c) you will have to distinguish between longitudinal (compression) and transverse (torsion) modes of vibration.

8. What additional effects would you expect to observe in a Kundt's tube if the frequency of the exciting sound is gradually increased far above the customary pitch?

Chapter 10

Quantization in Wave Mechanics

10.1. Stationary de Broglie waves

The basic feature of the early quantum theory was that it led to discrete stationary states for all bound systems. However, the form of the wave equations (9.57) and (9.58) does not appear to differentiate between different mechanical systems. If there is any difference between the stationary states of bound electrons and the progressive waves describing ionized electrons, for instance, then this difference must be a feature of the solutions of the wave equation rather than one of the form of the wave equation itself. To discuss this difference intelligently, we must first make one further observation concerning the general physical significance of the de Broglie waves.

We had agreed to consider the absolute square of the wave function ψ in configuration space as a measure of the probability of finding the system in that particular configuration. The expression (9.31), defining the average value of an x-coordinate, is merely an application of this interpretation. If we designate the probability of finding for the three coordinates x_k values placing the particle within a specified spatial domain V by the symbol $P(V)$, then $P(V)$ is given by the definition

$$P(V) \int_{-\infty}^{\infty} |\psi|^2 \, dx = \int_{V} |\psi|^2 \, dx. \tag{1}$$

Naturally, the probability of finding the particle somewhere at all, without restrictions concerning its location, must be 1, and definition (1) yields this result if we let V approach the total space. However, this defining equation, which is basic to our interpretation of the ψ-function, loses all meaning if the integral on the left-hand side diverges. Thus our definition of local probability leads to no reasonable answer to a question concerning the average location, or concerning the probability of finding a particle in a particular

203

domain, if its momentum is known with complete accuracy and if the appropriate wave function is, therefore, a plane de Broglie wave. In general, we cannot expect to get reasonable answers to reasonable physical questions unless the integral of $|\psi|^2$, extended over all of configuration space, exists. But if that integral exists, then we can always multiply the wave function itself by a suitable factor so that

$$\int_{-\infty}^{\infty} |\psi|^2 \, dx = 1. \tag{2}$$

A wave function that satisfies eq. (2) is said to be *normalized*. If ψ is normalized in configuration space, then its Fourier transform, A, is at the same time normalized in momentum space, according to eq. (9.38). In the remainder of this book we shall usually assume that whatever wave functions occur are normalized. Functions that cannot possibly be normalized, such as plane de Broglie waves, will usually be excluded from our considerations, on the ground that they call for certain types of information that can be supplied only approximately in nature. A momentum of a free particle known with complete accuracy is one abstraction usually not admissible in wave mechanics.

In the case of the free particle, we indicated the complementary nature of experiments designed to measure either the location or the momentum of a particle. Likewise, experiments designed to measure the energy of a system do not always have the same result. Let us assume that the classical relationship between the Hamiltonian and the energy remains preserved, in other words, that the Hamiltonian equals the energy in any conservative system, provided we use a static coordinate system (that we have not carried out a canonical transformation involving the time t). If we wish to determine the energy of the system, we should measure that function of its q_k and p_k known as the Hamiltonian. But even for a free particle, if we go, for instance, into momentum space and use the representation (9.51) for the wave function, the energy will have a probability distribution determined by the range of the coordinates p from which nonvanishing contributions have been drawn. The energy of a system will be determined completely only if the contributions from all points of momentum space are identical or, in configuration space, if all points of configuration space contribute the same value of the Hamiltonian.

According to either Schrödinger equation (9.57) or (9.58), the Hamiltonian or the energy times the wave function equals $(-\hbar/i)$ times the partial time derivative of the wave function. Hence the relative contribution of a domain $\mathbf{dx}$ of configuration space to the average energy equals

$$E(\mathbf{x})|\psi|^2\,\mathbf{dx} = H(\mathbf{x})|\psi|^2\,\mathbf{dx} = -\frac{\hbar}{i}\,\frac{\partial\psi/\partial t}{\psi}\,|\psi|^2\,\mathbf{dx}$$

$$= -\frac{\hbar}{i}\,\psi^*\frac{\partial\psi}{\partial t}\,\mathbf{dx}. \tag{3}$$

As a result, we find that we must assign to the location $\mathbf{x}$ the energy $E(\mathbf{x})$:

$$E(\mathbf{x}) = -\frac{\hbar}{i}\,\frac{\partial\psi/\partial t}{\psi}. \tag{4}$$

The energy for the whole system will be sharply defined, and the result of a measurement clearly predictable, only if $E(\mathbf{x})$ is everywhere the same, i.e.

$$\frac{\partial\psi/\partial t}{\psi} = \text{const} = -\frac{i}{\hbar}\,E. \tag{5}$$

Then E on the right-hand side is *the* (sharply defined) *energy* of the system. Once we have measured the energy of a system (ideally, by determining its mass, for instance), the energy is sharply defined because it is a constant of the motion and will not change. Therefore we are assured that in any future redetermination we shall again measure exactly the same value we obtained originally. Thus, as the result of any energy determination, the wave function will satisfy condition (5). Interpreted as a differential equation, eq. (5) is easily integrated. The integral must possess the form

$$\psi(q_k, t) = \phi(q_k)e^{-\frac{i}{\hbar}Et}, \tag{6}$$

where ϕ is a function of the q_k only and is independent of t. $\phi(q_k)$ satisfies the differential equation

$$H\left(q_k, \frac{\hbar}{i}\frac{\partial}{\partial q_k}\right)\phi = E\,\phi, \tag{7}$$

which we can obtain by substituting expression (6) into the Schrödinger equation (9.57). The corresponding equation in momentum space is

$$A(p_k, t) = B(p_k)e^{-\frac{i}{\hbar}Et},$$

$$H\left(-\frac{\hbar}{i}\frac{\partial}{\partial p_k}, p_k\right)B = E\,B. \tag{8}$$

The two equations (7) and (8) are known as the *time-independent forms of the Schrödinger equation* in configuration space and in momentum space, respectively. Whenever we ask for energy levels, we must look for solutions of the time-independent Schrödinger equation. A system will possess discrete energy levels whenever solutions of eqs. (7) and (8) exist only for discrete values of the parameter E on the right-hand side. In such a case, the values of E for which solutions exist are called the *eigenvalues* or *characteristic values* of the problem. The corresponding solutions $\phi(q_k)$ and $B(p_k)$ are called *eigenfunctions* or *characteristic functions*.

In classical physics, we call the solutions of vibration problems in which the dependence on time is purely trigonometric *normal modes* or *stationary states* of the system. In wave mechanics the first designation is not very common, but it is quite customary to refer to the solutions corresponding to a definite value of the energy as *stationary states* of the wave-mechanical system. In the following sections we shall determine stationary states of a few physically significant systems.

10.2. The rigid rotator

As a first example, we shall treat once more the case of the diatomic symmetric molecule, but this time with the simplifying assumption that the binding force between the two atoms has such a pronounced minimum that the distance between them, r_0, may be considered rigid. Using again spherical coordinates and referring to expression (7.34), we find that the Hamiltonian of a rigid rotator is given by the expression

$$H = \frac{1}{m'\,r_0^2}\,(p_\theta^2 + \sec^2\theta \cdot p_\phi^2). \tag{9}$$

The denominator $m'\,r_0^2$ is, incidentally, twice the moment of inertia of the molecule with respect to the center of mass.

If we were to apply our "dictionary" directly, for instance the formula (7), to go over to the wave equation, replacing p_θ by $\dfrac{\hbar}{i} \dfrac{\partial}{\partial \theta}$ and so forth, we should encounter a serious difficulty: In classical physics, the sequence of coordinates in a product is immaterial; for instance, pq equals qp. But if we construct the corresponding expression using the wave-mechanical operators on the wave function (multiplication by q, differentiation with respect to q), it does make a considerable difference whether we differentiate first or multiply first. The only instance where the dictionary can be used with real confidence is that of rectilinear coordinates, in terms of which the kinetic energy is a function of the p-coordinates only, whereas the potential energy depends only on the q_k's. Hence it is the better part of valor to formulate the wave equation first in rectilinear coordinates and to carry out the transformation into spherical coordinates afterward. In rectilinear coordinates, the expression for the intrinsic kinetic energy of the two mass points is

$$K \psi = -\frac{\hbar^2}{m'} \left(\frac{\partial^2 \psi}{\partial x^2} + \frac{\partial^2 \psi}{\partial y^2} + \frac{\partial^2 \psi}{\partial z^2} \right) = -\frac{\hbar^2}{m'} \nabla^2 \psi. \qquad (10)$$

The Laplacian in spherical coordinates is well known. We have

$$\nabla^2 \psi = \frac{1}{r^2} \left\{ \frac{\partial}{\partial r} \left(r^2 \frac{\partial \psi}{\partial r} \right) + \sec \theta \left[\frac{\partial}{\partial \theta} \left(\cos \theta \frac{\partial \psi}{\partial \theta} \right) + \sec \theta \frac{\partial^2 \psi}{\partial \phi^2} \right] \right\}. \qquad (11)$$

The first term is obviously the contribution of radial motion and must be excluded in the case of the rigid rotator. The wave-mechanical analogue to expression (9) is, therefore,

$$H \psi = -\frac{\hbar^2}{m' r_0^2} \sec \theta \left[\frac{\partial}{\partial \theta} \left(\cos \theta \frac{\partial \psi}{\partial \theta} \right) + \sec \theta \frac{\partial^2 \psi}{\partial \phi^2} \right], \qquad (12)$$

and we must try to find solutions to the partial differential equation

$$\frac{\hbar^2}{m' r_0^2} \sec \theta \left[\frac{\partial}{\partial \theta} \left(\cos \theta \frac{\partial \psi}{\partial \theta} \right) + \sec \theta \frac{\partial^2 \psi}{\partial \phi^2} \right] + E \psi = 0, \qquad (13)$$

which represents the time-independent Schrödinger equation (in configuration space) for the rigid rotator.

We shall admit an expression as a solution only if it is unique, that is, if for a given direction in space the value of ψ is uniquely determined. This condition is not entirely trivial, since the same direction in space may be described in terms of an infinity of angles ϕ that differ from each other by integral multiples of 2π. Our condition of uniqueness implies that ψ is a periodic function of ϕ with the period 2π. Accordingly, we can expand the hypothetical solution of eq. (13) into a Fourier series having the form

$$\psi(\theta, \phi) = \sum_{m=-\infty}^{\infty} F_m(\theta) \, e^{im\phi}. \tag{14}$$

If we substitute this expression back into the equation, we get

$$\sum_{m=-\infty}^{\infty} \left\{ \frac{\hbar^2}{m' \, r_0^2} \sec\theta \left[\frac{d}{d\theta}\left(\cos\theta \, \frac{dF_m}{d\theta} \right) - \sec\theta \, m^2 \, F_m \right] + E \, F_m \right\} e^{im\phi} = 0. \tag{15}$$

But whenever the value of a Fourier series expansion is zero for every value of the argument, each Fourier coefficient must vanish separately. Thus we obtain an infinite set of separate ordinary differential equations for the Fourier coefficients F_m:

$$\frac{\hbar^2}{m' \, r_0^2} \sec\theta \left[(\cos\theta \, F_m')' - m^2 \sec\theta \, F_m \right] + E \, F_m = 0$$
$$(m = -\infty, \cdots, \infty). \tag{16}$$

For each Fourier component separately, the angular momentum about the z-axis, p_ϕ, which is now represented by the differential operator $\frac{\hbar}{i} \frac{\partial}{\partial\phi}$ in configuration space, has a definite value. If we apply this operator to a single Fourier component, we get

$$\frac{\hbar}{i} \frac{\partial}{\partial\phi} (F_m \, e^{im\phi}) = m\hbar \cdot F_m \, e^{im\phi},$$
$$p_\phi = m\hbar, \tag{17}$$

where m is our old acquaintance, the magnetic quantum number. So far, the new wave-mechanical quantization reproduces our former results, but with one difference. There is nothing to prevent us from considering solutions of the wave equation that are linear combinations of several of these Fourier components. But a solution of this mixed type will not have a sharply determined angular momentum about the z-axis.

Now we shall turn to the solution of the individual equations (16). The argument θ ranges from $-\pi/2$ to $\pi/2$. We shall first simplify the equation by introducing as a new argument sin θ, which we may call s. In terms of s, eq. (16) turns into

$$\frac{\hbar^2}{m' r_0^2} \left\{ \frac{d}{ds} \left[(1 - s^2) \frac{dF_m}{ds} \right] - \frac{m^2}{1 - s^2} F_m \right\} + E F_m = 0$$

$$(-1 \leq s \leq 1). \quad (18)$$

This equation has coefficients that become infinite at the two boundaries of the domain of definition. In such cases one has to apply the Fuchs theory, which permits us to determine whether at these points the solutions of the differential equation remain finite. A complete presentation of the Fuchs theory would lead far afield, though knowledge of it is almost a necessity for the practicing theoretical physicist. A fairly short presentation will be found in Margenau and Murphy[1] and a more comprehensive treatment in Frank and Mises,[2] to mention two references. As far as our present needs are concerned we must expand the coefficients of the differential equation into Laurent series (power series that start with negative powers) about the singular points. If we carry out this expansion about the point $s = -1$, replacing the variable s for this purpose by

$$s = \sigma - 1, \quad (19)$$

we find for the first terms of these expansions

$$\frac{\hbar^2}{m' r_0^2} \left(2\sigma F_m'' + 2 F_m' - \frac{m^2}{2\sigma} F_m \right) + \cdots = 0. \quad (20)$$

Having obtained the differential equation in this form, we attempt a solution, also in the form of a Laurent series in σ:

$$F_m = \sigma^\alpha \sum_0^\infty c_\nu \sigma^\nu \qquad (c_0 \neq 0). \quad (21)$$

[1] H. Margenau and G. M. Murphy, *The Mathematics of Physics and Chemistry*, Van Nostrand, 1943, p. 69.

[2] P. Frank and R. von Mises (editors), *Die Differential- und Integralgleichungen der Mechanik und Physik*, 2 vols., 2nd ed., Vieweg, 1930 and 1935; reprinted by M. Rosenberg, New York. The treatment of linear differential equations with singular coefficients begins on p. 317 of Vol. I.

The question is whether the first nonvanishing term has a positive or a negative power of σ; in other words, we must determine the correct value of α. If we substitute our trial solution (21) into eq. (20), we find immediately a condition to be satisfied by the terms multiplied by c_0, the so-called *indicial equation:*

$$\alpha^2 - \tfrac{1}{4}m^2 = 0, \qquad \alpha = \pm\tfrac{1}{2}|m|. \tag{22}$$

There will then be two independent solutions in the vicinity of the point $s = -1$, one beginning with a positive and another beginning with a negative power of cos θ. The same result can be obtained by the same method for the point $s = 1$. These two solutions form a *fundamental system,* that is, *every* solution is a linear combination of these two. Naturally, we wish to exclude the solution starting with a negative power of σ. But whether the solution which is regular at -1 is identical with the solution which remains regular at 1 depends on the differential equation as a whole and more particularly on the choice of the one disposable parameter E. In other words, our requirement of regularity at the two poles will produce quantization of the energy. In order to obtain the regular solution, we shall split the behavior at the two poles off F_m and expand the remainder into a power series, thus setting

$$F_m = (1 - s^2)^{\frac{|m|}{2}} \sum_0^\infty a_k s^k. \tag{23}$$

This trial solution must now be substituted into eq. (18). We find for the coefficients the recurrence formula

$$a_{k+2} = \frac{(m + k)(m + k + 1) - \eta}{(k + 1)(k + 2)} a_k$$

$$\left(k = 0, 1, \cdots ; \eta = \frac{m' r_0^2 E}{\hbar^2}\right). \tag{24}$$

First, we find that in this recurrence formula all the even powers are tied together, and so are the odd powers, but the coefficients of the even powers are independent of the coefficients of the odd powers, and vice versa. Second, unless some one of the a_k (either in the odd or in the even sequence) vanishes, and consequently also all the following coefficients in that sequence, the coefficients either increase consistently after some value $k = K$ or, in the case of

$m = 0$, at least decrease so slowly that the series diverges for $s = \pm 1$. Because the sign of consecutive coefficients no longer changes beyond K, this divergence is a certain sign of a real infinity in the function represented by our power series. Thus F_m will be regular throughout the range of the argument s only if the sequence of the coefficients a_k breaks off. The recurrence formula (24) shows that a_l will be the highest nonvanishing coefficient if E satisfies the condition

$$E = \frac{\hbar^2}{m' \, r_0^2} \, l(l + 1) \qquad (l \geq |m|). \tag{25}$$

Such a breaking off of the series is possible only if we start only one of the two sequences, either the odd or the even one. Then, in that sequence, eq. (25) must be satisfied for some one $k = l$.

We find that the energy is not given by entirely the same expression we encountered in the phase-integral quantization. Spectroscopic evidence confirms the correctness of the new rather than the old expression. It was known previously that rotational bands obeyed "half-odd quantization." In rotational transitions, one always observes transitions changing the azimuthal quantum number by 1. Now the difference between the two energy levels corresponding to l and to $l + 1$ is

$$\epsilon_{l,l+1} = \frac{\hbar^2}{m' \, r_0^2} \, 2(l + 1) \qquad (l = 0, 1, \cdot \cdot \cdot), \tag{26}$$

whereas the difference between two neighboring energy levels determined by the old formula (7.41) is

$$\epsilon_{k,k+1} = \frac{\hbar^2}{m' \, r_0^2} \, (2k + 1) \qquad (k = 0, 1, \cdot \cdot \cdot). \tag{27}$$

In the one case, the frequencies of the lowest lines of a rotational band are as the numbers $1 : 2 : 3$, whereas according to formula (27) they are as $1 : 3 : 5$. Actually, the situation is usually still a little different. In molecular spectra, unless we go to the extreme infrared, we observe the rotational transitions coupled with vibrational jumps. Again the rotational quantum number *must* change by ± 1. The "band" will then be found on both sides of the nominal frequency that would be radiated or absorbed if only the vibrational quantum number could change. The distance of the actual lines forming the band from that mid-point according to the older quantum theory would be proportional to the numbers ± 1, ± 3, ± 5, $\cdots$, and therefore evenly spaced; according to the wave-mechanical quantization the figures should be ± 1, ± 2, ± 3, $\cdots$, with the omission of zero, and hence the center of the band should be marked by a gap in the otherwise evenly spaced lines. This gap is invariably found, and the superiority of the new over the old formula thus established.

The calculations just performed are applicable in all problems possessing spherical symmetry. But instead of furnishing the value of the rotational energy, they merely give us the term that is to be introduced into the remaining radial part of the Hamiltonian. If we use the expression (11) for the Laplacian and consider that the time-independent Schrödinger equation for a single particle in a potential $V(\mathbf{x})$ must be

$$- \frac{\hbar^2}{2m} \nabla^2 \psi + V(\mathbf{x})\, \psi = E\, \psi, \tag{28}$$

the radial portion of the Schrödinger equation with a spherically symmetric potential $V(r)$ must be

$$- \frac{\hbar^2}{2m} \frac{1}{r^2} [(r^2\, R')' - l(l+1)\, R] + V(r)\, R = E\, R, \tag{29}$$

$$\psi = Y_l(\phi,\, \theta)\, R(r).$$

This is the form of the equation with which we shall, for instance, start off the quantization of the hydrogen atom. The functions $Y(\phi, \theta)$, which determine the angular dependence of the wave function in *all* spherically symmetric problems, have been studied extensively and are known as *spherical harmonics* and more particularly as *associated Legendre polynomials*. They occur not only time and again in quantum-mechanical calculations but also in classical vibrational problems having spherical symmetry. Wave functions with values of $l = 0$, 1, 2, $\cdots$, are still designated as s-waves, p-waves, d-waves, and so forth, throughout contemporary physical literature.

At this point we can clear up another difficulty created by the older quantum theory. The reader will remember how difficult it was to reconcile results obtained about the permissible trajectories of systems in different coordinate systems. This trouble does not

arise in wave mechanics.   First of all, we get quantization of energy
levels only if we try to determine sharp energy levels, that is if we
search for stationary waves.   Then, in degenerate situations, there
will be more than one possible wave function for a given energy
level.   In the rigid rotator, for instance, the energy is given by the
quantum number l alone, and to each value of l there belong altogether $(2\,l + 1)$ different and linearly independent wave functions
with values of m from $-l$ to l.   Now a wave function with a given
value of l and a given value of m is a stationary wave, to be sure,
but so is a linear combination of several wave functions having the
same l but different m's.   If we wish to determine the angular
momentum about a particular axis, we may do so without disturbing the sharpness of the energy level; but determinations of the
angular momentum about two different axes are usually incom-
patible, leading to different sets of wave functions among all those
belonging to a given value of l.   And although one set of functions
may be obtained as linear combinations of the functions of the
other set, each set of separate functions permits the accurate definition of the angular momentum component about *its* axis only.   In
all other cases of degeneracy, the situation is exactly the same.

10.3. The harmonic oscillator

Next we shall treat the harmonic oscillator, but to simplify
matters we shall restrict ourselves to one that has only one degree of
freedom.   The classical Hamiltonian of such an oscillator has the
form

$$H = \frac{1}{2}\left(\frac{p^2}{m} + k\,q^2\right). \tag{30}$$

Before going over to the corresponding Schrödinger equation, we
shall carry out a change in scale, setting

$$(k\,m)^{\frac{1}{4}}\,q = x, \qquad (k\,m)^{-\frac{1}{4}}\,p = y. \tag{31}$$

This transformation is canonical, since the Poisson bracket between
the new variables still equals 1.   It turns the Hamiltonian into

$$H = \frac{\omega}{2}\,(x^2 + y^2) = E \tag{32}$$

where ω, as usual, is the classical angular frequency of the oscillator.

The Schrödinger equation of this problem is

$$\frac{\omega}{2}\left(x^2\,\psi \,-\, \hbar^2\,\frac{d^2\psi}{dx^2}\right) \,=\, E\,\psi. \tag{33}$$

This equation has an essential singularity at infinity, according to the Fuchs theory. Under these conditions, the solutions must be transcendentals, and we shall examine the character of the solutions at infinity. For large values of x, we may disregard the term on the right-hand side: asymptotically, the solutions will resemble solutions of the equation

$$\psi'' \,-\, \frac{x^2}{\hbar^2}\,\psi \,=\, 0. \tag{34}$$

The solutions of this last equation are approximated by

$$\psi \sim e^{-\frac{1}{2\hbar}x^2}, \qquad \psi \sim e^{\frac{1}{2\hbar}x^2}. \tag{35}$$

One of these functions drops off for large positive and negative values of the argument, the other increases rapidly. No solution that behaves in such a manner is square-integrable, and hence the second type of solution must be rejected as physically unreasonable. But such unreasonable solutions exist as possibilities at both ends of the range of our configuration space, for large positive and for large negative values of x. Our requirement that the solution which behaves reasonably at the negative end should be identical with the acceptable solution at the positive end will again place restrictions on the parameter E, which will result in quantization of the energy.

To study the solutions of the complete equation (33), we split off the desired behavior at both ends and try our luck with a representation of the form

$$\psi \,=\, f(x)\, e^{-\frac{1}{2\hbar}x^2}, \tag{36}$$

in which the remainder of ψ, $f(x)$, should increase so moderately for large positive and negative values of x that the product (36) is square-integrable. $f(x)$ satisfies the differential equation

$$f'' \,-\, \frac{2}{\hbar}\,x\,f' \,+\, \left(\frac{2}{\omega}\,\frac{E}{\hbar^2} \,-\, \frac{1}{\hbar}\right)f \,=\, 0. \tag{37}$$

Except at infinity, the coefficients of this equation are analytic functions. Among the solutions there must be those which increase only moderately if at all, and those which, because we split off the factor $\exp(-x^2/2\hbar)$, will increase as rapidly as the function $\exp(x^2/\hbar)$. To find out what are the conditions for either solution to arise, we shall expand $f(x)$ into a power series,

$$f(x) = \sum_0^\infty a_n x^n. \tag{38}$$

By substituting this series into eq. (37), we obtain a recurrence formula for the coefficients:

$$a_{n+2} = \frac{2}{\hbar^2} \frac{\hbar(n + \frac{1}{2}) - E/\omega}{(n + 1)(n + 2)} a_n \qquad (n = 0, 1, \cdots). \tag{39}$$

This series converges for all values of x. But it is not difficult to show that the function thus represented is transcendental and increases at the same rate as the function $\exp(x^2/\hbar)$ for large values of the argument at both ends. The only manner in which we can avoid this behavior is by choosing E so that the series (38) breaks off after a finite number of terms. If a_n is to be the last nonvanishing coefficient, we must choose E to be

$$E = (n + \tfrac{1}{2})\hbar\,\omega \qquad (n = 0, 1, \cdots). \tag{40}$$

Again, this result is slightly different from the one obtained earlier, eq. (8.12). Although the spacing of the energy levels is the same as before, even the very lowest level has a non-vanishing energy, $\frac{1}{2}\hbar\,\omega$, which is called the *zero-point energy*. In this case, no experimental decision between the two formulas is possible, because in an experiment we always measure the *difference* between two energy levels. But we can supply an intuitive explanation for the presence of the zero-point energy in the wave-mechanical oscillator. Classically, the state of rest corresponds to the oscillator being permanently at the center, but a particle at a particular point in space and in a state of specified velocity cannot be represented by any de Broglie wave. The state of lowest energy in wave mechanics is one in which the probability distribution of position and the probability distribution of momentum are adjusted so that the total energy is as small as possible, consistent with the limitations imposed by the complementary character of position sharpness and momentum sharpness.

In a three-dimensional oscillator, the zero-point energy equals $\frac{3}{2}\hbar\,\omega$; more generally, the zero-point energy equals $\frac{1}{2}\hbar\,\omega$ for each degree of freedom, regardless of whether in a complicated system some or all of the frequencies of the classical normal modes coincide or whether they are all different.

10.4. The hydrogen atom

In treating the hydrogen atom, we shall start with the wave equation (29), in which the angular part of the Hamiltonian has been integrated and quantized. For the hydrogen atom, the radial wave equation becomes

$$-\frac{\hbar^2}{2m}\left[R'' + \frac{2}{r}R' - \frac{l(l+1)}{r^2}R\right] - \left(\frac{e^2}{r} + E\right)R = 0$$
$$(l = 0, 1, \cdots; 0 \le r \le \infty). \quad (41)$$

The coefficients of this differential equation become singular both at zero and at infinity. We must consider these two points separately.

At $r = 0$, the terms with the highest singularities are

$$-\frac{\hbar^2}{2m}\left[R'' + \frac{2}{r}R' - \frac{l(l+1)}{r^2}R\right] + \cdots = 0. \quad (42)$$

If we attempt again a Laurent series expansion and call the power of the first nonvanishing term α, then the indicial equation for α is

$$\alpha(\alpha + 1) - l(l + 1) = 0, \quad (43)$$

with the two solutions

$$\alpha = l, \qquad \alpha = -(l + 1). \quad (44)$$

Only the first of these two solutions is acceptable.

At infinity, the differential equation (41) has an "essential singularity"; that is, no Laurent series is possible. We can study again the asymptotic behavior of the solutions at infinity by considering only the largest parts of the coefficients at infinity. The reduced equation is

$$-\frac{\hbar^2}{2m}R'' - ER + \cdots = 0, \quad (45)$$

with the solutions

$$R = e^{\frac{i}{\hbar}\sqrt{2mE}\,r}, \qquad R = e^{-\frac{i}{\hbar}\sqrt{2mE}\,r} \quad (46)$$

for positive energies and the solutions

$$R = e^{\frac{1}{\hbar}\sqrt{2m\epsilon}\, r}, \qquad R = e^{-\frac{1}{\hbar}\sqrt{2m\epsilon}\, r}$$

$$(\epsilon = -E) \quad (47)$$

for negative energies.

Physically, we know that positive energies correspond to free particles; asymptotically, both possible solutions (46) correspond to spherical de Broglie waves with amplitudes which, in a more careful estimate, drop off as r^{-1}. These waves are not square-integrable, and, of course, in a stationary situation the location of a free particle cannot be estimated even approximately.

In the case of negative energy, the electron is bound, and we should be able to obtain square-integrable solutions. But eqs. (44) and (47) show that at zero and at infinity only one each of the two solutions is acceptable. Again, our requirement that the acceptable solution at one end should be identical with the acceptable solution at the other end of the domain of definition leads to a quantization of the energy.

Our procedure for obtaining the desired eigenfunctions and eigenvalues is the same as before. We split the acceptable behavior at the two end points off the function $R(r)$, setting

$$R(r) = f(r)\, r^l\, e^{-\frac{1}{\hbar}\sqrt{2m\epsilon}\, r}. \qquad (48)$$

If we substitute this expression into eq. (41), we obtain a differential equation for the new unknown $f(r)$:

$$-\frac{\hbar^2}{2m}\left(f'' + 2\frac{l+1}{r}f'\right) + \hbar\sqrt{\frac{2\epsilon}{m}}\left(f' + \frac{l+1}{r}f\right) - \frac{e^2}{r}f = 0. \quad (49)$$

We shall attempt to solve this equation by means of a power-series expansion:

$$f(r) = \sum_0^\infty a_s r^s \qquad (a_0 \neq 0), \qquad (50)$$

which leads to the recurrence formula for the coefficients

$$a_{s+1} = \frac{2m}{\hbar^2}\frac{\hbar\sqrt{\frac{2\epsilon}{m}}(s+l+1) - e^2}{(s+1)(s+2l+1)}\, a_s. \qquad (51)$$

Again, the coefficients have all the same sign after some value $s \geq s_0$. They drop just rapidly enough to represent a transcendental function of the asymptotic behavior at infinity that makes the function R as a whole an exponentially increasing function. We must, therefore, require that the power series expansion break off after a finite number of terms. The series will break off if we give ϵ one of the values

$$\epsilon = \frac{m\,e^4}{2\,\hbar^2\,n^2}, \qquad n = l + s + 1 = 1,\,2,\,\cdots$$

$$(n \geq l + 1,\, l \geq 0). \quad (52)$$

In the case of the hydrogen atom, wave mechanics leads again to the Rydberg formula.

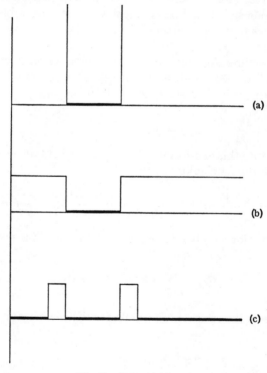

Fig. 8.   Potential boxes.

Problems

1. Consider a one-dimensional problem with a potential box
  (a) When the walls are infinitely high.
  (b) When the walls have finite height but are infinitely thick.
  (c) When the walls have both finite thickness and height.
These three possibilities are illustrated in Fig. 8.   In the last case, there are no stationary square-integrable cases, but there are solutions that depend on the time with a "complex" frequency.   In this case, the solutions in which the waves outside the box are directed toward infinity are of special interest, because Gamow's theory of radioactive (alpha-) decay is based on the assumption that atomic nuclei are surrounded by such finite potential barriers.

2. Work out the hydrogen atom in confocal parabolic coordinates.

3. Determine the wave solutions of a three-dimensional box with infinitely high potential walls that has the shape of the interior of a sphere. Determine in particular the distribution of the characteristic energy levels and their multiplicities.

Chapter 11

Approximation Methods

The problems we have dealt with so far are about the only cases of Schrödinger equations that can be solved in closed form. We have omitted the discussion of a particle in a closed box with rigid walls. That case is useful primarily as a model that can be treated with very elementary mathematical tools, but it does not represent realistically any situation ever encountered in elementary particle physics. There are, however, innumerable cases in particle physics where the setting up of the Hamiltonian and the Schrödinger wave equation is straightforward but in which solutions can be obtained only in approximate form. The problems encountered in atomic physics are essentially twofold. In a given range of energies, the possible classical states of a system may fill only a finite volume in phase space; in that case, we are interested in finding the discrete energy levels and the characteristic functions that go with them. Or the classical states corresponding to the given energy bracket will fill an infinite volume of phase space; then by far the greatest part of that infinite volume will represent force-free motion, and we are faced with the problem of *scattering*, in which we are interested in knowing how many particles approaching the region of appreciable forces will be deflected from their original direction and through how large an angle. For both of these types of problem, a variety of methods is available, some of which we shall discuss in this chapter.

11.1. The WBK(J) method[1]

The method to be discussed first is not only useful in many calculations but also has fundamental interest in that it shows most

---

[1] This method was developed at about the same time by several workers, among them most prominent Wentzel, Brillouin, Kramers, and Jeffreys. It is customarily identified by the initials of these three or four investigators.

succinctly the relationship between wave mechanics, the older quantum theory, and classical mechanics. It turns out that the older formulations of the laws of nature may be interpreted, from the point of view of wave mechanics, as consecutive steps in a systematic approximation method.

Suppose we wish to investigate a problem involving such high momenta that the average de Broglie wave length is small compared with the dimensions of the system. In that case, if we have a free particle, the wave functions will be approximated locally by *plane* de Broglie waves. If the particle is bound, the wave will locally look like a sinusoidal stationary wave. We shall treat the case of the progressive wave first.

Assuming that the above conditions are satisfied, we shall give the wave function in configuration space, ψ, such a form that we introduce separately a (real) function for the amplitude of the wave and another (also real) function for its phase, thus:

$$\psi(q_k, t) = A(q_k, t)\, e^{\frac{i}{\hbar} S(q_k, t)}. \tag{1}$$

If the de Broglie wave is plane, the function A becomes constant, and S becomes a linear function of the coordinates and the time.

If we carry out the processes of differentiation that occur in the Schrödinger equation, we find that

$$-\frac{\hbar}{i} \frac{\partial \psi}{\partial t} = -\left(\frac{\partial S}{\partial t} + \frac{\hbar}{i} \frac{\partial \ln A}{\partial t} \right) \psi \tag{2}$$

and
$$\frac{\hbar}{i} \frac{\partial \psi}{\partial q_k} = \left(\frac{\partial S}{\partial q_k} + \frac{\hbar}{i} \frac{\partial \ln A}{\partial q_k} \right) \psi. \tag{3}$$

The idea behind the WBK(J) method is to try for an approximate solution by assuming that the derivatives of the amplitude are small compared with the derivatives of the phase angle, and the second derivatives of the latter are small compared with the first derivatives. Both these assumptions are automatically incorporated into our mathematical scheme if we treat $\hbar$ as a small quantity and expand the rigorous expressions for A and S into power series with respect to increasing powers of $\hbar$. If we first consider the terms in which ψ is multiplied by terms free of $\hbar$ and, incidentally, real, we find that whenever the classical Hamiltonian contains a factor q_k in a term, ψ in the Schrödinger equation must be multiplied by q_k; but for each factor p_k in the classical Hamiltonian, ψ in the Schrödinger equation must be multiplied by $\partial S/\partial q_k$. Thus these very first terms in the approximation method will yield the equation

$$\left[H\left(q_k, \frac{\partial S_0}{\partial q_k}, t \right) + \frac{\partial S_0}{\partial t} \right] \psi = 0, \qquad (4)$$

S_0 being the $\hbar$-free term in the power expansion of S, and so on. Inasmuch as ψ does not vanish, we find that S_0 satisfies the classical Hamilton-Jacobi equation!

So far, we have obtained no equation for the lowest term in the series expansion for A, A_0. We can get such an equation if we collect all the terms linear in $\hbar/i$. But here a difficulty arises. In the previous step, we had always considered the contributions obtained if we differentiate the exponent of expression (1) and never the coefficient A. Now we shall collect those terms in which the coefficient is differentiated just once. If in the Schrödinger equation the differentiation symbol stands to the right of all other factors q_k or $\partial S_0/\partial q_k$, the coefficient to be differentiated is just A_0. But if the differentiation symbol stands farther to the left, everything to the right must be included as well. If we use rectilinear coordinates in configuration space, we know that half of the differentiation symbols stand at the extreme right and half at the extreme left. At present we are in no position to analyze what happens under different conditions (we shall do so in the next chapter), and so for just now the following calculation can be justified only in rectilinear coordinates.

If we collect all the terms indicated in one equation and omit the joint factor $\frac{\hbar}{i} \psi$, we get the equation

$$\frac{1}{2} \left[\frac{\partial}{\partial q_k} \left(\frac{\partial H}{\partial p_k} A_0 \right) + \frac{\partial H}{\partial p_k} \frac{\partial A_0}{\partial q_k} \right] + \frac{\partial A_0}{\partial t} = 0. \qquad (5)$$

If we multiply this equation by $2A_0$, the result is an *equation of continuity for the probability density* A_0^2 (which equals $|\psi_0|^2$):

$$\frac{\partial}{\partial q_k} \left(\frac{\partial H}{\partial p_k} A_0^2 \right) + \frac{\partial}{\partial t} (A_0^2) = 0 \qquad \left(\frac{\partial H}{\partial p_k} = \dot{q}_k \right). \qquad (6)$$

If we were to continue the calculation, we should next collect all the terms quadratic in $\hbar$, to get an equation for S_1, and so forth. Instead of carrying out these steps, we shall comment on the information obtained so far.   Our results show that classical mechanics, at least in the case of a free particle, may be considered as that approximation to wave mechanics in which the de Broglie wave length is treated as negligibly small.   This result explains not only why classical mechanics can be partially successful without thereby invalidating the basic tenets of wave mechanics, but also indicates clearly the limits of validity of classical mechanics.   We also find that the classical analogue to a solution of the Schrödinger wave equation is not a *single* mechanical trajectory but a *field* of trajectories represented by a solution of the Hamilton-Jacobi equation, and endowed with a density distribution in configuration space whose integral equals unity.   One of the faults of the older quantum mechanics, from our present viewpoint, is that it considered individual quantized trajectories rather than selected fields of trajectories in configuration space.

Now we shall turn to the bound state.   All bound states are characterized by stationary waves with nodal surfaces at infinity (and usually elsewhere as well), but there need not be nodes with respect to every one of the generalized coordinates of configuration space.   To give but two examples: In our treatment of a single bound particle in a central-force field, the radial dependence of the wave function will have nodes for all but the lowest state, and for large values of r the wave function must drop sufficiently rapidly that it remains square-integrable.   But for the angular part the dependence on ϕ has no nodes, for the simple reason that a circulating flux of probability density about the z-axis is not only possible in a stationary situation but even necessary whenever a nonvanishing value of the quantum number m implies a definite value for the z-component of the angular momentum.   Therefore we should be ill advised if we tried to introduce nodes with respect to each and every one of the coordinates q_k.

Thus we are faced with one or the other of two possibilities.   If the coordinate q_k is *periodic* in the sense that two different values of q_k correspond actually to the same coordinate surface, then our condition of uniqueness of the wave function must be that if we travel through the whole range of q_k once, then the phase angle

$S/\hbar$ must have increased by an integral multiple of 2π:

$$\Delta S = \oint \frac{\partial S}{\partial q_k} \, dq_k = \oint p_k \, dq_k = 2\pi n\hbar = nh.$$

(Do not sum over the index k.)   (7)

Or the variable is of the *nonperiodic* type. Then, with respect to that variable, it is better to set up the wave function in the form of a stationary wave:

$$\psi = A(q) \sin\left[\frac{1}{\hbar} S(q)\right] e^{-\frac{i}{\hbar} Et}.$$

(8)

Let us consider the example of a particle in a central-force field. There the coordinate r is of the nonperiodic type, and we must solve eq. (10.29). If we substitute expression (8) into this equation, we find terms multiplied by various powers of $\hbar$, starting with the zeroth power, and also terms multiplied by $\sin(S/\hbar)$ and terms multiplied by $\cos(S/\hbar)$. To the extent that we consider solutions with many nodes, that is, solutions with short wave lengths, we may try to equate the sine terms and the cosine terms to zero separately. But in so doing, we must be prepared for difficulties that will arise because our assumption of short wave lengths will not hold throughout the range of r.

If we proceed as indicated, we shall first find a number of terms free of $\hbar$ and multiplied by $\sin(S/\hbar)$, yielding the condition

$$\frac{1}{2m} S_0'^2 = E - V(r).$$

(9)

Also, there are a number of terms linear in $\hbar$ and multiplied by $\cos(S/\hbar)$; these terms together yield the relation

$$2S_0' A_0' + A_0 S_0'' + \frac{2}{r} A_0 S_0' = 0,$$

$$r^2 A_0^2 S_0' = \text{const.}$$

(10)

The first equation, (9), is a simple Hamilton-Jacobi equation for the radial dependence alone. It furnishes a real increase for S over the range of r between the classical perihelion and the classical aphelion. Outside this range the increase in S is purely imaginary; therefore expression (8) will not be purely oscillatory outside the limits of the classical orbit but (apart from the slow dependence of A on r)

will exhibit exponential increase or decrease because of the appearance of hyperbolic functions. Equation (10) is of questionable validity outside the classical orbit, since the premise of short wave lengths there is completely unrealistic, and without that assumption eq. (10) should contain terms from the next approximation. For whatever this equation may be worth, though, it discourages us from looking for a compensatory exponential drop in A_0. We can start a purely exponential drop at the limits of the classical orbit if at the dividing point (where the potential energy equals E) the real part of S_0 vanishes. That will be the case if both the perihelion and the aphelion are nodal points, that is, if the number of wave lengths between them is half-integral:

$$\Delta S_0 = \int_{r_p}^{r_a} \frac{dS_0}{dr}\, dr = \frac{1}{2} \oint p_r\, dr = n\,\pi\,\hbar = \frac{n}{2}\,h. \tag{11}$$

This condition again is equivalent to the old phase-integral quantization.

Summing up our present interpretation of the phase-integral quantization, we may say that this method corresponds to the most elementary diffraction theory in optics, in which we use Huygens's principle for the construction of wave fronts but at the same time recognize the existence of definite phase angle values on these wave fronts, which are then used to determine diffracted intensities.

11.2. Time-independent perturbation theory without degeneracies

Frequently we encounter a situation in which a system moves under the influence of forces that can be divided into a set of prevailing forces, determining the principal features of the system, and a set of much weaker *perturbing* forces, modifying but not completely obliterating the characteristics determined by the prevailing forces. The approximation methods to be presented in this and the following sections are designed to cope with this situation. In order to have some specific set of circumstances in mind, the reader might think of an atom whose electrons are subject not only to the internal forces of the atom but also to an external applied electric or magnetic field.

In this section we shall address ourselves to the simplest conceivable case: that both the prevailing and the perturbing forces are time-independent and that the system has only single (nondegenerate) discrete energy levels. In later sections we shall consider more involved cases. In order to keep the calculations to the irreducible minimum, we shall consider a single particle in rectilinear canonical coordinates. The time-independent Schrödinger equation in configuration space is then

$$-\frac{\hbar^2}{2m} \nabla^2 \psi + V \psi = E \psi \qquad (V = \overset{0}{V} + \kappa \overset{1}{V}). \qquad (12)$$

$\overset{0}{V}$ is the potential of the prevailing forces, and $\kappa \overset{1}{V}$ is the potential of the perturbing forces. The small parameter κ has been introduced because we shall expand the solution of eq. (12) into a power series in ascending powers of κ:

$$\psi = \overset{0}{\psi} + \kappa \overset{1}{\psi} + \kappa^2 \overset{2}{\psi} + \cdots. \qquad (13)$$

$\overset{0}{\psi}$ is a solution of the unperturbed problem,

$$-\frac{\hbar^2}{2m} \nabla^2 \overset{0}{\psi} + \overset{0}{V} \overset{0}{\psi} = \overset{0}{E} \overset{0}{\psi}, \qquad (14)$$

and we have assumed that the only square-integrable solutions existing are $\overset{0}{\psi}_1, \overset{0}{\psi}_2, \cdots, \overset{0}{\psi}_k, \cdots$, each belonging to a different value of the energy, $\overset{0}{E}_k$. The whole purpose of the perturbation theory is to ascertain systematically the higher approximations if the zeroth-order approximation (the solutions of the unperturbed problem) is known. Naturally, the theory must furnish us with two separate pieces of information, the perturbed energy levels and the perturbed characteristic functions. We shall obtain both.

Before we can launch into the perturbation theory proper, we must first discuss two mathematical properties of the unperturbed solutions, which we shall need. The first property is the *orthogonality* of the characteristic functions; the second is the *expansion theorem for arbitrary functions*. First the orthogonality theorem: We claim that the integral I_{ik},

$$I_{ik} \equiv \int_{-\infty}^{\infty} \overset{0}{\psi}_i^* \overset{0}{\psi}_k \, \mathbf{dx} = 0 \qquad (i \neq k), \qquad (15)$$

vanishes whenever i and k are different.   For proof, we replace first
one and then the other of the two factors under the integral from the
wave equation by the expression

$$\overset{0}{\psi_i} = \frac{1}{\overset{0}{E_i}}\left(V\overset{0}{\psi_i} - \frac{\hbar^2}{2\,m}\nabla^2\overset{0}{\psi_i}\right).$$ (16)

Thus we get for I_{ik} two different expressions,

$$\begin{aligned}
I_{ik} &= \frac{1}{\overset{0}{E_i}}\int\left(V\overset{0}{\psi_i^*}\overset{0}{\psi_k} - \frac{\hbar^2}{2\,m}\nabla^2\overset{0}{\psi_i^*}\cdot\overset{0}{\psi_k}\right)\mathbf{dx}\\
&= \frac{1}{\overset{0}{E_k}}\int\left(V\overset{0}{\psi_i^*}\overset{0}{\psi_k} - \frac{\hbar^2}{2\,m}\overset{0}{\psi_i^*}\nabla^2\overset{0}{\psi_k}\right)\mathbf{dx}.
\end{aligned}$$ (17)

But we can prove that the two integrals (without the factors in
front) are equal if only the wave functions are square-integrable.
Their difference

$$\begin{aligned}
\int_{\mathrm{I}} - \int_{\mathrm{II}} &= \frac{\hbar^2}{2\,m}\int(\overset{0}{\psi_i^*}\nabla^2\overset{0}{\psi_k} - \overset{0}{\psi_k}\nabla^2\overset{0}{\psi_i^*})\,\mathbf{dx}\\
&= \frac{\hbar^2}{2\,m}\oint(\overset{0}{\psi_i^*}\,\mathrm{grad}\,\overset{0}{\psi_k} - \overset{0}{\psi_k}\,\mathrm{grad}\,\overset{0}{\psi_i^*})\cdot\mathbf{n}\,dS,
\end{aligned}$$ (18)

a surface integral because of Green's theorem.[1]   Since the surface
integral is to be extended over a surface at infinity, it will vanish;
square-integrability imposes on the wave functions a more rapid
drop than is necessary to ensure the vanishing of the surface integral
in question.   But in eq. (17) these two *equal* integrals are multiplied
by different factors (since we have assumed the absence of degeneracies); therefore both the two integrals on the right, and I_{ik} itself,
must vanish.   If all the characteristic functions are normalized, we
call the set of characteristic functions a set of *orthonormal* functions
or, for short, an orthonormal set.

The *expansion theorem* deals with the representation of an arbitrary square-integrable function $f(\mathbf{x})$ by a series of orthonormal
functions ψ_k.   Suppose we set ourselves the task of finding that sum

---

[1] Green's theorem is a special application of Gauss's theorem.   To prove it
one must interpret the Laplacian as the divergence of a gradient and also carry
out an integration by parts in each term under the integral (18).

F of given orthonormal functions,

$$F = \sum_{k=1}^{\infty} c_k \, \psi_k, \tag{19}$$

which deviates as little as possible from the given function f. As a measure of deviation, we form the absolute square of the difference $(f - F)$ and integrate this positive-definite function over the whole domain of the coordinates $\mathbf{x}$:

$$\Delta^2 = \int (f^* - F^*)(f - F) \, d\mathbf{x}. \tag{20}$$

Δ^2 will vanish only if f and F are "almost everywhere" equal, and for most purposes this means equal everywhere except where f has points of discontinuity. Regardless of whether Δ^2 can be made to vanish, we wish to adjust the coefficients c_k so that Δ^2 becomes as small as possible. If we substitute for F in eq. (20) the complete expansion (19), we find that the expression to be minimized is

$$\Delta^2 = \int f^* f \, d\mathbf{x} + \sum_{k=1}^{\infty} c_k^* \, c_k - \sum_{k=1}^{\infty} \left[c_k \int f^* \, \psi_k \, d\mathbf{x} + c_k^* \int f \, \psi_k^* \, d\mathbf{x} \right].$$
$$\tag{21}$$

The partial derivatives of Δ^2 with respect to the various c_k must vanish:

$$\frac{\partial \Delta^2}{\partial c_k} = c_k^* - \int f^* \, \psi_k \, d\mathbf{x} = 0$$

$$c_k = \int f \, \psi_k^* \, d\mathbf{x}, \qquad c_k^* = \int f^* \, \psi_k \, d\mathbf{x}. \tag{22}$$

Thus we find that the coefficient of each function in the orthonormal set is completely determined, regardless of the choice of the other functions, as long as that choice does not violate the orthonormality of the set.

If we choose the coefficients in the expansion in accordance with eq. (22), we find that Δ^2 takes the value

$$\Delta^2 = \int |f|^2 \, d\mathbf{x} - \sum_1^{\infty} |c_k|^2 \geq 0, \tag{23}$$

leading to *Bessel's inequality*,

$$\sum_1^{\infty} |c_k|^2 \leq \int |f|^2 \, d\mathbf{x}. \tag{24}$$

The results obtained so far do not completely exhaust the expansion theorem. The remaining question is whether Δ^2 can be made zero for all square-integrable functions $f(x)$. If it can be, we call the orthonormal set ψ_k *complete*. We shall not prove it here, but the fact is that the characteristic functions of a Hamiltonian of the form (14) comprise a complete orthonormal set if all possible states are bound, and this statement completes the expansion theorem. We shall now return to our perturbation problem.

Collecting all the terms in eq. (12) that are linear in κ, we get for the function $\overset{1}{\psi}_k$ the condition

$$-\frac{\hbar^2}{2m}\nabla^2 \overset{1}{\psi}_k + \overset{0}{V}\overset{1}{\psi}_k + \overset{1}{V}\overset{0}{\psi}_k = \overset{0}{E}_k \overset{1}{\psi}_k + \overset{1}{E}_k \overset{0}{\psi}_k. \tag{25}$$

If we multiply this last equation by $\overset{0}{\psi}_i^*$ and integrate over all space, we get

$$-\frac{\hbar^2}{2m}\int \overset{0}{\psi}_i^* \nabla^2 \overset{1}{\psi}_k\, \mathbf{dx} + \int \overset{0}{\psi}_i^* V_0 \overset{1}{\psi}_k\, \mathbf{dx} + \int \overset{0}{\psi}_i^* \overset{1}{V} \overset{0}{\psi}_k\, \mathbf{dx}$$

$$= \overset{0}{E}_k \int \overset{0}{\psi}_i^* \overset{1}{\psi}_k\, \mathbf{dx} + \overset{1}{E}_k \delta_{ik}, \quad (26)$$

the last term because of the orthonormality of the unperturbed characteristic functions. The first term can be transformed with the help of Green's theorem and because of the vanishing of the surface integral at infinity:

$$\int \overset{0}{\psi}_i^* \nabla^2 \overset{1}{\psi}_k\, \mathbf{dx} = \int \overset{1}{\psi}_k \nabla^2 \overset{0}{\psi}_i^*\, \mathbf{dx}. \tag{27}$$

Because of the zeroth-order equation, we have

$$-\frac{\hbar^2}{2m}\nabla^2 \overset{0}{\psi}_i^* + \overset{0}{V}\overset{0}{\psi}_i^* = \overset{0}{E}_i \psi_i^*, \tag{28}$$

and hence eq. (26) can be given the form

$$\int \overset{0}{\psi}_i^* \overset{0}{\psi}_k \overset{1}{V}\, \mathbf{dx} = (\overset{0}{E}_k - \overset{0}{E}_i)\int \overset{0}{\psi}_i^* \overset{1}{\psi}_k\, \mathbf{dx} + \overset{1}{E}_k \delta_{ik}. \tag{29}$$

(The summation convention is not to apply to any of these equations!) Equation (29) holds whether we choose the two indices i and k equal or different. But now we must distinguish these two choices, because they give us different bits of information. Setting

$i = k$, we find

$$\overset{1}{E_k} = \int \overset{1}{V} \, |\overset{0}{\psi_k}|^2 \, \mathbf{dx}. \tag{30}$$

For all other choices we get

$$\int \overset{0}{\psi_i^*} \overset{1}{\psi_k} \, dx = \frac{1}{\overset{0}{E_k} - \overset{0}{E_i}} \int \overset{1}{V} \overset{0}{\psi_i^*} \overset{0}{\psi_k} \, \mathbf{dx} \qquad (i \neq k). \tag{31}$$

Equation (30) tells us how to determine the disturbed energy level. All we have to do is to integrate the perturbing potential over all space, using the absolute square of the unperturbed wave function for weighting. Equation (31), on the other hand, furnishes us with the integrals that we need, according to eq. (22), for expanding the perturbation in terms of the unperturbed wave functions. Only the coefficient of the function $\overset{0}{\psi_k}$ remains undetermined, and we may set it equal to zero. The first-order perturbation functions are therefore

$$\overset{1}{\psi_k} = \sum_{i \neq k} \frac{\overset{0}{\psi_i}}{\overset{0}{E_k} - \overset{0}{E_i}} \int \overset{1}{V} \overset{0}{\psi_i^*} \overset{0}{\psi_k} \, \mathbf{dx}. \tag{32}$$

Equations (30) and (32) are the fundamental equations of perturbation theory. For many purposes, however, it is necessary to go over to second-order and even higher terms. The procedure is the same in all orders.

11.3. Degeneracies

If some of the energy levels of the unperturbed case coincide, if they are *degenerate*, the method developed in Section 11.2 must be modified. First of all, the proof of orthogonality of the characteristic functions given previously is based on the argument that the two energies E_i and E_k, which appear in eq. (17), are different (unless $i = k$). If there are several independent characteristic functions belonging to the same energy level, then any linear combination of these functions is again a characteristic function. Although not every conceivable set of such degenerate characteristic functions is orthonormal to begin with, we can always construct a set of linear combinations that has that property. In what follows, we shall assume that this has been done.

But even though we can again assume that all the eigenfunctions are orthonormal, the procedure followed in the preceding section cannot be carried through entirely. As we come to eq. (32), some of the denominators in that expression for the expansion coefficients of the first-order perturbation may vanish, leading to impossible results. We must, therefore, proceed more cautiously. The perturbation may remove the degeneracy, and if that happens, only certain linear combinations of the degenerate zeroth-order characteristic functions are suitable for the starting of the perturbation calculation. If we use the wrong combinations for a start, we shall get contradictions as we attempt to determine the first-order corrections. Accordingly, we shall introduce into eq. (25) as a zeroth-order solution a linear combination of the $\overset{0}{\psi}_k$ belonging to the same level, with unknown coefficients u_α, which will be determined subsequently. Equation (25) then assumes the form

$$-\frac{\hbar^2}{2m}\nabla^2\overset{1}{\psi}_k + \overset{0}{V}\overset{1}{\psi}_k + \overset{1}{V}\sum_{\alpha=1}^{n} u_\alpha\overset{0}{\psi}_{k\alpha} = \overset{0}{E}_k\overset{1}{\psi}_k + \overset{1}{E}_k\sum_{\alpha=1}^{n} u_\alpha\overset{0}{\psi}_{k\alpha}, \quad (33)$$

where n is the number of degenerate characteristic functions belonging to the same level $\overset{0}{E}_k$. The secondary index α serves to identify the different eigenfunctions belonging to the same unperturbed energy level $\overset{0}{E}_k$. Next we shall multiply this whole equation in turn by each one of the degenerate unperturbed eigenfunctions $\overset{0}{\psi}_{k\beta}^*$. The result is

$$-\frac{\hbar^2}{2m}(\overset{0}{\psi}_{k\beta}, \nabla^2\overset{1}{\psi}_k) + (\overset{0}{\psi}_{k\beta}, \overset{0}{V}\overset{1}{\psi}_k) + \sum_{\alpha=1}^{n} u_\alpha(\overset{0}{\psi}_{k\beta}, \overset{1}{V}\overset{0}{\psi}_{k\alpha})$$

$$= \overset{0}{E}_k(\overset{0}{\psi}_{k\beta}, \overset{1}{\psi}_k) + \overset{1}{E}_k\sum_{\alpha=1}^{n} u_\alpha(\overset{0}{\psi}_{k\beta}, \overset{0}{\psi}_{k\alpha})$$

$$= \overset{0}{E}_k(\overset{0}{\psi}_{k\beta}, \overset{1}{\psi}_k) + \overset{1}{E}_k u_\beta \qquad (\beta = 1, \cdots, n). \quad (34)$$

In order to shorten the notation, we have introduced for the integrals that arise the abbreviating symbol

$$\int \phi^* \chi \, d\mathbf{x} \equiv (\phi, \chi). \quad (35)$$

With the help of Green's theorem, we prove as usual that

$$(\overset{0}{\psi}_{k\beta}, \nabla^2 \overset{1}{\psi}_k) = (\nabla^2 \overset{0}{\psi}_{k\beta}, \overset{1}{\psi}_k). \qquad (36)$$

Then in eq. (34) the first two terms on the left cancel with the first term on the right, and we have left:

$$\sum_{\alpha=1}^{n} [(\overset{0}{\psi}_{k\beta}, \overset{1}{V} \overset{0}{\psi}_{k\alpha}) - \delta_{\beta\alpha} \overset{1}{E}_k]u_\alpha = 0, \qquad (\beta = 1, \cdots, n). \quad (37)$$

Thus we have a set of n linear homogeneous equations for the n unknowns u_α. It is well known that a nonvanishing solution will exist only if the determinant of the coefficients vanishes. If we further abbreviate the notation by writing

$$\int \overset{0}{\psi}_{k\beta}^* \overset{1}{V} \overset{0}{\psi}_{k\alpha} \, \mathbf{dx} \equiv (\overset{0}{\psi}_{k\beta}, \overset{1}{V} \overset{0}{\psi}_{k\alpha}) \equiv \overset{1}{V}_{\beta\alpha}, \qquad (38)$$

we find that the necessary condition for a nonvanishing zeroth-order solution is

$$\det |\overset{1}{V}_{\beta\alpha} - \delta_{\beta\alpha} \overset{1}{E}_k| = \det \begin{vmatrix} \overset{1}{V}_{11} - \overset{1}{E}_k, & \overset{1}{V}_{12} & , \cdots \\ \overset{1}{V}_{21} & , & \overset{1}{V}_{22} - \overset{1}{E}_k, \cdots \\ & \cdots & \end{vmatrix} = 0. \quad (39)$$

A very similar equation must be solved in the theory of elasticity if we look for principal directions of the stress tensor or the strain tensor (M&E, pp. 80 ff.). Again, eq. (39) is called the *secular equation* of the problem, and we can use it as a determining equation for the unknown $\overset{1}{E}_k$.

On the strength of the original definition for the symbol $\overset{1}{V}_{\beta\alpha}$, these n^2 quantities satisfy the relationship

$$\overset{1}{V}_{\beta\alpha}^* = \overset{1}{V}_{\alpha\beta}, \qquad (40)$$

and it is said that these n^2 numbers form a *Hermitian matrix*. In the realm of square arrays of complex numbers, Hermiticity is the analogue to symmetry for similar arrays of real numbers.

We shall use the property of Hermiticity to prove two important properties of the solutions. First, *all the solutions $\overset{1}{E}_k$ of the secular* *equation are real.* To prove it, we take eqs. (37), multiply each of them by u_β^*, and add the n resulting expressions:

$$\sum_{\alpha,\beta=1}^{n} u_\beta^* \overset{1}{V}_{\beta\alpha} u_\alpha - \overset{1}{E}_k \sum_{\beta=1}^{n} |u_\beta|^2 = 0. \tag{41}$$

Because of the Hermiticity, the first term is a real number. The coefficient of $\overset{1}{E}_k$ is real, nonvanishing, and positive definite. Therefore all roots of the secular equation are real.

Second, we shall prove the property of orthogonality for two different sets of solutions for the $\overset{1}{E}_k$ if they belong to two different roots of the secular equation, say

$$\overset{1}{E}_k = \overset{\mathrm{I}}{\epsilon}, \qquad \overset{1}{E}_k = \overset{\mathrm{II}}{\epsilon}. \tag{42}$$

Again we write down eqs. (37) for the two solutions, once after taking the conjugate complex:

$$\sum_{\alpha=1}^{n} \overset{1}{V}_{\beta\alpha} \overset{\mathrm{I}}{u}_\alpha - \overset{\mathrm{I}}{\epsilon} \overset{\mathrm{I}}{u}_\beta = 0,$$
$$\sum_{\alpha=1}^{n} \overset{1}{V}_{\beta\alpha}^* \overset{\mathrm{II}}{u}_\alpha^* - \overset{\mathrm{II}}{\epsilon} \overset{\mathrm{II}}{u}_\beta^* = 0. \tag{43}$$

Then we multiply the first equation by $\overset{\mathrm{II}}{u}_\beta^*$, the second by $\overset{\mathrm{I}}{u}_\beta$, subtract the results from each other, and sum over all β. Our result is

$$\sum_{\alpha,\beta=1}^{n} (\overset{1}{V}_{\beta\alpha} \overset{\mathrm{II}}{u}_\beta^* \overset{\mathrm{I}}{u}_\alpha - \overset{1}{V}_{\beta\alpha}^* \overset{\mathrm{I}}{u}_\beta \overset{\mathrm{II}}{u}_\alpha^*) = (\overset{\mathrm{I}}{\epsilon} - \overset{\mathrm{II}}{\epsilon}) \sum_{\beta=1}^{n} \overset{\mathrm{I}}{u}_\beta \overset{\mathrm{II}}{u}_\beta^*. \tag{44}$$

Because of the Hermiticity, the double sum vanishes. To show that it does, we must first apply eq. (40) to the second term in the double sum and then interchange the symbols for the two summation indices α and β. The result of these operations is that the second term becomes identical with the first, except for the sign, and they cancel. Thus the left-hand side of eq. (44) vanishes. The right-hand side is a product, and one of the two factors must vanish. If the two perturbation energies $\overset{\mathrm{I}}{\epsilon}$ and $\overset{\mathrm{II}}{\epsilon}$ are different, it follows immediately that

$$\sum_{\beta=1}^{n} \overset{\mathrm{II}}{u}_\beta^* \overset{\mathrm{I}}{u}_\beta = 0 \equiv (\overset{\mathrm{II}}{u}, \overset{\mathrm{I}}{u}). \tag{45}$$

In this case, the perturbing potential has served to *remove the degeneracy*. As a result, an energy level that is single in the unperturbed system splits up into several closely adjacent energy levels in the perturbed system. Such systems of energy levels are called *multiplets* in spectroscopy, and the appearance of such multiplets is often referred to as the *fine structure* of the originally single level.

The other possibility is that the roots $\overset{\text{I}}{\epsilon}$ and $\overset{\text{II}}{\epsilon}$ of the secular equation are equal. Here the perturbing potential has failed to remove the degeneracy, and the u_α remain undetermined, since any linear combination of solutions belonging to the same multiple root ϵ is again a solution of the wave equation up to the first order. Subsequent orders of the perturbation calculation may or may not remove the degeneracy, or any order may remove the degeneracy *partially*, splitting the energy level into $m < n$ different levels. All these contingencies actually arise in physically interesting situations, for instance in the theory of the Stark effect on polar molecules, where the degeneracy of the rigid rotator with respect to m remains unchanged in the first-order perturbation but becomes partially removed in the second-order perturbation.

The perturbation theory applied to degenerate systems puts into sharper focus the whole question of alternative methods of quantization, which we had occasion to discuss within the framework of the older quantum theory in Section 8.2. We find now that in a degenerate system it is always possible to replace one set of orthonormal eigenfunctions belonging to one energy level by another set of orthonormal functions, the latter set consisting of suitable linear combinations of the former. But if a small modification of the force field, a perturbation, removes the degeneracy, only certain combinations even in the zeroth-order calculation are adapted to the modified problem. However, the correct set of combinations is not always the same; it depends on the coefficients in the secular equation (39), and these coefficients are determined by the perturbing potential. It may appear strange that a very small perturbing potential will determine the choice of linear combinations in the unperturbed system. Such a large effect by small causes appears to contradict our usual experience about the continuous dependence of the effect on the cause, the cause in this case being the Schrödinger equation and the effect the characteristic functions.   The physical explanation of this apparent paradox is that we have looked specifically for *stationary* solutions.   In the case of an almost degenerate system, all the combinations of $\psi_{k\alpha}^{0}$ are very nearly stationary, but only the solutions of the secular equation are completely stationary.   If we start with a wrong combination, we shall find that slow, "secular" changes take place; and the smaller the perturbing forces that remove the degeneracy, the slower are these changes.   But if we look for completely stable states, then we shall find that these depend critically on the nature of the perturbing potential, no matter how small we choose it.   In other words, it is the functional dependence of V^{1} on the coordinates, not the amplitude factor κ in eq. (12), that determines the correct zeroth-order combinations.   In the next section we shall find just what happens when we start with the wrong combination.

11.4. Time-dependent perturbation theory

In this section we shall describe the methods that apply when we are interested in *transitions* from one stationary state to another. Let us consider a system that in the absence of perturbations possesses only discrete stationary states.   Some of the states may be degenerate but need not be so.   If we apply a perturbation that is itself a function of the time, for instance an external alternating electric or magnetic field, there will be no stationary perturbed levels; nevertheless, we may represent the instantaneous wave function at any time as the linear superposition of the characteristic functions of the unperturbed eigenfunctions $\phi_{k}^{0} e^{-\frac{i}{\hbar} E_{k}^{0} t}$, because of the expansion theorem.   The coefficients of this expansion will then be themselves functions of the time t, and they will be an indication of the change in probability of finding any one particular state ϕ_{k}^{0}. This probability can be realized in a conceptual experiment if we can switch off the perturbing forces completely and then find in which state is our (now unperturbed) system.

Time-dependent perturbation theory is also possible if the applied perturbation itself is constant in time.   Although the methods presented in the last two sections are then applicable, we may also, with perfect justification, shift our inquiry and, instead of asking for the new energy levels, ask for the rapidity with which a certain unperturbed state changes over into some other unperturbed state.   Thus the time-dependent methods are applicable for both time-dependent and constant perturbing forces.

One more remark is necessary before we can launch into the theory proper.   How are we going to measure the probability of finding any particular state if the wave function is a mixture of several unperturbed eigenfunctions?   Such a mixture would have the form

$$\psi(\mathbf{x},\, t) \;=\; \sum_{k=1}^{\infty} c_k(t)\, \overset{0}{\phi}_k(\mathbf{x})\, e^{-\frac{i}{\hbar}\overset{0}{E}_k t}. \tag{46}$$

It would not do to set the probabilities equal to the expansion coefficients c_k themselves, because these expansion coefficients will in general be complex and their sum will not be equal to unity, though the sum of the individual probabilities—the probability of finding the system in *some* state—must be 1.   But the expansion theorem, which enables us to set Δ^2 in eq. (23) equal to zero, tells us that the sum of the absolute squares of the c_k equals 1 provided the wave function $\psi(\mathbf{x},\, t)$ is normalized.   Therefore we shall assume that the probability of finding the state $\overset{0}{\phi}_k$ is determined by the real non-negative quantity $|c_k|^2$.

To start our development itself, we shall substitute the expansion (46) into the time-dependent Schrödinger equation,

$$-\frac{\hbar^2}{2\,m}\,\nabla^2\psi + (\overset{0}{V} + \kappa\overset{1}{V})\,\psi + \frac{\hbar}{i}\,\frac{\partial\psi}{\partial t} = 0, \tag{47}$$

and thus obtain a system of ordinary differential equations of the first order for the c_k.   Straightforward calculation yields first

$$-\frac{\hbar^2}{2\,m}\sum_k c_k\,\nabla^2\overset{0}{\phi}_k\, e^{-\frac{i}{\hbar}\overset{0}{E}_k t} + (\overset{0}{V} + \kappa\overset{1}{V})\sum_k c_k\,\overset{0}{\phi}_k\, e^{-\frac{i}{\hbar}\overset{0}{E}_k t}$$

$$+ \sum_k \left(\frac{\hbar}{i}\,\dot{c}_k - \overset{0}{E}_k\, c_k\right)\overset{0}{\phi}_k\, e^{-\frac{i}{\hbar}\overset{0}{E}_k t} = 0 \qquad \left(\dot{c}_k \equiv \frac{dc_k}{dt}\right). \tag{48}$$

Because the $\overset{0}{\phi}_k$ are assumed to be solutions of the unperturbed wave equation, three terms cancel mutually, leading to the simpler set of equations

$$\kappa \overset{1}{V} \sum_k c_k \overset{0}{\phi_k} e^{-\frac{i}{\hbar} \overset{0}{E_k} t} + \sum_k \frac{\hbar}{i} \dot{c}_k \overset{0}{\phi_k} e^{-\frac{i}{\hbar} \overset{0}{E_k} t} = 0. \qquad (49)$$

Let us now multiply this equation by the factor $e^{\frac{i}{\hbar} \overset{0}{E_l} t} \overset{0}{\phi_l}$ and integrate over **x**. If we use again the abbreviating notation introduced in eqs. (35) and (38), we find that the integration disposes of the space-dependent functions and that we are left with differential equations for the c_k:

$$\dot{c}_l + \frac{i}{\hbar} \sum_{k=1}^{\infty} \kappa \overset{1}{V}_{lk} e^{\frac{i}{\hbar}(\overset{0}{E_l} - \overset{0}{E_k})t} c_k = 0 \qquad (l = 1, 2, \cdots). \quad (50)$$

These equations form an infinite set for an infinite number of unknowns, the c_k. A solution in closed form is usually out of the question, but there are a number of special situations we shall examine. Let us start with the assumption that the perturbation itself does not depend on the time and that the V_{lk} are therefore constants. Then the coefficients of the equations are trigonometric functions, and it is reasonable to look for solutions that are also sinusoidal functions of the time. However, this approach, though successful, in general will not lead to new knowledge. Such solutions will incorporate into the time-dependence of the c_k the additional small frequencies appearing in the exponentials of the stationary perturbed eigenfunctions. In general, then, in such solutions the phase angle of the c_k will gradually change linearly in time, but the change in absolute magnitude will be minute, and it is only the magnitude of the c_k that measures probability. The reason for the slightness of the change can be understood thus: The coefficients of eq. (50) are small, because they contain the small factor κ; at the same time they oscillate rapidly, at atomic frequencies. Unless the induced change in c_k on the left is appreciable during half a period of oscillation of the coefficients, the next half-period will induce a cancellation of the effect of the first half-period.

The exception to this general rule is the possibility that some of the coefficients may not oscillate rapidly, because the two energy levels E_k and E_l are either closely adjacent or even identical. In that case, considerable changes in the magnitudes of the two coefficients involved are possible, both in the degenerate and in the nearly degenerate case. Let us assume the simplest possible case, that only two energy levels, call them a and b, are closely adjacent or coincident. We may disregard all the other terms in eqs. (50) and retain merely those involved in transitions between a and b. The two equations to be considered are then

$$\dot{c}_a + \frac{i}{\hbar} \kappa (\overset{1}{V}_{aa} c_a + \overset{1}{V}_{ab} e^{i\omega_{ab} t} c_b) = 0,$$

$$\dot{c}_b + \frac{i}{\hbar} \kappa (\overset{1}{V}_{ba} e^{-i\omega_{ab} t} c_a + \overset{1}{V}_{bb} c_b) = 0 \qquad (51)$$

$$\left[\overset{1}{V}_{aa}, \overset{1}{V}_{bb} \text{ real}, \quad \overset{1}{V}_{ba} = \overset{1}{V}_{ab}^{*}, \quad \omega_{ab} = \frac{1}{\hbar} (E_a - E_b) \right].$$

These two equations (which are admittedly only approximately valid, but actually contain all the interesting aspects of the situation) can be solved in closed form. We shall try sinusoidal dependence, but not the same for the two coefficients. Let us introduce

$$c_a = a_a e^{i(\omega + \frac{1}{2}\omega_{ab})t},$$
$$c_b = a_b e^{i(\omega - \frac{1}{2}\omega_{ab})t}, \qquad (52)$$

where the amplitudes a_a and a_b and the frequency ω remain to be determined. If we substitute our trial expression back into the differential equations (51), we get

$$(\hbar \omega + \kappa \overset{1}{V}_{aa} + \tfrac{1}{2} \hbar \omega_{ab}) a_a + \kappa \overset{1}{V}_{ab} a_b = 0,$$

$$\kappa \overset{1}{V}_{ab}^{*} a_a + (\hbar \omega + \kappa \overset{1}{V}_{bb} - \tfrac{1}{2} \hbar \omega_{ab}) a_b = 0. \qquad (53)$$

These constitute a set of homogeneous linear equations for the amplitudes a_a and a_b, which possess nonvanishing solutions only if the determinant of the coefficients vanishes:

$$\hbar^2 \omega^2 + \kappa (\overset{1}{V}_{aa} + \overset{1}{V}_{bb})\hbar \omega + \tfrac{1}{2} \hbar \omega_{ab} \kappa (\overset{1}{V}_{bb} - \overset{1}{V}_{aa}) - \tfrac{1}{4} \hbar^2 \omega_{ab}^2$$
$$+ \kappa^2 \overset{1}{V}_{aa} \overset{1}{V}_{bb} - \kappa^2 |V_{ab}|^2 = 0. \qquad (54)$$

This condition is a typical secular equation for the frequency ω. The two solutions are

$$\hbar \omega = \tfrac{1}{2}\kappa (\overset{1}{V}_{bb} - \overset{1}{V}_{aa}) \pm \sqrt{\kappa^2 |\overset{1}{V}_{ab}|^2 + \tfrac{1}{4} \hbar^2 \Omega^2}$$

$$\left[\Omega = \omega_{ab} + \frac{\kappa}{\hbar} (\overset{1}{V}_{aa} - \overset{1}{V}_{bb}) \right]: \qquad (55)$$

As a result, we get two different sets of relations between the coefficients a_a and a_b. If we choose the positive sign for the root in eq. (55), we have

$$\left(\tfrac{1}{2}\hbar\,\Omega + \sqrt{\kappa^2|\overset{1}{V}_{ab}|^2 + \tfrac{1}{4}\hbar^2\,\Omega^2}\right) a_a^+ + \kappa\overset{1}{V}_{ab}\,a_b^+ = 0, \qquad (56)$$

or $\quad \kappa\overset{1}{V}_{ab}^*\,a_a^+ + \left(\sqrt{\kappa^2|\overset{1}{V}_{ab}|^2 + \tfrac{1}{4}\hbar^2\,\Omega^2} - \tfrac{1}{2}\hbar\,\Omega\right) a_b^+ = 0. \qquad (57)$

Equations (56) and (57) are equivalent. If, on the other hand, we choose the negative sign for the root, we shall get the two equivalent relations

$$\left(\tfrac{1}{2}\hbar\,\Omega - \sqrt{\kappa^2|\overset{1}{V}_{ab}|^2 + \tfrac{1}{4}\hbar^2\,\Omega^2}\right) a_a^- + \kappa\overset{1}{V}_{ab}\,a_b^- = 0,$$
$$\kappa\overset{1}{V}_{ab}^*\,a_a^- - \left(\sqrt{\kappa^2|\overset{1}{V}_{ab}|^2 + \tfrac{1}{4}\hbar^2\,\Omega^2} + \tfrac{1}{2}\hbar\,\Omega\right) a_b^- = 0. \qquad (58)$$

The most general solution of our problem is a linear combination of these alternatives, but each one by itself represents a stationary possibility. A short calculation will show that if ω_{ab} vanishes and hence if we have a degenerate case, then the secular equation (54) is just the one we would have encountered in the time-independent degenerate-perturbation calculation of Section 11.3; and if Ω is assumed large, then the solution with ω^+ and a^+ represents the perturbed level b, whereas the solution with the negative signs for the root represents the perturbed level a of the theory of Section 11.2.

We may wish to consider the case in which the perturbation is "switched on" at the time zero and where previously the system was definitely in state a. To work out this situation, we must find a linear combination so that at the designated time the probability for b vanishes. Again, if ω_{ab} is large, this initial condition calls for a large value of the a^-, with just a small admixture of the a^+, because, rigorously, our initial condition leads to

$$a_b^+ + a_b^- = 0, \qquad (59)$$

and to satisfy it we must have $a_a^+ \ll a_a^-$. But what if the two energy levels are closely adjacent? Our solutions show that we may expect a serious mixture of the two stationary solutions if

$$\kappa|\overset{1}{V}_{ab}| \not\ll \hbar\,\Omega. \qquad (60)$$

In that case, the coefficients in eqs. (56), (57), and (58) are all of the same order of magnitude. As a result, the actual magnitude of the coefficients c_a and c_b,

$$
\begin{aligned}
c_a &= e^{\frac{i}{2}\omega_{ab} t}\, (a_a^+ \, e^{i\omega^+ t} + a_a^- \, e^{-i\omega^- t}),\\
c_b &= e^{-\frac{i}{2}\omega_{ab} t}\, (a_b^+ \, e^{i\omega^+ t} + a_b^- \, e^{-i\omega^- t}),
\end{aligned}
\tag{61}
$$

depends on the phase relations between the two terms in each. Originally, the phases of c_b are 180° apart. The largest probability for b will be found when they are in phase; and since the beat frequency is $(\omega^+ - \omega^-)$, that will be the case after a time

$$
t = \frac{\pi}{\omega^+ - \omega^-} = \frac{\pi}{2\sqrt{\dfrac{\kappa^2}{\hbar^2}\,|\overset{1}{V}_{ab}|^2 + \tfrac{1}{4}\Omega^2}}
\tag{62}
$$

The *rate* at which the probability changes depends on both this time constant and on the maximum amplitude that the b-probability can achieve before decreasing again. This amplitude is a complicated quantity, which, however, is of the order of magnitude of 1; that is, it is neither very small, nor greater than 1. We may, therefore, say that the average rate at which the probability changes is of the order of the inverse of the expression (62), provided, of course, that ω_{ab} is not large compared with $\dfrac{\kappa}{\hbar}\,|\overset{1}{V}_{ab}|$. Under these circumstances, the average rate at which transitions occur will be of the order of magnitude of $\dfrac{1}{\hbar}\,\kappa|\overset{1}{V}_{ab}|$.

Now we shall consider another important possibility, namely, that the perturbing potential is not constant but has a sinusoidal dependence on the time t. This situation occurs first of all in the case that monochromatic radiation is incident on an otherwise isolated system.

11.5. Semiclassical radiation theory

Let us consider the transitions induced by a perturbing force that is sinusoidal,

$$
\overset{1}{V} = A(\mathbf{x}) \cos (\omega t + \delta).
\tag{63}
$$

For the wave function we shall use expression (46) again, in which the time-dependence of the unperturbed wave functions is introduced explicitly, so that the (slow) time-dependence of the coefficients c_k is a direct consequence of the perturbation. If we substitute expression (46) and the perturbing potential (63) into the time-dependent Schrödinger equation (47), we get the following differential equations for the c_k:

$$\dot{c}_l + \frac{i}{\hbar} \kappa \sum_k A_{lk} \cos (\omega t + \delta) e^{\frac{i}{\hbar}(\overset{0}{E}_l - \overset{0}{E}_k)t} c_k = 0,$$

$$A_{lk} = \int \overset{0}{\phi}_l^* \overset{0}{\phi}_k A(\mathbf{x}) \, d\mathbf{x}.$$

(64)

This set of equations plays the same role as eqs. (50) in the case of a constant perturbing potential. The method of finding solutions is quite similar to the previous calculation. We shall again look for solutions in which the c_k are sinusoidal.

Transitions will not take place to any considerable extent if the coefficients of the c_k on the right-hand side oscillate rapidly, for the reasons discussed in the previous section. But whereas for time-independent perturbations transitions take place between closely adjacent levels, particularly between states belonging to the same unperturbed degenerate energy level, the condition in our present case is that the absolute magnitude of the frequency

$$\omega_{lk} = \frac{1}{\hbar} (E_l - E_k),$$

(65)

$|\omega_{lk}|$, differs only slightly from the applied perturbing frequency ω.

Let us consider that for two particular states denoted by subscripts a and b there is near-resonance in this sense, and for no other sets of states; then again we may disregard all terms that do not directly refer to a or b. Thus we get

$$\dot{c}_a + \frac{i}{\hbar} \kappa A_{ab} \cos (\omega t + \delta) e^{i\omega_{lk}t} c_b = 0,$$

$$\dot{c}_b + \frac{i}{\hbar} \kappa A_{ba} \cos (\omega t + \delta) e^{-i\omega_{lk}t} c_a = 0$$

(66)

$$(A_{ba} = A_{ab}^*).$$

We now set

$$\cos (\omega t + \delta) = \tfrac{1}{2}[e^{i(\omega t + \delta)} + e^{-i(\omega t + \delta)}].$$

(67)

In the expression

$$\tfrac{1}{2}[e^{i(\omega t+\delta)} + e^{-i(\omega t+\delta)}]\, e^{i\omega_{lk}t}, \tag{68}$$

one of the two terms will have a slow time-dependence but the other will not; which one is the interesting term depends on whether ω_{lk} is a positive or a negative quantity. In any case let us call the *small* difference

$$\omega \pm \omega_{lk} = \Delta. \tag{69}$$

Then we may omit the fast-changing term in eqs. (66), and we are left with the system of equations

$$\dot{c}_a + \frac{i}{\hbar}\, \kappa\, e^{i\delta}\, A_{ab}\, e^{i\Delta t}\, c_b = 0,$$
$$\dot{c}_b + \frac{i}{\hbar}\, \kappa\, e^{-i\delta}\, A_{ab}^*\, e^{-i\Delta t}\, c_a = 0. \tag{70}$$

We shall solve these equations again by sinusoidal functions. We set

$$c_a = e^{i(\omega'+\frac{1}{2}\Delta)t}\, a_a,$$
$$c_b = e^{i(\omega'-\frac{1}{2}\Delta)t}\, a_b, \tag{71}$$

choosing the difference in time-dependence of c_a and c_b so that both terms in each equation assume the same functional dependence on t. The final set of equations for the new constants a_a, a_b is

$$\left(\omega' + \frac{1}{2}\Delta\right) a_a + \frac{\kappa}{\hbar}\, e^{i\delta}\, A_{ab}\, a_b = 0,$$
$$\frac{\kappa}{\hbar}\, e^{-i\delta}\, A_{ab}^*\, a_a + \left(\omega' - \frac{1}{2}\Delta\right) a_b = 0. \tag{72}$$

These equations can be solved only if the frequency ω' is chosen so that the determinant of the coefficients vanishes. Thus ω' obeys the equation

$$\omega'^2 = \frac{1}{4}\Delta^2 + \frac{\kappa^2}{\hbar^2}\,|A_{ab}|^2. \tag{73}$$

This equation is much simpler than the corresponding (54), and consequently the remainder of the calculation is fairly brief. We shall first work out the relations obeyed by the coefficients a_a, a_b. Depending on the choice of sign in the expression for ω', we get

$$a_a^+ = -\hbar \, e^{i\delta} \frac{|\omega'| - \frac{1}{2}\delta}{\kappa \, A_{ab}^*} \, a_b^+,$$

$$a_a^- = \hbar \, e^{i\delta} \frac{|\omega'| + \frac{1}{2}\delta}{\kappa \, A_{ab}^*} \, a_b^-. \tag{74}$$

If we let the perturbing potential tend to zero, the "$+$" solution is the one in which we have a pure b state, and the "$-$" solution goes over into a pure a state.

We shall now consider an initial state that is purely a. In that case, we must choose our two coefficients a_b^- and a_b^+ so that the initial amplitude of the b state vanishes:

$$a_b^+ + a_b^- = 0. \tag{75}$$

We can now easily determine the amplitudes of both states for all times other than $t = 0$. The two expressions are

$$c_a = 2 \, e^{\frac{i}{2}\Delta t} \, e^{i\delta} \frac{\hbar \, a_b^-}{\kappa \, A_{ab}^*} \, (|\omega'| \cos |\omega'|t + \frac{i}{2}\Delta \sin |\omega'|t),$$

$$c_b = -2i \, a_b^- \, e^{-\frac{i}{2}\Delta t} \sin |\omega'|t. \tag{76}$$

a_b^- must be chosen so that initially $|c_a|^2$ equals unity. With this normalization, we find after a brief calculation that the absolute squares of the coefficients c_a and c_b are, respectively,

$$|c_a|^2 = 1 - |c_b|^2$$

and
$$|c_b|^2 = \frac{\epsilon^2}{\hbar^2} |A_{ab}|^2 \frac{\sin^2 |\omega'|t}{\omega'^2}. \tag{77}$$

The result just obtained is approximate insofar as we have disregarded the contributions of all rapidly oscillating terms in the equations. Nevertheless, formulas (77) are quite adequate for most purposes. They give information both on how large the maximum probability for transitions can become and at which rate the probability for the induced state (b) increases. Complete transition to the new state will take place (at some particular time) only if Δ vanishes, that is, in accordance with eq. (69), if resonance is perfect. Even then, transitions will occur back and forth at a regular rhythm. With imperfect resonance, there is always a finite minimum for the probability of finding state a.

The speed with which the state of maximum b-probability is reached depends, of course, on the frequency parameter ω', which is given by eq. (73). This frequency is always finite if there is a finite perturbing force constant κA_{ab}, but it has its least value for perfect resonance. If the resonance is very poor, the oscillations will be very rapid but small in amplitude, and they will not differ from any of the other small oscillations that we have systematically disregarded.

These results have been confirmed and applied in great detail in the so-called *molecular-beam resonance method* initiated by I. I. Rabi and coworkers.[1] In this method, a molecular beam that is homogeneous with respect to the velocity of the particles and, as far as possible, with respect to their internal states, is passed through a magnetic or electric field oscillating at a controlled frequency. Transitions of the molecules are observed as a function either of the perturbing frequency or, very often, of the level separation, which itself is a magnetically or electrically induced perturbation separation and can be varied continuously by the experimenter. These experiments have been used for precision determinations of magnetic dipole and electric quadrupole moments.

We shall not go through the complete theory of the Rabi method but shall apply our results to the transitions in an atom induced by a field of electromagnetic *radiation*. Let us consider some atom whose electronic states are completely determined by some Schrödinger equation with a Hamiltonian $\overset{0}{H}$ and with certain wave functions $\psi_k = \phi_k \exp\left(- \frac{i}{\hbar} E_k t \right)$ and energy levels E_k. We assume that this atom is acted on by a field of radiation, with all frequencies and all directions of propagation represented, and we ask what transitions will be observed if the atom is known to be initially in a state a. Naturally, transitions may take place to all other states, and therefore we shall ask more particularly at which rate transitions occur into the state b.

In carrying out the calculations, we shall use an approach that, strictly speaking, is inconsistent. Though we shall treat the atom quantum-mechanically, we shall deal with the radiation field as if

---

[1] Rabi, Millman, Kusch, and Zacharias, *Phys. Rev.*, **55**, 526 (1939).

the electric and magnetic field strengths were ordinary classical quantities. Actually, we know that the radiation field itself must have quantum properties; probably the strongest evidence to this effect is the success of Planck's theory of cavity radiation. Nevertheless, the interaction between an atom and radiation can be represented fairly well by the "semiclassical" method that we shall follow here, except that we are unable to obtain a reasonable theory of the *spontaneous emission*, the fact that an excited atom will drop spontaneously into a lower state and emit a photon in the process. The consistent treatment of the radiation problem requires considerably more conceptual and mathematical tools than we shall bring to bear on the problem; if the reader will keep in mind the limited validity of the derivations that will follow, the semiclassical treatment also is rather instructive in teaching us how time-dependent problems are to be treated in quantum mechanics.

If we go back for a moment to expression (77), we find that initially the state b is produced at a vanishing rate; only when the probability of finding b is already finite will this probability continue to increase (for a while) at a nonvanishing rate. In the case of incident *radiation*, which in nature is never strictly monochromatic, we can and shall obtain right from the start a rate of formation for b that is different from zero. We shall represent the incident radiation by means of a large sum of single-frequency components, thus:

$$\kappa \overset{1}{V}_{ab} \equiv \kappa \int \phi_a^* \overset{1}{V} \phi_b \, dV = \sum_s \alpha_s \cos (\omega_s t + \delta_s). \qquad (78)$$

In radiation as it occurs in nature, the phase relations between different frequency components are completely random. They must be, because any nonrandom relationship would have to single out a particular origin in time (say an instant when all different vibrations or waves are in phase with each other). As for the amplitudes, we cannot work out a connected theory unless there is a possibility of defining an intensity per unit band width of frequency, some quantity of the dimension of ergs per cm^3 per cycle. Since wave intensities are generally proportional to the squared amplitude (rather than the amplitude itself), we shall assume that for a band width chosen neither too small nor too large it is possible to define a quantity $J(\omega)$,

$$J(\omega) = \frac{1}{2\Omega} \sum_s \alpha_s^2 \qquad (\omega - \Omega \leq \omega_s \leq \omega + \Omega), \qquad (79)$$

and that J is a smooth function of its argument. The actual energy density per unit band width will always be proportional to J, but the constant of proportionality will depend on the particular type of wave considered.

We shall now consider an instant of time $t > 0$ but close enough to $t = 0$ to make the probability of finding b still very small. In that case, because of the randomness of the phases, we may assume that the probability of finding state b is simply the algebraic sum of all the probabilities induced by the individual single-frequency waves, or, according to eq. (77),

$$|c_b|^2 = \frac{1}{\hbar^2} \sum_s \alpha_s^2 \frac{\sin^2 |\omega_s'|t}{\omega_s'^2} \qquad \left(\omega_s'^2 = \frac{1}{4}\Delta_s^2 + \frac{1}{\hbar^2}\alpha_s^2 \right). \qquad (80)$$

We cannot carry out this summation rigorously, but we shall determine an approximate expression. First of all, if the amplitudes of the individual waves are sufficiently small, we may replace, for small values of t only, ω_s' by $\frac{1}{2}\Delta_s$. Obviously, for large values of Δ_s, this substitution is harmless. For small values of Δ_s, that is, near the resonance peak, the error made in ω_s' is considerable, but not the error in the value of $(\sin |\omega_s'|t/\omega_s')^2$, since this value tends to t^2, regardless of the value of ω_s'. Thus the substitution

$$|c_b|^2 \sim \frac{1}{\hbar^2} \sum_s \alpha_s^2 \frac{\sin^2 \frac{1}{2}\Delta_s t}{\frac{1}{4}\Delta_s^2} \qquad (81)$$

for the better formula (80) is actually quite harmless as long as t is sufficiently small, and we shall be interested primarily in the value of expression (80) as t tends to zero.

Next, using the defining equation (79), we shall replace the sum in (80) by an integral,

$$|c_b|^2 \sim \frac{1}{\hbar^2} \int_{\omega=-\infty}^{\infty} J(\omega) \frac{\sin^2 [\frac{1}{2}(|\omega_{ab}| - \omega)t]\, d\omega}{\frac{1}{4}(|\omega_{ab}| - \omega)^2} \qquad \left[\omega_{ab} = \frac{1}{\hbar}(E_a - E_b) \right]. \qquad (82)$$

In this integral, the factor J is a smooth function of the argument, while the other factor has a sharply peaked maximum for $\Delta = 0$.

We can get a pretty good approximation by putting J in front of the integral, giving its argument the value at the peak:

$$|c_b|^2 \sim \frac{1}{\hbar^2} J(|\omega_{ab}|) \int_{-\infty}^{\infty} \frac{\sin^2 \frac{\omega'}{2} t}{\frac{1}{4}\omega'^2} d\omega'. \tag{83}$$

Thus we end up with the expression

$$|c_b|^2 \sim \frac{2\pi}{\hbar^2} J(|\omega_{ab}|) t \qquad \left(\int_{-\infty}^{\infty} \frac{\sin^2 x \, dx}{x^2} = \pi \right). \tag{84}$$

As a result of our introduction of broad-band radiation, the probability of the state b, being zero initially, has a nonvanishing rate of increase. This rate is, at least at first,

$$\frac{d|c_b^2|}{dt} \bigg|_{t=0} = \frac{2\pi}{\hbar^2} J(|\omega_{ab}|). \tag{85}$$

Equation (85) holds both when the atom is raised to a higher energy level and when it is dropped to a lower level. We call these two processes *absorption* of radiation and *induced emission*, respectively. That $|c_b^2|$ increases linearly with time (instead of quadratically) can be understood in such a way that at first a relatively broad frequency band causes transitions from a to b, but this band narrows down very rapidly as the trigonometric function in eq. (77) begins to decrease. This rapid contraction of the contributing band is responsible for the modified dependence of $|c_b^2|$ on the time t.

Equation (85) completes our task, except insofar as we have yet to relate the function J to the radiation intensity per unit band width of an electromagnetic radiation field. In electrostatic (Gaussian) units, the contribution of a single-frequency plane wave to the energy density of the radiation field equals

$$I_s = \frac{1}{8\pi} \mathcal{Q}_s^2, \tag{86}$$

$$\mathcal{Q}_s = \max |\mathbf{E}_s| = \max |\mathbf{B}_s|.$$

$\mathcal{Q}_s$ is the amplitude of both the electric and the magnetic vectors. The total energy density U per unit band width of a radiation field is related to the quantities $\mathcal{Q}_s$ in the same manner as the function J is related to the amplitudes α_s by means of eq. (79). Our task is to relate the amplitude of a single plane wave of amplitude a_s to the value of the resulting expression α_s, as it occurs in eq. (78). We shall confine ourselves to the consideration of a single bound electron.

Such an electron is bound to its atom by some conservative potential. In the presence of an electromagnetic field, and in the nonrelativistic approximation (which for most purposes is perfectly adequate in the realm of atomic energies), the total Hamiltonian of such an electron, without quantum-physical modifications, is

$$H = \frac{1}{2\,m}\left(\mathbf{p} - \frac{e}{c}\mathbf{A}\right)^2 + e\,\Phi + V(\mathbf{x}) \tag{87}$$

[cf. M&E, p. 241, eq. (9.23)]. The relationship between the canonical momentum vector and the velocity is given by the relation

$$\mathbf{p} = m\,\dot{\mathbf{x}} + \frac{e}{c}\mathbf{A}. \tag{88}$$

In other words, in the presence of a magnetic potential $\mathbf{A}$, the momentum differs from the usual mechanical expression, but the difference is very small. We can represent an electromagnetic plane wave solely by means of a vector potential $\mathbf{A}$, without a scalar potential, with the added condition that the divergence of $\mathbf{A}$ vanish:

$$\text{div } \mathbf{A} = 0. \tag{89}$$

With these assumptions, and for small radiation intensities, we can set the Hamiltonian expression as

$$H = \frac{1}{2\,m}\mathbf{p}^2 + V(\mathbf{x}) - \frac{e}{m\,c}\mathbf{p}\cdot\mathbf{A}. \tag{90}$$

In this expression, we shall treat the last term as the perturbing term.

If we go over to the quantum-mechanical treatment, the Schrödinger equation that corresponds to the nonquantum Hamiltonian (90) is

$$-\frac{\hbar^2}{2\,m}\nabla^2\psi + V(\mathbf{x})\,\psi - \frac{e\,\hbar}{m\,c\,i}\mathbf{A}\cdot\nabla\psi + \frac{\hbar}{i}\frac{\partial\psi}{\partial t} = 0. \tag{91}$$

A question might arise as to whether the partial derivative in the perturbing term should not include the vector potential, but in view of the condition (89), such an inclusion would add nothing.

Evidently, if ϕ_a and ϕ_b are two solutions of the unperturbed time-independent Schrödinger equation, then $\kappa \overset{1}{V}_{ab}$ is given by the expression

$$\kappa \overset{1}{V}_{ab} = -\frac{e\,\hbar}{m\,c\,i} \int \phi_a^* \, \mathbf{A} \cdot \nabla \phi_b \, dV. \tag{92}$$

This expression can be further transformed and then assumes a form that is rather suggestive of its physical significance.

First we shall make use of the fact that the wave length of visible light (which is responsible for most of the atomic transitions) exceeds atomic dimensions by a factor of the order of 10^3 and that, therefore, $\mathbf{A}$ is virtually constant throughout the domain in which the other two factors in the integrand of eq. (92) are significantly different from zero. Thus we may place $\mathbf{A}$ in front of the integral.

Because of the connecting equations

$$\mathbf{B} = \operatorname{curl} \mathbf{A}, \qquad \mathbf{E} = -\frac{1}{c} \frac{\partial \mathbf{A}}{\partial t}, \tag{93}$$

the amplitude of the electric field strength is ω/c times the amplitude of the vector potential. If the amplitude of the electric field strength is again denoted by α_s and if the unit direction of the electric field strength (which depends on its polarization) is denoted by $\mathbf{s}_s$, then eq. (92) turns into

$$\alpha_s = -\frac{\hbar}{i} \frac{e}{m\,\omega} \, \alpha_s \, \mathbf{s}_s \cdot \int \phi_a^* \, \nabla \phi_b \, dV. \tag{94}$$

In this expression we must now evaluate the integral

$$\mathbf{p}_{ab} \equiv \frac{\hbar}{i} \int \phi_a^* \, \nabla \phi_b \, dV. \tag{95}$$

To do so, we may attempt to form the analogy in wave mechanics to the classical principle that the momentum is m times the velocity, and that the velocity is the time derivative of the "radius vector" (the combination of the coordinates of the particle). Accordingly, we shall form the time derivative of the expression

$$\mathbf{x}_{ab} = \int \psi_a^* \, \mathbf{x} \, \psi_b \, dV = e^{\frac{i}{\hbar}(E_a - E_b)t} \int \phi_a^* \, \mathbf{x} \, \phi_b \, dV. \tag{96}$$

If we make use of the fact that the wave functions ψ_a, ψ_b obey the unperturbed Schrödinger equation, we may proceed as follows:

$$\frac{d\mathbf{x}_{ab}}{dt} = \frac{i}{\hbar}(E_a - E_b)\mathbf{x}_{ab}$$

$$= \frac{i}{\hbar}\int\left[\left(V\psi_a^* - \frac{\hbar^2}{2m}\nabla^2\psi_a^*\right)\mathbf{x}\,\psi_b - \psi_a^*\,\mathbf{x}\left(V\psi_b - \frac{\hbar^2}{2m}\nabla^2\psi_b\right)\right]dV$$

$$= \frac{\hbar}{2im}\int(\nabla^2\psi_a^*\,\mathbf{x}\,\psi_b - \psi_a^*\,\mathbf{x}\,\nabla^2\psi_b)\,dV$$

$$= \frac{\hbar}{2im}\int(\psi_a^*\,\nabla\psi_b - \nabla\psi_a^*\,\psi_b)\,dV$$

$$= \frac{\hbar}{im}\int\psi_a^*\,\nabla\psi_b\,dV. \tag{97}$$

Our result is that

$$\mathbf{p}_{ab} = m\frac{d\mathbf{x}_{ab}}{dt} = \frac{i}{\hbar}m(E_a - E_b)\,\mathbf{x}_{ab} \tag{98}$$

and

$$\alpha_s = -\frac{e}{\omega}(E_a - E_b)\,\mathfrak{C}_s\,\mathbf{s}_s\cdot\mathbf{x}_{ab} \sim -e\hbar\,\mathfrak{C}_s\,\mathbf{s}_s\cdot\mathbf{x}_{ab} \qquad (\omega\approx\omega_{ab}). \tag{99}$$

If we are to substitute this expression for α_s into eq. (85) and thus to obtain the final expression for the rate at which the probability for state b increases (the rate of transitions, in customary terminology), we must be able to tell something about the collimation and the polarization of the incident beam of radiation. If we assume, first, that the beam is perfectly collimated and that it is also perfectly polarized, then the vector $\mathbf{s}_s$ is the same for all the component plane waves, and we may replace the dot product by the magnitude of the vector $\mathbf{x}_{ab}$, multiplied by the cosine of the angle θ between the vector $\mathbf{x}_{ab}$ and the direction of the electric vector of the incident polarization. In that case, using the relationship between the individual amplitudes $\mathfrak{C}_s$ and the radiation intensity U, we get

$$\frac{d|c_b|^2}{dt} = 8\pi e^2\hbar^2\cos^2\theta\,|\mathbf{x}_{ab}|^2\,U. \tag{100}$$

If, on the other hand, the radiation is completely random, we must average over all possible values of the angle θ from 0 to π, and we get, instead of eq. (100),

$$\frac{d|c_b|^2}{dt} = \tfrac{8}{3}\pi \, e^2 \, \hbar^2 \, |\mathbf{x}_{ab}|^2 \, U. \tag{101}$$

There remains only one question to discuss, and that is the properties and the significance of the integral that we have denoted by $\mathbf{x}_{ab}$.

Let us consider a single electron in a central-force field bound to the origin of the coordinate system.   In spherical coordinates, we have found previously that the wave functions corresponding to stationary states can be represented as products of three factors, the first of which is a function of r only, the second a function of θ, and the last one a function of ϕ.   The integral called for by eq. (96) can also be carried out as the product of three separate integrals over the three spherical coordinates, inasmuch as each of the three rectangular coordinates x, y, and z, is also a product:

$$x = r \cos \theta \cos \phi,$$
$$y = r \cos \theta \sin \phi, \tag{102}$$
$$z = r \sin \theta.$$

The question arises under what circumstances any one of the three integrals x_{ab}, y_{ab}, or z_{ab} may be expected to be different from zero. The answer is particularly simple if we consider only radiation incident along the z-axis.   In that case, the electric vector is bound to lie in the x,y-plane, and the component z_{ab} of the vector $\mathbf{x}_{ab}$ will certainly be perpendicular to the vector $\mathbf{s}_s$ and therefore will make no contribution.   Consequently, for the integral over the angle ϕ, we have to evaluate the two single integrals

$$X_{ab} = \int_0^{2\pi} e^{i(m_b - m_a)\phi} \cos \phi \, d\phi,$$
$$Y_{ab} = \int_0^{2\pi} e^{i(m_b - m_a)\phi} \sin \phi \, d\phi. \tag{103}$$

If we replace the two trigonometric functions by their complex representations, it is clear immediately that either of the two integrals (103) can be nonzero only if the two quantum numbers m_a and m_b differ exactly by 1. By means of a similar consideration of the integral over the angle θ, it is possible to show that no component of the vector $\mathbf{x}_{ab}$ will differ from zero unless the quantum numbers l_a and l_b differ exactly by 1.

Our whole theory is only approximative, to be sure. But to the extent that it is valid, we find that electromagnetic radiation will cause transitions only between states for which the changes in l and m obey the *selection rules*

$$\Delta l = \pm 1, \qquad \Delta m = \pm 1. \tag{104}$$

In fact, though transitions that disobey these selection rules are found occasionally, spectral lines that correspond to such "forbidden" transitions are always weak, because their occurrence is due to a higher approximation.

Now for the significance of $\mathbf{x}_{ab}$. Since the absolute square of a wave function is to be interpreted as the probability density for the electron if it is in the state described by that function, the integral $\mathbf{x}_{aa}$ represents the center of mass of the probability distribution. In a central-force field and in a stationary state, this center of mass always coincides with the origin because the absolute square of the angular parts of the wave function is centrosymmetric (the value at two directly opposite points is always the same). But if we form a nonstationary state that is composed of only the states a and b, then, because of the different time-dependence of these two states, we shall have "beats" with the angular frequency ω_{ab}, and we shall also have an off-center probability distribution that circulates about the center at the beat frequency. Such a mixed state will therefore embody an oscillating probability distribution for the charge that is capable of interacting with an incident electromagnetic wave. But the selection rules tell us that only mixtures between certain states will lead to such off-center distributions. Other mixtures may, however, lead to distributions with an oscillating quadrupole moment or higher moment of the probability distribution, and these higher moments may interact with the radiation field in higher approximations of the calculations. The "permitted" transitions, those which satisfy the selection rules (104), are also often called *dipole transitions*, for obvious reasons.

Problems

1. Discuss the most common examples of quantum-theoretical models (particle in a box, harmonic oscillator, and so on) from the point of view of the WBK method of approximate treatment.

2. In the actual solution of problems involving several degrees of freedom, it is always important to find coordinate systems into which the problem "separates." Discuss the concept of separability from the point of view of the nodal surfaces of characteristic solutions.

3. Consider the problem of scattering in an inverse-square field (Rutherford scattering) in terms of the WBK approximation method. Construct first a system of Huygens wave fronts by solving the classical Hamilton-Jacobi equation of the system corresponding to an incident plane wave. By solving the "conservation law" (6) as well, you can construct an approximate wave function.

4. Modify Problem 3 by assuming in addition to the inverse-square force law a small, spherically symmetric perturbing potential, such as $r^{-1}e^{-kr}$ (Yukawa potential). The physical significance of such a potential is that scattering under the combined influence of Coulomb forces and nuclear forces probably obeys such a law.

5. Using time-independent perturbation theory, work out the first-order Zeeman effect on the assumption that the wave functions of the unperturbed atom are perfectly known.

6. Consider a nonstationary solution of a problem involving degeneracies removed by a perturbing potential. Obtain approximate solutions by means of the WBK method and study the motion of the system of nodal surfaces under the influence of the perturbing potential. Compare your results with those obtained by means of time-dependent perturbation calculations (Section 11.4).

Chapter 12

The Abstract Theory

So far, we have presented quantum mechanics in terms of the early Schrödinger theory, which was formed in close analogy to the optics and diffraction theory of classical physics. In spite of this classical background, we found at every turn that the Schrödinger theory is not a classical theory, that it operates with concepts alien to the classical physicist. For a more complete understanding of the new theory, it is of the greatest importance to ascertain to what extent the wave picture is essential to its physical content and to what extent accidental. In this chapter we shall find that within the wave-mechanical formulation there is hidden a more abstract theory, a theory capable of many representations, of which wave mechanics is just one. An understanding of the abstract theory has made it possible to modify quantum mechanics further, to endow it with features that possess no classical analogue, and thus to incorporate not only the electronic spin but to assign to the forces between nuclear particles new properties (*exchange forces*) which are apparently required by the properties of the atomic nuclei but which are exceedingly hard to picture in terms of any classical model.

12.1. Observables

To penetrate to the core of the new physics, we shall ask ourselves which features or statements of quantum mechanics correspond directly to physical facts. The wave functions themselves cannot be determined or observed experimentally, but energy levels can. So likewise can configurations, values for the momentum, the angular momentum, and many other physical properties that are meaningful in terms of both classical and quantum physics. Then how does quantum physics predict the value of such an *observable?* So far, we have not given a uniform answer to this question. As the first step of our analysis, we shall collect the partial answers given up to now and then attempt to discover their common denominator.

Let us begin with the configuration of a mechanical system, that is, with the individual coordinates. We find that in general a system does not have a well-defined configuration but rather a probability distribution of all possible configurations. The only exception, if we want to call it that, is a wave function that is a Dirac delta function; with a delta function for any particular coordinate, that coordinate is known and predictable with certainty. But the delta function cannot be normalized, the integral over its square always diverges, and hence most of the integrals required to determine the expectation values of other observables diverge. Ordinarily, we must exclude non-normalizable functions as wave functions.

For any other wave function, we cannot predict with certainty the result of an experiment measuring a particular coordinate x_k, but we can predict the distribution that will be obtained when measurements are carried out on a large number of identical systems. The mean value of x_k is given by the integral

$$\bar{x}_k = \int_V \psi^* x_k \psi \, dV, \tag{1}$$

the integral to be extended over the whole configuration space. If we wish merely to ascertain the rms width of the probability distribution for the coordinate x_k, we may do so by forming the expectation value of its square, $\overline{x_k^2}$, and subtracting from it the square of its expectation value,

$$\overline{\Delta x_k^2} \equiv \overline{(x_k - \overline{x_k})^2} = \overline{x_k^2} - \overline{x_k}^2$$

$$= \int_V \psi^* (x_k - \overline{x_k})^2 \psi \, dV \tag{2}$$

$$= \int_V \psi^* x_k^2 \psi \, dV - \left(\int_V \psi^* x_k \psi \, dV \right)^2 \geq 0.$$

This expression cannot become negative, and it will be different from zero for all wave functions that are square-integrable.

Of course there is more to a distribution function than merely its centroid $\overline{x_k}$ and its rms spread. If we wish to ascertain all its properties, we must determine the answers to an infinity of questions, all of which may be put into this form; "What is the probability of the coordinate x_k being found in a specified range of values?" If the specified range is denoted by the limits m and n, then the answer to the question is furnished by an integral having the form

$$P(m, n) = \int_V \psi^* f(x_k) \, \psi \, dV,$$
$$f(x_k) = 1, \qquad x_k \, \varepsilon \, (m, n), \qquad (3)$$
$$f(x_k) = 0, \qquad x_k \, \text{\reflectbox{ε}} \, (m, n).$$

The function $f(x_k)$ is, to be sure, not analytic or even continuous, but it is otherwise a well-defined function of its argument. Naturally, this function must be constructed separately for any range (m, n) conceivable, but it exists, and thus all conceivable questions concerning the probability distribution of x_k can be answered by means of integrals to be extended over the whole configuration space.

Let us now turn to another type of observable, a linear momentum component p_k. In Section 9.3, we found that wave equations can be formulated in momentum space just as well as in configuration space. If we stick to the single-particle case and treat it in rectangular coordinates, we know, moreover, that the wave function $A(\mathbf{p}, t)$ in momentum space will be normalized automatically if its Fourier transform in configuration space, $\psi(\mathbf{x}, t)$ is normalized, because

$$\int |A|^2 \, \mathbf{dp} = \int |\psi|^2 \, \mathbf{dx},$$
$$A(\mathbf{p}, t) = (2\pi\hbar)^{-3/2} \int_{\mathbf{x}} \psi(\mathbf{x}, t) \, e^{-\frac{i}{\hbar}\mathbf{p}\cdot\mathbf{x}} \, \mathbf{dx}. \qquad (4)$$

This relationship is a mathematical identity that forms an integral part of Fourier theory. Thus there is nothing more natural than to assume that the probability of finding the momentum component p_k within a given range (r, s) is given by the integral

$$P(r, s) = \int A^* f(p_k) \, A \, \mathbf{dp},$$
$$f(p_k) = 1, \qquad p_k \, \varepsilon \, (r, s), \qquad (5)$$
$$f(p_k) = 0, \qquad p_k \, \text{\reflectbox{ε}} \, (r, s),$$

to be extended over all momentum space! This was, in fact, the attitude adopted in Section 9.2. By the same token, the expectation value of an arbitrary power of the momentum $\overline{p_k^N}$, is given by the integral

$$\overline{p_k^N} = \int A^* \, p_k^N \, A \; \mathbf{dp}. \tag{6}$$

We shall now transform this integral into one that is defined in configuration space. If we introduce again the Fourier transform of the function A, which is the function ψ, we obtain, after a number of transformations very similar to those carried out in Section 9.2 in the derivation of the expression (9.38),

$$
\begin{aligned}
p_k^N &= \int \psi^* \left(\frac{\hbar}{i}\right)^N \frac{\partial^N \psi}{\partial x_k^N} \, \mathbf{dx}, \\
\overline{p_1^{N_1} \, p_2^{N_2} \, p_3^{N_3}} &= \int \psi^* \left(\frac{\hbar}{i}\right)^{N_1+N_2+N_3} \frac{\partial^{N_1+N_2+N_3} \psi}{\partial x_1^{N_1} \, \partial x_2^{N_2} \, \partial x_3^{N_3}} \, \mathbf{dx}.
\end{aligned}
\tag{7}
$$

These integrals are somewhat similar to integrals (1), (2), and (3). They differ in that in (7) the expectation value is formed by an integral in which ψ is not multiplied by certain functions of x_k but is subjected to the differentiation operator $\dfrac{\hbar}{i}\dfrac{\partial}{\partial x_k}$ as often as is required by the power N of the corresponding momentum component p_k.

Expression (7) permits us to derive a formula for every analytic function of the momentum components $f(\mathbf{p})$, provided that the series of integrals (7) converges. This convergence depends, of course, both on the function f and on the wave function ψ. In particular, step functions with respect to momentum components of type (5) can usually be approximated by polynomials in p_k to any desired degree of accuracy in any finite domain. If the wave function ψ drops off fast enough toward infinity, say exponentially, then this domain can always be chosen so that on the outside the contribution to the integrals (7) (of which in the case of an approximation by polynomials there is only a finite number) is less than an arbitrary small amount ϵ. Thus in principle we may use the wave function ψ in configuration space to determine in complete detail the probability distribution of the momentum components. The less detailed questions as to the centroid of the distribution and its rms spread can, of course, be dealt with by working out just two of the integrals (7).

We shall now consider a third important physical quantity of a mechanical system, its energy. We shall confine our attention first to the type of system in which all possible states of the system are bound states. In the harmonic oscillator, just one example of this type, all the solutions of the time-independent Schrödinger equation (10.7) are discrete, normalizable wave functions ϕ_k, each belonging to a particular energy level E_k (some of which may coincide).

Because of the expansion theorem discussed in Section 11.2, the most general solution of the time-dependent Schrödinger equation (9.57) can in this case be represented as a series expansion in terms of the stationary solutions,

$$\psi = \sum_k c_k \psi_k = \sum_k c_k \phi_k e^{-\frac{i}{\hbar}E_k t}. \tag{8}$$

If ψ is to be normalized, then because of the orthonormality properties of the ϕ_k (cf. Section 11.2 again), the coefficients c_k satisfy the relationship

$$\sum_k |c_k|^2 = 1. \tag{9}$$

The probability of finding the kth state in an experiment designed to determine the state of a system equals the absolute square of the appropriate coefficient, $|c_k|^2$. Therefore the probability distribution for the quantity E is discontinuous, and the probability of finding E_k equals $|c_k|^2$ (if that level is single; in a degenerate level, the probability simply equals the sum of the squared coefficients belonging to that level). If we wish to determine the expectation value for any function of the energy, $f(E)$, we must set

$$\overline{f(E)} = \sum_k |c_k|^2 f(E_k). \tag{10}$$

On the other hand, we can also attempt to get the expectation value of the energy by means of another approach. In Section 9.3, we replaced the energy E of classical physics by the differential operation $-\frac{\hbar}{i}\frac{\partial}{\partial t}$ in order to obtain the wave equation. In analogy to expressions (7), we might try to define the expectation value of the function E^N by the expression

$$\overline{E^N} = \int \psi^* \left(-\frac{\hbar}{i}\right)^N \frac{\partial^N \psi}{\partial t^N} \, dx \tag{11}$$

and to approximate arbitrary functions $f(E)$ by means of polynomials. We shall find that the two expressions (10) and (11) are equivalent. If we substitute the expansion (8) for the wave function ψ, we get

$$-\frac{\hbar}{i}\frac{\partial\psi}{\partial t} = \sum_k c_k E_k \phi_k e^{-\frac{i}{\hbar}E_k t} = \sum_k c_k E_k \psi_k \tag{12}$$

and

$$\left(-\frac{\hbar}{i}\right)^N \int \psi^* \frac{\partial^N \psi}{\partial t^N} \, d\mathbf{x} = \int \left(\sum_{k'} c_{k'}^* \, \phi_{k'}^* \, e^{\frac{i}{\hbar}E_{k'} t}\right)$$
$$\left(\sum_k c_k E_k^N \phi_k e^{-\frac{i}{\hbar}E_k t}\right) d\mathbf{x}$$
$$= \sum_{k'}\sum_k c_{k'}^* \, c_k \, E_k^N \, e^{\frac{i}{\hbar}(E_{k'}-E_k)t} \int \phi_{k'}^* \, \phi_k \, d\mathbf{x}$$
$$= \sum_k |c_k|^2 \, E_k^N, \tag{13}$$

because of the orthonormality relations between the characteristic functions. Thus the representation of the expectation value of $f(E)$ by means of an integral patterned after the earlier integrals (3) and (7) is equivalent to the representation by means of a series.

We may attempt to use this result in reverse and see whether we can also obtain series expressions for the expectation values of coordinate or momentum functions. All we have to do to follow up this idea is to introduce into integrals (3) and (7) the series expansion (8). Let us start with an integral of the type

$$\bar{f} = \int \psi^* f(\mathbf{x}) \psi \, d\mathbf{x}, \tag{14}$$

where $f(\mathbf{x})$ is to be an arbitrary function defined on configuration space. If we introduce the expansion (8), we get, after carrying out a calculation similar to eq. (13),

$$\bar{f} = \sum_i \sum_k c_i^* f_{ik} c_k, \tag{15}$$

where $\qquad f_{ik} \equiv \int_{\mathbf{x}} \phi_i^* f(\mathbf{x}) \phi_k \, d\mathbf{x}.$

In this instance, the expectation value f is determined by a double sum that cannot be reduced to a single sum. The continuous function f in the integral has been replaced by a square array of numbers f_{ik}. If f is a real function (as it must be if it is to represent an observable physical quantity), these numbers satisfy the relationship

$$f_{ik} = f_{ki}^*, \tag{16}$$

which is an obvious consequence of their definition. We shall call a square array of numbers like f_{ik} a *matrix*. If a matrix satisfies relationship (16), we shall call it a *Hermitian* matrix. Bilinear forms in a set of numbers c_k and the conjugate complex set c_k^* will have real values regardless of the choice of the c_k if and only if the matrix of the coefficients of the form is Hermitian. We can prove this assertion by comparing the form with its conjugate complex,

$$\bar{f}^* = \left(\sum_{i,k} c_i^* f_{ik} c_k \right)^* = \sum_{i,k} c_k^* f_{ik}^* c_i$$

$$= \sum_{i,k} c_i^* f_{ki}^* c_k, \tag{17}$$

$$\bar{f} - \bar{f}^* = \sum_{i,k} c_i^* (f_{ik} - f_{ki}^*) c_k.$$

The numbers f_{ik} are determined by the integrals indicated in eq. (15). But is it possible to construct these numbers for complicated functions by going back to simpler building blocks? We can venture a fairly general answer by giving the rules for determining the matrices corresponding to sums and to products. First, if the function f is the sum of two or more terms $a, b, \cdots$,

$$f(x) = a(x) + b(x) + \cdots, \tag{18}$$

then the matrix element f_{ik} is the sum of the corresponding matrix elements $a_{ik}, b_{ik}, \cdots$,

$$f_{ik} = a_{ik} + b_{ik} + \cdots. \tag{19}$$

If the function f is equal to the product ab, and if the matrices a_{ik} and b_{ik} are known, we can proceed as follows: Let us set

$$f_{ik} = \int \phi_i^* \, a(\mathbf{x}) \, b(\mathbf{x}) \, \phi_k \, \mathbf{dx}. \tag{20}$$

Into this expression we shall introduce the matrix elements corresponding to the two factors a and b. First we determine the expansion of the function $b(\mathbf{x})\,\phi_k(\mathbf{x})$ in terms of the orthonormal functions ϕ_l:

$$b(\mathbf{x})\,\phi_k(\mathbf{x}) = \sum_l d_l\,\phi_l(\mathbf{x}). \tag{21}$$

The coefficients d_l are as yet unknown. But we can determine them easily if we multiply both sides of eq. (21) by one function ϕ_m^* and then integrate. On the two sides of the equation we get

$$b_{mk} = d_m, \tag{22}$$

and therefore

$$b(\mathbf{x})\,\phi_k(\mathbf{x}) = \sum_l b_{lk}\,\phi_l(\mathbf{x}). \tag{23}$$

If we substitute this expression back into integral (20), we get immediately

$$\begin{aligned}
f_{ik} &= \sum_l \int \phi_i^*\,a(\mathbf{x})\phi_l\,\mathbf{dx}\,b_{lk} \\
&= \sum_l a_{il}\,b_{lk},
\end{aligned} \tag{24}$$

and that is our result. To the extent that arbitrary functions of the coordinates can be approximated by polynomials, their corresponding matrices can be constructed, at least approximatively, from the basic matrices x_{ik}, y_{ik}, and z_{ik}.

In view of the fact that the sequence of factors ab or ba in the integral (20) is immaterial, the matrices a_{ik} and b_{ik} satisfy the relationship

$$\sum_l a_{il}\,b_{lk} = \sum_l b_{il}\,a_{lk}. \tag{25}$$

Two matrices with this property are said to *commute* with each other. We have now found that all matrices that correspond to functions of the coordinates commute with each other and that all those which correspond to real functions of the coordinates are Hermitian.

We shall now turn to the expectation values of *functions of the momenta*. Instead of going through a very lengthy calculation, we may simply define the matrices of functions of the momentum components, $f(p)$, in terms of integrals to be carried out in momentum space. To this end, we must introduce the Fourier transforms of the functions $\phi_k(\mathbf{x})$ in momentum space, the $\alpha_k(\mathbf{p})$. In momentum space the α_k also form an orthonormal system of functions, and all the relationships that we have derived for the matrices of coordinate functions will also hold for the matrices of momentum functions.

Of course it is also possible to define these matrices in terms of integrals in configuration space, and we shall show that the two definitions are equivalent. That is, we assert that

$$F_{ik} = \int_{\mathbf{p}} \alpha_i^* F(\mathbf{p}) \, \alpha_k \, d\mathbf{p}$$
$$= \int_{\mathbf{x}} \phi_i^* F\left(\frac{\hbar}{i} \nabla\right) \phi_k \, d\mathbf{x}, \tag{26}$$

where, in analogy to eq. (9.26), $\alpha_k(\mathbf{p})$ is defined by the equation

$$\alpha_k(\mathbf{p}) = (2\pi\hbar)^{-\frac{3}{2}} \int_{\mathbf{x}} \phi_k(\mathbf{x}) \, e^{-\frac{i}{\hbar}\mathbf{p}\cdot\mathbf{x}} \, d\mathbf{x}. \tag{27}$$

Because of the manner in which we can construct F_{ik} from the matrices for the three rectangular momentum components, we may confine our proof to the latter. Equation (26) then follows automatically. To avoid an inflation of subscripts, in the following few equations we shall omit the subscript x in p_x. We have then to prove that

$$p_{ik} = \int_{\mathbf{p}} \alpha_i^* \, p \, \alpha_k \, d\mathbf{p} = \int_{\mathbf{x}} \phi_i^* \frac{\hbar}{i} \frac{\partial \phi_k}{\partial x} \, d\mathbf{x}, \tag{28}$$

and so on. The proof proceeds in these steps:

$$\int_{\mathbf{x}} \phi_i^* \frac{\hbar}{i} \frac{\partial \phi_k}{\partial x} \, d\mathbf{x}$$

$$= (2\pi\hbar)^{-3} \int_{\mathbf{x}}\int_{\mathbf{p}'}\int_{\mathbf{p}} e^{-\frac{i}{\hbar}\mathbf{p}'\cdot\mathbf{x}} \alpha_i^*(\mathbf{p}') \frac{\hbar}{i} \frac{\partial}{\partial x} [e^{\frac{i}{\hbar}\mathbf{p}\cdot\mathbf{x}} \alpha_k(\mathbf{p})] \, d\mathbf{p} \, d\mathbf{p}' \, d\mathbf{x}$$

$$= (2\pi\hbar)^{-3} \int_{\mathbf{x}}\int_{\mathbf{p}'}\int_{\mathbf{p}} e^{\frac{i}{\hbar}(\mathbf{p}-\mathbf{p}')\cdot\mathbf{x}} \alpha_i^*(\mathbf{p}') \, p \, \alpha_k(\mathbf{p}) \, d\mathbf{p} \, d\mathbf{p}' \, d\mathbf{x}$$

$$= \int_{\mathbf{p}} \alpha_i^*(\mathbf{p}) \, p \, \alpha_k(\mathbf{p}) \, d\mathbf{p}. \tag{29}$$

Thus we find that the matrix definition based on integrals in configuration space is completely equivalent to that involving integrals in momentum space.

In eq. (23), we found that to multiply one of the orthonormal functions $\phi_k(\mathbf{x})$ by an arbitrary function $f(\mathbf{x})$ is equivalent to forming a linear combination of the $\phi_l(\mathbf{x})$, with the matrix elements b_{lk} being the coefficients. We may give the matrix elements p_{lk} a similar meaning. If we start again with a function $\phi_k(\mathbf{x})$ and then apply to it the differentiation operator $\dfrac{\hbar}{i}\dfrac{\partial}{\partial x}$, the result will again be a linear combination of the $\phi_l(\mathbf{x})$:

$$\frac{\hbar}{i}\frac{\partial \phi_k}{\partial x} = \sum_i d_i\, \phi_i. \tag{30}$$

If we multiply both sides of this equation by ϕ_l^* and integrate, we find

$$p_{lk} = d_l \tag{31}$$

so that we have

$$\frac{\hbar}{i}\frac{\partial \phi_k}{\partial x} = \sum_l p_{lk}\, \phi_l. \tag{32}$$

All the matrices that correspond to functions in momentum space, $F(\mathbf{p})$, commute with each other. However, the matrices corresponding to a coordinate and to its conjugate momentum component do not commute, as we shall show now. Let us again call such a pair x and p, suppressing the subscript x or 1 for the sake of brevity. Let us start with an arbitrary wave function ϕ,

$$\phi = \sum_k c_k\, \phi_k, \tag{33}$$

and let us multiply it by x. The result will be

$$x\phi = \sum_{k,l} x_{lk}\, c_k\, \phi_l, \tag{34}$$

because of eq. (23). If we now differentiate the product with respect to x, we shall have

$$\frac{\hbar}{i}\frac{\partial}{\partial x}(x\,\phi) = \frac{\hbar}{i}\left(x\frac{\partial \phi}{\partial x} + \phi\right)$$

$$= \sum_{i,k,l} p_{il}\, x_{lk}\, c_k\, \phi_i. \tag{35}$$

On the other hand, starting with the same function ϕ, we may first differentiate and then multiply by x, with the result

$$x \frac{\hbar}{i} \frac{\partial \phi}{\partial x} = \sum_{i,k,l} x_{il} \, p_{lk} \, c_k \, \phi_i. \tag{36}$$

Now if we subtract the expression (36) from (35), we find

$$\frac{\hbar}{i} \phi = \frac{\hbar}{i} \sum_i c_i \, \phi_i = \sum_{i,k,l} (p_{il} \, x_{lk} - x_{il} \, p_{lk}) c_k \, \phi_i; \tag{37}$$

and since the c_k are, after all, arbitrary,

$$\sum_l (p_{il} \, x_{lk} - x_{il} \, p_{lk}) = \frac{\hbar}{i} \, \delta_{ik}. \tag{38}$$

δ_{ik} is the Kronecker symbol, whose value is 0 or 1, depending on whether the two subscripts i, k are different or equal. This result is a co-called *commutation relation*. It shows that the matrices of two canonically conjugate observables do not commute but that their commutator equals $(\hbar/i)$, multiplied by the matrix whose elements are Kronecker symbols.

If two matrices do not commute with each other, we can show that the probability distributions for the corresponding physical observables cannot be made arbitrarily sharp at the same time. More precisely, we shall show that the product of their rms spreads has a nonzero lower limit.

Consider two observables A and B, with corresponding matrices A_{ik} and B_{ik}. Let their commutator be C_{ik}:

$$\sum_l (A_{il} \, B_{lk} - B_{il} \, A_{lk}) = C_{ik}. \tag{39}$$

The expectation value of A is

$$\bar{A} = \sum_{i,k} c_i^* \, A_{ik} \, c_k, \tag{40}$$

and the mean square spread of its probability distribution is

$$\overline{\Delta A^2} = \sum_i a_i^* \, a_i,$$
$$a_i = \sum_l A_{il} \, c_l - A c_i, \qquad A_{li}^* = A_{il}. \tag{41}$$

Corresponding formulas hold for the observable B. The product of the mean square spreads of A and B is

$$\overline{\Delta A^2}\,\overline{\Delta B^2} = \sum_i a_i^* a_i \sum_b b_i^* b_i$$

$$\geq \left| \sum_i a_i^* b_i \right|^2. \tag{42}$$

The last line is a consequence of Schwarz's inequality. If we work out the expression $\sum_i a_i^* b_i$, we find, by straight substitution from the defining equation, the second of (41), that

$$\sum_i a_i^* b_i = \sum_{i,k,l} c_k^* A_{ki} B_{il} c_l - \bar{A}\,\bar{B}. \tag{43}$$

We have assumed that both matrices A_{ik} and B_{ik} are Hermitian. In that case, their product $\sum_l A_{il} B_{lk}$ is the sum of a Hermitian and an anti-Hermitian matrix,

$$\sum_i A_{ki} B_{il} = \tfrac{1}{2} \sum_i (A_{ki} B_{il} + B_{ki} A_{il}) + \tfrac{1}{2} \sum_i (A_{ki} B_{il} - B_{ki} A_{il})$$

$$= \tfrac{1}{2} \sum_i (A_{ki} B_{il} + B_{ki} A_{il}) + \tfrac{1}{2} C_{kl},$$

$$\tfrac{1}{2} \sum_i (A_{li} B_{ik} + B_{li} A_{ik})^* = \tfrac{1}{2} \sum_i (A_{ki} B_{il} + B_{ki} A_{il}),$$

$$(C_{lk}^* = -C_{kl}). \tag{44}$$

A bilinear form in the c_i and c_i^* of which the coefficients are anti-Hermitian is always purely imaginary (its conjugate complex is its negative). Therefore, if we form the absolute square of expression (43), we get

$$\left| \sum_i a_i^* b_i \right|^2 = \tfrac{1}{4} \left| \sum_{k,l} c_k^* C_{kl} c_l \right|^2$$

$$+ \left[\tfrac{1}{2} \sum_{i,k,l} c_k^*(A_{ki} B_{il} + B_{ki} A_{il})c_l - \bar{A}\,\bar{B} \right]^2, \tag{45}$$

and both squares in this sum are positive definite. It follows that

$$\overline{\Delta A^2}\,\overline{\Delta B^2} \geq \tfrac{1}{4}\bar{C}^2. \tag{46}$$

The commutator (38) is a particularly simple matrix. Its expectation value equals $\hbar/i$, regardless of the choice of wave function. It follows for two canonically conjugate observables, such as x and p_x, that their rms spreads satisfy the inequality

$$\Delta x \, \Delta p_x \geq \tfrac{1}{2} \, \hbar. \tag{47}$$

This result is known as *Heisenberg's uncertainty relation*. Equation (47) is the quantitative statement mentioned in Section 9.2 but then not proved.

We shall summarize the most important of our results so far: All physical observables can be represented by Hermitian matrices that enable us to calculate all results of possible physical significance if the expansion coefficients of the wave function are known. Not all of these matrices will commute; if two of them do not, no wave function can be found in which both probability distributions are arbitrarily narrow.

12.2. Operators. Transformation theory

Altogether, we have found that the essential physical predictions of quantum theory can be obtained in at least three different forms: as integrals in configuration space, as integrals in momentum space, and as infinite sums over algebraic expressions. What is the common feature of these different *representations?*

When we multiply a wave function in configuration space by a function $f(x)$ or when we differentiate it once or several times, we start with one function and obtain another function. When we multiply a series of numbers c_k by a set of numbers A_{ik} and sum over the subscript k, we obtain a new set of numbers d_i:

$$\sum_k A_{ik} c_k = d_i. \tag{48}$$

In all these cases, multiplication of the wave function, differentiation, and multiplication of a sequence by a matrix all adjoin to a certain mathematical object (the wave function, the c_k) a new object of the same type according to a definite set of instructions. We may say that the operations of multiplication, differentiation, and so forth *map* a set of certain objects on itself in a definite manner. A set of instructions that can be used to effect a mapping of a set of specified mathematical objects either on itself or on another set is called an *operator*. Multiplication of wave functions by a specified function $f(x)$, and the other processes just mentioned, are merely a few examples of operators.

The representations we have studied involve typically the introduction of operators taking the place of classical dynamical variables. In addition, every representation includes an instruction on how to obtain the expectation values of all physically interesting operators when the wave function is given. Finally, every representation must contain the equivalent of a Schrödinger equation, that is, information on how a physical system will change with time. This last point we shall consider in detail in the following section. Right now we shall study the properties of the operators that we have to deal with in quantum theory.

The most general definition of an operator is rather vague—too vague to be very useful. The instruction "starting with any function $f(x)$, form the integral of its square over the domain (0, 1); then take the numerical value of the integral, round it off to the nearest integer, and finally look up in the dictionary the first word appearing on the page bearing that number," is an operator that maps a certain set of functions on a certain set of words. But this operator is not likely to play an important role either in pure mathematics or in theoretical physics. The operators we have to deal with now, which in quantum theory are to represent observables, and the mathematical objects that represent wave functions alike have certain properties, regardless of the representation chosen. We shall now ascertain these properties and then use them in the study of the operators. Because the term "wave function" is usually reserved to representations in configuration space, we shall call the objects to which our operators are applied simply *states*, a neutral designation that does not imply anything about the manner of representation.

(1) *The states form a linear set.* That is to say, if we have two states designated by M and N, respectively, then the expression

$$P = \alpha M + \beta N \tag{49}$$

is defined and represents another state. The symbols α and β here stand for ordinary complex numbers.

(2) It is possible to find an (infinite) set of states which are linearly independent of each other and which form a *complete base set*. By these statements we mean that there is no linear combina-

tion of states within the set that vanishes, and that all states can be represented as linear combinations of the base set.

(3) For any two states M and N there exists a *bilinear form* (M, N), an ordinary number, usually complex, that depends on the sequence of the two states so that

$$(M, N)^* = (N, M) \qquad (50)$$

always. Automatically, for any one state the form (M, M) must be real. Usually we call the number (M, N) the *dot product* or *scalar product* of the two states M and N, in analogy to the terminology of vector calculus; by the same token, we call the real number (M, M) the *norm* of the state M. If we multiply the state M by a suitable ordinary number, we can make its norm equal to unity. A state whose norm is 1 is said to be *normalized*.

The dot product is realized in the wave-function representation by an integral of the form $\int \phi_M^* \phi_N \, \mathbf{dx}$, where ϕ_M and ϕ_N are the representations of the states M and N, respectively. In momentum space, the corresponding integral is $\int \alpha_M^* \alpha_N \, \mathbf{dp}$. Finally, in the matrix formulation, the dot product has the form of a series, $\sum_k c_k^{(M)*} c_k^{(N)}$. All these representations, as the reader can easily convince himself, have all the properties enumerated above.

From these general properties, it is possible to prove the existence of *complete orthonormal base sets*, but the choice of such a base set is by no means unique. There are infinitely many complete orthonormal base sets, and every one of them leads to a different representation.

(4) All the *operators* we have to deal with *operate on states; the result of the operation is another state.* It is true that most of the operators used in quantum theory are not capable of operating on all the states. For instance, in wave mechanics the function $(1 + x^2)^{-\frac{1}{2}}$ is a suitable (though not normalized) wave function in a one-dimensional configuration space. If we multiply it by x, the resulting function is not square-integrable and hence does not represent a state. We cannot assert that an operator maps the totality of all states on the totality of all states without excluding many operators that are important for our purposes. But such an all-inclusive applicability is not necessary for an operator to be useful.

We must merely restrict its applicability to those states where the result of the operation is another well-defined state.

(5) Our operators are *linear*. That means if we apply the operator $\mathcal{P}$ to a linear combination of states such as (49) (provided the operator is applicable to both M and N), we have

$$\mathcal{P}(\alpha M + \beta N) = \alpha \mathcal{P} M + \beta \mathcal{P} N. \tag{51}$$

(6) All operators that represent physical observables are *Hermitian:* that is, for any two states M and N to which they are applicable they satisfy the condition

$$(M, \mathcal{P} N) = (\mathcal{P} M, N). \tag{52}$$

The reader can convince himself that all the operators and matrices we have introduced so far are in fact Hermitian. Hermiticity is both necessary and sufficient to assure that every expectation value is real. This proof can be carried out on the basis of the following assumption:

(7) In a state M, the expectation value of an observable A is given by the expression

$$\bar{A} = (M, \mathcal{Q} M) \tag{53}$$

where $\mathcal{Q}$ is the operator corresponding to the physical quantity A.

(8) The *identity operator 1* is the operator that carries each state over into itself. For any state M to which the operators $\mathfrak{x}$ (representing the physical coordinate x) and $\mathfrak{p}$ (representing the canonically conjugate momentum p) are applicable, we have the relationship

$$\mathfrak{p} \, \mathfrak{x} \, M - \mathfrak{x} \, \mathfrak{p} \, M = \frac{\hbar}{i} \, M \tag{54}$$

or
$$\mathfrak{p} \, \mathfrak{x} - \mathfrak{x} \, \mathfrak{p} = \frac{\hbar}{i} \, 1. \tag{55}$$

All operators corresponding to canonical variables *not conjugate* to each other *commute;* that is,

$$\mathfrak{a} \, \mathfrak{b} = \mathfrak{b} \, \mathfrak{a}. \tag{56}$$

All classical observables have operators corresponding to them which are built up from the basic canonical operators $\mathfrak{q}_k$ and $\mathfrak{p}_k$ in the same manner as the corresponding classical quantities. But in the case of noncommuting operators, the sequence must be chosen so that the resulting operator is Hermitian. This rule, though obviously necessary, is in general not sufficient to determine the sequence uniquely. In the event of difficulties, appeal must be made to independent experimental evidence.

The Hamiltonian, because of its appearance in the Schrödinger equation, is by far the most important operator that must be built up from the canonical observables q_k and p_k. In simple problems of atomic mechanics, all difficulties of sequence can be obviated by first constructing the Hamiltonian in rectilinear coordinates. The potential energy is then a function of the q_k only, and the kinetic energy depends only on the p_k; thus no noncommuting operators appear as factors in a product. If the problem then must be integrated in some other coordinate system, we can apply the methods of wave mechanics (transforming the Laplacian, which invariably appears in the expression for the kinetic energy) as in Chapter 10, or if desired we can formulate similar procedures in some other representation.

In more involved situations, for instance in the quantization of radiation fields, any product involving noncommuting factors must be symmetrized in order to assure Hermiticity for the resulting product, but that requirement alone may not be sufficient to determine the sequence of the operators. These problems are not yet solved; we must realize that the adoption of a particular Hamiltonian is equivalent to the adoption of a particular theory (that is, a set of laws of nature) whose validity can be checked only as a whole.

Purely formally, we note that the two requirements that the Hamiltonian be Hermitian and that it go over into the corresponding classical Hamiltonian if we let $\hbar$ go to zero (and with it all the commutators) are necessary but are by no means sufficient to determine the quantum-theoretical Hamiltonian uniquely. Hence quantum mechanics presents us with a freedom of choice for the laws of nature that has no counterpart in classical physics.

The rules just formulated determine the transition from classical to quantum physics, except that we have said nothing concerning the dependence on time. We shall deal with that question in the next section. Right now we shall concern ourselves with the transition from the abstract theory, which deals only with relationships between states (identified by some symbols but otherwise not represented by particular mathematical objects) and operators, to particular representations.

Let us choose an arbitrary complete orthonormal base set, so that for any two members of the set, A_i, A_k,

$$(A_i, A_k) = \delta_{ik}. \tag{57}$$

Consider an arbitrary state M. According to our assumption concerning the completeness of the A_i, there exists an infinite set of numbers c_i so that

$$M = \sum_i c_i A_i. \tag{58}$$

As the first step, we shall determine this set of numbers. To do so we form the dot products (A_k, M) for each value of k. We find

$$(A_k, M) = \sum_i c_i (A_k, A_i) = c_k. \tag{59}$$

The infinite set of numbers (A_k, M), the coefficients of the expansion, serve as a complete identification of the state M and thus may be considered one of its possible representations.

If two states M and N are represented by the numbers c_i and d_i, respectively, then the dot product (M, N) can be found in this manner. First, because of eq. (50), we have

$$(M, A_k) = c_k^*. \tag{60}$$

If we then multiply each eq. (60) by its appropriate d_k and add, we get

$$\sum_k d_k (M, A_k) = (M, N) = \sum_k c_k^* d_k. \tag{61}$$

As a matter of fact, the expansion coefficients we introduced earlier were expansion coefficients with respect to a particular set of orthonormal states, the characteristic states of a Hamiltonian operator. The whole formalism developed then, however, was independent of the particular source of our orthonormal set.

Let us now turn to the representation of operators. If we apply the operator $\mathcal{P}$ to a state M, represented by the coefficients c_i, and if the result of the operation is the state N, represented by the coefficients d_i, evidently we have, because of the linearity of the operator,

$$\mathcal{P} M = N,$$

$$\sum_i d_i A_i = \mathcal{P} \left(\sum_k c_k A_k \right) = \sum_k c_k \mathcal{P} A_k. \tag{62}$$

In order to solve for the coefficients d_i, we form the dot product by A_l:

$$d_l = \sum_k (A_l, \mathcal{O} A_k) c_k = \sum_k P_{lk} c_k. \tag{63}$$

In other words, the matrix P_{lk} is the array of numbers by which the c_k must be multiplied if we are to obtain the representation of the state N.

In mathematics, matrices are widely used to represent linear operators. Just as in vector and tensor calculus it has become customary to drop all symbols indicating summation of index pairs, an abbreviating notation is generally used in matrix operations. What we do is to suppress all indices referring to matrices and to have it understood that if several symbols denoting matrices follow each other, then the last index of the matrix to the left is identical with the first index of the matrix to the right, and the two are to be treated as dummies (are to be summed over). In what follows, we shall use boldface Greek letters to denote the rows of numbers (such as c_i) representing a state, and a special Roman alphabet to denote matrices representing operators. For instance, eq. (63) will be written in the form

$$\mathbf{v} = \mathsf{P}\,\mathbf{\mu}. \tag{64}$$

Occasionally we have used products of operators. The symbol $\mathcal{O}\mathcal{B}$ denotes the operator which does the same thing to any state M that would be accomplished if we applied to M first the operator $\mathcal{B}$ and then to the result the operator $\mathcal{O}$. In other words, the operator equation

$$\mathcal{C} = \mathcal{O}\,\mathcal{B} \tag{65}$$

and the matrix equation

$$\mathsf{C} = \mathsf{A}\,\mathsf{B} \tag{66}$$

are short for

$$\mathcal{C}\,M \equiv \mathcal{O}\,\mathcal{B}\,M,$$
$$\mathsf{C}\,\phi \equiv \mathsf{A}\,\mathsf{B}\,\phi, \tag{67}$$

for any state M to which these operators can be applied. We require a special symbol for the matrix whose elements are Kronecker symbols. This matrix is the *identity matrix* or unit matrix. It carries any row of numbers c_i over into itself. We shall denote it by the symbol 1. Equation (38) can be rewritten more succinctly in the form

$$\mathsf{p}_r \, \mathsf{x}_s - \mathsf{x}_s \, \mathsf{p}_r = \frac{\hbar}{i} \, \delta_{rs} \, \mathbf{1}, \tag{68}$$

where the subscripts r and s refer to coordinate axes; the matrix indices are suppressed.

Before we go over to a consideration of the dynamics of quantum theory, we must take up *transformation theory*. We have found that we can represent abstract states and operators by means of matrices, by introducing a complete set of orthonormal states A_i. Suppose we wish to go over to a representation in which the base set has been chosen differently, say as a set A_i'. The coefficients of an expansion of the state M with respect to this new base set will be denoted by c_i'. What will happen to our whole formalism?

Obviously, we have

$$M = \sum_i c_i \, A_i = \sum_k c_k' \, A_k'. \tag{69}$$

In order to obtain a relationship between the two different sets of coefficients, we form the dot product of this equation by A_m'. The result is

$$c_m' = \sum_i u_{mi} \, c_i, \qquad u_{mi} = (A_m', \, A_i), \tag{70}$$

because of the orthonormality of the new base set as well as the old one. The coefficients u_{mi} also form a matrix, which we shall denote by the symbol u. Therefore we can rewrite eq. (70) in the form

$$\phi' = \mathsf{u} \, \phi. \tag{71}$$

But we must remember that u does not represent a physical observable. (In the abstract theory it lacks meaning, inasmuch as ϕ and ϕ' are two different representations of the same state!) Hence there is no reason why it should obey the condition (16) or (41), each of which holds for the representation of Hermitian operators. Instead, the matrix u satisfies another condition. The coefficients u_{mi} lead from one set of orthonormal states to another. Thus they are somewhat analogous to the cosines, in ordinary geometry, between the axes of two different rectangular (Cartesian) coordinate systems. If we form the dot product $(A_i, \, A_k)$ between two of the old base states, we can represent each one in terms of the A_m'. The result, in accordance with eq. (61), is

$$(A_i, A_k) = \delta_{ik} = \sum_m u_{mi}^* u_{mk}. \qquad (72)$$

By adding one further element to our notation, we can give this condition a simpler form. We call two matrices A and B *Hermitian conjugates* of each other if

$$B_{ik} = A_{ki}^*. \qquad (73)$$

A Hermitian matrix is one that equals its own Hermitian conjugate. It is customary to denote the Hermitian conjugate by an asterisk, so that eq. (73) may be rewritten in the form

$$\mathsf{B} = \mathsf{A}^*. \qquad (74)$$

Thus the condition satisfied by a *Hermitian matrix* is

$$\mathsf{A}^* = \mathsf{A}, \qquad (75)$$

and eq. (72), the condition for u, turns into

$$\mathsf{u}^* \mathsf{u} = 1. \qquad (76)$$

We call the matrix u a *unitary matrix*.

Provided certain conditions of convergence are satisfied, any Hermitian matrix A may be used for the construction of a unitary matrix by means of the exponential series. The reader can convince himself quite easily that the matrix v,

$$\mathsf{v} = e^{i\mathsf{A}} \equiv \sum_0^\infty \frac{(i\,\mathsf{A})^n}{n!}, \qquad (77)$$

is unitary.

The unitary matrix u provides for the transition from one representation ϕ of the state M to another, ϕ'. But this same matrix also provides the transition from one operator representation to another. If the operator $\mathcal{P}$ transforms a state M into a state N, as in eqs. (62) and (63), and if we denote the representations of these two states by the symbols ϕ, ϕ' and χ, χ', respectively, then we must have for the representations of $\mathcal{P}$

$$\chi = \mathsf{P}\,\phi, \qquad \chi' = \mathsf{P}'\,\phi'. \qquad (78)$$

If we now substitute the old representations in the first equation by means of eq. (71) in reverse, we get first

$$u^* \chi' = P u^* \phi' = u^* P' \phi'. \qquad (79)$$

To solve this equation for P', we must multiply from the left by u;

$$u P u^* \phi' = P' \phi'. \qquad (80)$$

This relationship must hold for any ϕ'. Therefore

$$P' = u P u^*, \qquad (81)$$

the desired relationship.

Expectation values of observables are pure numbers, possessing physical meaning. They must be unaffected by the transition from one representation to another. Indeed, we have

$$\bar{A}' = \phi^{*'} A' \phi' = (\phi^* u^*)(u A u^*)(u \phi)$$
$$= \phi^* A \phi = \bar{A}. \qquad (82)$$

Previously, we have seen that all physically meaningful questions can be formulated in terms of expectation values. In particular, questions concerning the probability distribution of a certain physical variable or even a combination of such variables ("What is the probability that x will be found to have values between x_1 and x_2 and, at the same time, y will lie between y_1 and y_2?") can be reformulated as questions for the expectation value of a function that equals 1 for favorable and 0 for unfavorable outcomes of the experiment. Therefore, once we have shown that expectation values are independent of the representation, we know that physically all choices of representation are equivalent.

12.3. Dynamics

In the wave-mechanical representation, the dependence of a state on time was determined by the Schrödinger equation,

$$\frac{\partial \psi}{\partial t} = - \frac{i}{\hbar} H \left(x, \frac{\hbar}{i} \nabla \right) \psi. \qquad (83)$$

Without questioning the correctness of that equation, we shall now proceed to reformulate it so that it deals with physically observable quantities, that is, expectation values.

Let us consider some physical quantity A, a function of the canonical coordinates. Let the corresponding operator be α. Then if A is a representation of the state of the system at the time

t, the expectation value of A is, in general, also a function of the time t:

$$\bar{A}(t) = \psi^*(t) \, \mathsf{A} \, \psi(t). \tag{84}$$

Its rate of change may be determined with the help of the Schrödinger equation (83), reinterpreted as a matrix equation

$$\dot{\psi} = -\frac{i}{\hbar} \mathsf{H} \, \psi, \qquad \dot{\psi}^* = \frac{i}{\hbar} \psi^* \, \mathsf{H}^* = \frac{i}{\hbar} \psi^* \, \mathsf{H}, \tag{85}$$

and comes out as

$$\begin{aligned}
\dot{\bar{A}} &= \dot{\psi}^* \, \mathsf{A} \, \psi + \psi^* \, \mathsf{A} \, \dot{\psi} \\
&= \frac{i}{\hbar} \psi^* \, (\mathsf{H} \, \mathsf{A} - \mathsf{A} \, \mathsf{H}) \, \psi = \frac{i}{\hbar} \, (\overline{\mathsf{H} \, \mathsf{A} - \mathsf{A} \, \mathsf{H}}).
\end{aligned} \tag{86}$$

In this last equation, the time derivative of one expectation value is equated to the expectation value of another observable or operator. Consequently, this equation holds irrespective of the choice of representation. Once a mechanical system has been defined in terms of its Hamiltonian (operator), the time rate of change of any interesting expectation value, including probability distributions, is given by eq. (86).

At this point a new range of possibilities presents itself. We have assumed, as a matter of course, that the states and their representations are functions of time, and that the matrices representing physical observables are constant. But suppose we start with such a representation and then go over to another representation with the help of a unitary matrix u,

$$\mathsf{u} = e^{i\mathsf{G}}, \qquad \mathsf{u}^* = e^{-i\mathsf{G}} \tag{87}$$

(G being Hermitian), which is not constant in time. The new representation will involve matrices that are time-dependent. In general, the matrix A will go over into

$$\mathsf{A}' = e^{i\mathsf{G}} \, \mathsf{A} \, e^{-i\mathsf{G}}. \tag{88}$$

The time derivatives of ϕ' and A are the expressions

$$\begin{aligned}
\dot{\phi}' &= \dot{\mathsf{u}} \, \phi + \mathsf{u} \, \dot{\phi} = \left(\dot{\mathsf{u}} - \frac{i}{\hbar} \mathsf{u} \, \mathsf{H} \right) \phi, \\
\dot{\mathsf{A}}' &= \dot{\mathsf{u}} \, \mathsf{A} \, \mathsf{u}^* + \mathsf{u} \, \mathsf{A} \, \dot{\mathsf{u}}^* \neq 0.
\end{aligned} \tag{89}$$

In other words, through an appropriate choice of G we may distribute the dependence on time between the state representations and the operator representations in any way we choose. The Schrödinger equation (85) holds only for representations in which all the time-dependence is thrown into the state representations. Such representations are called *Schrödinger representations*.

We can choose G in such a manner that the state representations become constant. To do so, we must, according to eq. (89), satisfy the differential equation

$$\dot{u} = \frac{i}{\hbar} u\,H = 0. \tag{90}$$

This equation has a simple solution,

$$G = \frac{i}{\hbar} H\,t, \qquad u = e^{\frac{i}{\hbar}Ht}, \tag{91}$$

$$\dot{u} = \frac{i}{\hbar} H\,e^{\frac{i}{\hbar}Ht}.$$

With this particular unitary transformation, the matrices that represent observables become

$$A' = e^{\frac{i}{\hbar}Ht}\,A\,e^{-\frac{i}{\hbar}Ht}, \tag{92}$$

and their time derivatives are

$$\dot{A}' = \frac{i}{\hbar}\,(H\,e^{\frac{i}{\hbar}Ht}\,A\,e^{-\frac{i}{\hbar}Ht} - e^{\frac{i}{\hbar}Ht}\,A\,e^{-\frac{i}{\hbar}Ht}\,H)$$

$$= \frac{i}{\hbar}\,(H\,A' - A'\,H). \tag{93}$$

This type of representation, called a *Heisenberg representation*, is the diametric opposite of the Schrödinger representation. In Heisenberg representations, there is, of course, no differential equation for the time derivatives of the state representations, because these derivatives vanish. The Schrödinger equation is replaced by a differential equation for the observables (or their matrix representations), namely, eq. (93).

In the solution of practical problems, either the Schrödinger or the Heisenberg representation may be the more convenient. In perturbation theory, an intermediate between these two extreme possibilities is often used, the so-called *interaction representation*. In the interaction representation the characteristic states of the zeroth approximation are made to be constant in time, and as a result the time-dependence of the exact states directly represents transitions between these zeroth-order approximation states.

12.4. The harmonic oscillator

To show the usefulness of the matrix formalism, in the conclusion of this discussion we shall work through one example, one that we have already treated with the help of wave-mechanical methods. We shall calculate the energy levels of a one-dimensional harmonic oscillator.

In matrix algebra, this problem must be formulated as follows: Given the form of the Hamiltonian matrix as a function of the matrices x and p,

$$H = \frac{\kappa}{2} x^2 + \frac{1}{2m} p^2, \tag{94}$$

find those numbers E_k which permit solutions of the equation

$$H \phi_k = E_k \phi_k. \tag{95}$$

We shall choose as our base set the (unknown) characteristic states of the oscillator itself. In this representation, the matrix H takes the form

$$H_{mn} = E_m \delta_{mn}. \tag{96}$$

We know nothing as yet concerning the form of the matrices p and x, except that they satisfy the commutation relation,

$$p x - x p = \frac{\hbar}{i} 1, \tag{97}$$

and that they are Hermitian.

To simplify our problem, we shall start by introducing a new matrix a and its Hermitian conjugate a* by means of the definition

$$a = \frac{1}{\sqrt{2\hbar}} [(m \kappa)^{\frac{1}{4}} x + i(m \kappa)^{-\frac{1}{4}} p],$$

$$a^* = \frac{1}{\sqrt{2\hbar}} [(m \kappa)^{\frac{1}{4}} x - i(m \kappa)^{-\frac{1}{4}} p]. \tag{98}$$

We shall find it easier to determine this new matrix than x and p. a and a* satisfy the commutation relation

$$a a^* - a^* a = 1. \tag{99}$$

The Hamiltonian (94), in terms of this new matrix, becomes

$$\mathsf{H} = \hbar\,\omega(\mathsf{a}^*\,\mathsf{a} + \tfrac{1}{2}\mathsf{1}) = \hbar\,\omega\,(\mathsf{a}\,\mathsf{a}^* - \tfrac{1}{2}\mathsf{1}). \tag{100}$$

Let us multiply the first expression (100) from the left by a and the second expression from the right by a, and then subtract the two resulting equations from each other. We get

$$\mathsf{a}\,\mathsf{H} = \hbar\,\omega\,(\mathsf{a}\,\mathsf{a}^*\,\mathsf{a} + \tfrac{1}{2}\,\mathsf{a}),$$

$$\mathsf{H}\,\mathsf{a} = \hbar\,\omega\,(\mathsf{a}\,\mathsf{a}^*\,\mathsf{a} - \tfrac{1}{2}\,\mathsf{a}), \tag{101}$$

$$\mathsf{a}\,\mathsf{H} - \mathsf{H}\,\mathsf{a} = \hbar\,\omega\,\mathsf{a}.$$

Because of eq. (96), we have

$$a_{ik}\,E_k - E_i\,a_{ik} = \hbar\,\omega\,a_{ik} \tag{102}$$

or $\qquad\qquad (E_k - E_i - \hbar\,\omega)\,a_{ik} = 0. \tag{103}$

This last equation can be satisfied only if either the first or the second factor vanishes. We find then that the only matrix elements a_{ik} that do not vanish are those for which the difference between E_i and E_k equals $\hbar\,\omega$. So let us assemble a sequence of energy values in which each following element exceeds the preceding one by this amount, so that

$$E_n = E_0 + n\,\hbar\,\omega. \tag{104}$$

At this stage we do not yet know whether there is a first element in this sequence or whether the sequence starts with $n = -\infty$.

The only matrix elements a_{ik} different from zero are those in which the second index is greater by 1 than the first index. If we wish to satisfy the commutation relation (99), then, we find that

$$|a_{n,n+1}|^2 - |a_{n-1,n}|^2 = 1 \quad \text{if } n \text{ is not the first index in the sequence,}$$

$$|a_{n,n+1}|^2 \qquad\qquad = 1 \quad \text{if } n \text{ is the first index,} \tag{105}$$

showing that

$$|a_{n,n+1}| = \sqrt{\epsilon + n}. \tag{106}$$

This equation proves conclusively that there *is* a first element, because $|a_{n,n+1}|$ cannot become complex. We shall call this first index 0 and set

$$a_{n,n+1} = \sqrt{\epsilon + n} \qquad (n = 0, 1, \cdot\cdot\cdot). \tag{107}$$

Since there is a first state in the sequence, the second part of eq. (105) is applicable with $n = 0$,

$$|a_{01}|^2 = 1, \tag{108}$$

and ϵ comes out as 1.

If we substitute this result back into either of the two expressions for the Hamiltonian, (100), we find for the energy levels, as we did before,

$$E_n = (n + \tfrac{1}{2}) \hbar \omega \qquad (n = 0, 1, \cdot \cdot \cdot). \tag{109}$$

Besides, we have found a convenient form for the matrix **a** and, therefore, also for the matrices **x** and **p**. These forms are also useful in problems not involving the harmonic oscillator. Naturally, in other problems this choice for **x** and **p** will not produce a Hamiltonian as simple as (96). After all, if we expand with respect to the characteristic states of the Hamiltonian matrix (94), we cannot expect any matrix except this one to consist only of diagonal elements.

Problems

1. Determine the matrix elements x_{ik} and p_{ik} in terms of the characteristic functions of the time-independent Schrödinger equation for a one-dimensional particle in a box with rigid walls. In this case, the commutation relation (38) is not satisfied (you can verify this statement explicitly). Why?

Compare this situation with the one-dimensional harmonic oscillator where the corresponding matrices do satisfy eq. (38).

2. Recast the Schrödinger perturbation calculation, Sections 11.2 and 11.3, into the form of a matrix representation.

3. Set up the commutation relations between the three components of the angular momentum, basing your derivation on the definition of the angular momentum as the vector product of radius vector and linear momentum. Show that each component commutes with the square of the angular-momentum operator.

4. Starting with the commutation relations obtained in the preceding problem, find finite matrix representations for the components of the angular momentum and determine characteristic values. This you can do best by assuming that the square of the angular momentum and one component possess joint characteristic functions (which they do because they commute) and by attempting the expansions in terms of this set.

Chapter 13

Summary and Outlook

This book is devoted to those parts of physics which deal with the atomic and molecular structure of matter. Heat physics is concerned with the interchange of energy between the macroscopic and the microscopic degrees of freedom of matter. Quantum physics has proved its necessity, and has achieved its most brilliant successes, in treating the behavior of the electrons in the atom, the forces between the atoms in the molecule, and the forces that hold solids together—those which determine their heat capacity, their heat conductivity, their electric resistivity, and their magnetic properties.

In this book we have done no more than discuss the foundations of these vast fields; in quantum physics we have not even quite completed the discussion of the foundations. As for thermodynamics, a great deal of work has been done applying the general laws to the phase changes of pure substances, of solutions, alloys, and so forth. Another great field of applications lies in the great variety of chemical reactions whose equilibrium points are determined by the particular properties of each reaction and also by the general thermodynamic laws. A more recent field of application has been the treatment of reactions that take place at great speed, such as explosions and the burning of liquid or evaporated fuels in combustion chambers.

As for quantum mechanics, we have omitted the treatment of systems involving several identical particles. In the Hamiltonian of such systems, the coordinates of these identical particles appear, of course, in perfectly symmetrical fashion; for example, if in a helium atom we effect a complete exchange of the coordinates and momentum components of the two electrons, the energy of the system will remain the same. In classical physics this symmetry has no particular consequences, but in quantum physics it has the result that those states in which the interchange of all the particle coordinates leaves the state intact and those in which this interchange produces a change in sign are separated permanently; there can be no transitions between one type of state and the other, not even in the presence of perturbations. Apart from the fact that the so-called symmetrical states always have different energy levels from the antisymmetric states, one big difference is that certain energy levels possible with symmetrical states have no counterparts in antisymmetric states. Those levels in which two identical particles have completely identical quantum numbers can exist only in symmetric states.

Experience has taught us that the symmetry character of the state in this respect is an inherent property of the different types of particles. The states of several electrons are always antisymmetrical, and so are the states of several protons. Photons—if we want to call photons particles—always occur in symmetrical states. Apart from the analysis of spectra, where the *Pauli exclusion principle* (that no two electrons can have all quantum numbers in common) is of the greatest importance, this principle has also considerable statistical significance in systems involving large numbers of identical particles. An example is provided by the statistics of the "gas" of the relatively free electrons in the interior of a metal that are responsible for the conduction of both heat and electric current.

Another matter we have not treated is the fact that electrons and protons, and probably also most of the other elementary particles, possess an intrinsic angular momentum, the so-called *spin*, and an intrinsic magnetic dipole moment. This property of elementary particles is closely connected with certain features of the relativistic quantum mechanics, which was developed by Dirac. All these things are necessary for an understanding of the behavior of elementary particles, but apparently they are not sufficient in themselves.

Our present theories run into serious difficulties on two fronts. One is the interaction of the elementary particles inside the atomic nucleus. These particles, protons and neutrons, all move within about 10^{-13} cm, whereas intraatomic and intramolecular distances are of the order of 10^{-8} cm. Although a great deal of partially successful work has been done on nuclear forces, we still lack a basic understanding of the nature of nuclear forces; nor do we know exactly how they are related to the mesons, even though Yukawa proposed the first meson theory of nuclear forces as early as 1935.

The other field in which present theory is unsatisfactory is the quantization of physical fields. To the best of our present knowledge, we can deal mathematically with the electrons and with their interaction with the electromagnetic field. However, to complete the calculations even the most recent theories have to use certain semiempirical formal devices, to cope with serious divergences in the higher approximations of a perturbation calculation.

Probably contributing to both of these difficulties is our basic inability to account for the properties of the elementary particles. We know from experience that all electrons have the same charge and the same mass, but these facts do not form part of the foundations of quantum physics. We could apply the quantum-mechanical formalism just as well to a universe in which no two elementary particles are entirely alike. At present no approach shows much promise, although the problem is recognized by all workers in the field and many proposals have been made how to construct a theory of elementary particles.

At the conclusion of this last chapter, the epistemological questions raised by quantum mechanics deserve at least brief mention. In classical physics, we deal with a physical universe whose existence need not be questioned. It is there for all to see, and all the experimental physicist has to do is to measure every possible parameter as accurately as possible in order to find out, in principle, everything there is to that universe. In quantum mechanics, the theory predicts only probability distributions. True, for any one variable suitable measurements can narrow the range of possible values as much as desired, but automatically such measurements produce a very broad probability distribution for the canonically conjugate variable. That is the physical significance of Heisenberg's uncertainty relation.

The most nearly complete information obtainable about a quantum-mechanical system is summarized in its state. But this state is not itself the object of physical measurements. As a matter of fact, most measurements on a system change its state in an unpredictable fashion. If, for example, we know the energy and the linear momentum of a free particle with great accuracy, that particle's state is very nearly determined. Its wave function (in configuration space) will be an almost plane, almost monochromatic de Broglie wave. In momentum space, the wave function (that is, the Fourier transform of the de Broglie wave) will have a very large amplitude for a very narrow interval of momentum values and will be almost zero elsewhere. If we now subject our particle to a very precise measurement of its location, if we look at it with an "X-ray microscope" (since resolution is limited by the wave length of the radiation employed), interaction with the high-energy photons employed will invalidate all the information concerning momentum and energy that we had acquired previously, replacing it by information concerning position. The resulting wave function in configuration space will now be highly peaked in a narrow region and very small elsewhere, and its Fourier transform in momentum space will be broad and evenly distributed. However, until we have actually carried out this position measurement, until the electron has actually scattered a high-frequency photon, there is no way of predicting the location of the peak of the new wave function in configuration space.

Apparently the duality of quantum physics destroys the classical concept of causality. Here we have experiments whose outcome is unpredictable in spite of very nearly perfect information at the beginning. Coupled with this invalidation of classical causality, we face an invalidation of the concept of reality as applied to classical mechanical concepts. We have no right to assign to a free particle definite momentum and definite location *at the same time*, since we cannot determine these two types of quantities simultaneously; nor does quantum mechanics permit us to formulate a single possible "state" incorporating both these features.

One might argue that particles possess both location and momentum but that our experimental means are at present insufficient to determine both at the same time, and that quantum-mechanical descriptions of nature are incomplete in a manner to match our present experimental deficiencies. But we can devise experiments in which particles with known momentum behave differently from particles with known locations. Again merely as one example, consider electron diffraction by crystals. By accelerating slow electrons through a known electric potential, we can produce a stream of electrons that within narrow limits all have the same momentum and energy.   If we pass these electrons through a very thin layer of crystallized material, we obtain a diffraction pattern from the crystal grating which is closely similar to that obtained by means of the monochromatic X rays.   In more recent times the same experiment has been performed successfully with neutrons, which are much heavier and hence under ordinary circumstances behave more nearly like classical particles.   If, on the other hand, we determine the location of electrons very exactly by passing them through a system of very narrow slits or pinholes, the crystal diffraction patterns will resemble those made by unfiltered, "white" X rays, that is, mixtures of a wide range of frequencies.   In other words, we cannot collimate a stream of electrons perfectly both with respect to its cross section and its angle of divergence any more than we can do so for a beam of light.

Many of these consequences of Heisenberg's uncertainty principle have been confirmed experimentally.   Because of their obvious bearing on the meaning of reality of the physical universe and on the meaning of causality, quantum mechanics has led to a continuing reexamination of the epistemological foundations of the physical sciences.   One school of thought, the so-called *logical positivists*, believes that it is unnecessary to postulate an existence of the physical universe apart from our perceptions.   They argue that inasmuch as all our information about the universe consists of the results of observations, the most that can be asked of a physical theory is to describe the results of our observations and to predict the results of future observations.   Quantum mechanics achieves these aims to the extent that it not only predicts the results of *some* observations outright (if I have measured the momentum of a free particle at a time t_0, I can confidently predict the result of a new momentum measurement at a later time t_1), but also tells us when the results of these measurements will vary from time to time (as I repeat the same experiment under identical circumstances several times), and it furnishes probability distributions for the results of such cases.   According to the logical positivists, tacking questions about reality onto these legitimate aspects of a physical theory adds nothing but confusion.

Although the position of the logical positivists is logically unassailable, the same counterarguments apply that have been used against positivism and solipsism[1] in the past. It is hard to believe that there should be no intrinsic difference between the perceptions of a scientist and a lunatic, even though the lunatic may be quite as capable of predicting his future "observations." It is also very difficult to assign meaning to such obviously legitimate scientific inquiries as those into the history of the earth prior to the onset of life on this planet, the history of our solar system for the past 10^9 years, and so on. Hardly anyone doubts that many of the classical concepts that were created to formulate the laws of nature possess no reality (the "ether" is a clear-cut example) and correspond to earlier and even less perfect states of knowledge than the present; but most scientists feel intuitively that reality does attach to the physical universe as a whole and to its building blocks as well. We are simply not yet certain which of the present concepts will turn out to be these building blocks.

Bohr has taken the attitude that the fault of classical physics lies in that it attempts to discover physical reality in one object taken in isolation and that, as a result, causality and reality tend to evaporate before our eyes. He suggests that we should consistently look at the physical object *and* our measuring devices as the unit to which causality and reality must be applied. In his insistence on the inclusion of the means of observation with the object to be observed, Bohr approaches somewhat the position of the logical positivists without, however, accepting most of their ultimate philosophical consequences.

Einstein objects to Bohr's position on the grounds that it tends to emasculate physical reality beyond the point he is prepared to go to. Einstein, one of the early workers in quantum physics, has consistently held that quantum mechanics is a temporary state of the theory, which must be overcome ultimately by a theory that resembles classical field theory much more closely than it does quantum mechanics. Though agreeing that in any observation we make, our measuring equipment interferes with the objects we

---

[1] Solipsism is an epistemological theory generally credited to Bishop Berkeley (1685–1753), according to which reality attaches only to the Ego and its sensations, including sense perceptions, but not to the presumptive external causes of these sensations (the physical universe).

wish to observe he feels that in our theoretical description we ought to be able to conceive of the object apart from its interaction with the measuring instrument.

Naturally, within the space of a very few pages, it is quite impossible to report adequately on a controversy which is still in progress and which has engaged the most profound thinkers in the field. For the reader who wishes to examine the philosophical aspects of quantum mechanics, the most convenient collection of original contributions by the protagonists is undoubtedly the book *Albert Einstein: Philosopher-Scientist* (Library of Living Philosophers, Evanston, Ill., 1949). In fairness to the reader who does not propose to go back to the original literature, I shall sketch my own attitude, which undoubtedly is coloring my presentation. I feel very strongly that the physical universe is real and quite capable of existing even without our ministrations. On the other hand, I feel that the weight of the evidence supports quantum physics in that we ought not to attribute identifiable characteristics to individual electrons or other particles, or to their mechanical parameters, such as position and momentum. To just which aspect of modern theory one must ascribe the enduring quality of reality, I do not pretend to know. Our physical measuring instruments consist themselves of the same basic ingredients as the rest of the universe, and I do not believe that the interaction between a measuring device and the object to be measured is different in principle from the interactions of any other physical objects. Whether we care to read a dial or not, in other words whether we complete the observation or let the measuring instrument remain part of the unobserved universe, cannot affect the behavior of the instrument. On the other hand, quantum mechanics shows that in general we lack sufficient information concerning the initial relationship between object and measuring device to predict with certainty the result of the interaction. It is possible to construct exceptions to this general rule, however, just as in particular situations it is possible to predict the outcome of measurements.

Thus it would appear that at least some aspects of the wave function of de Broglie and Schrödinger contain the "reality" of a physical situation, but there remains the question whether we can analyze more precisely the effect of a measurement on this wave function than is usually done. My point of view would seem to lie somewhere between those professed by Bohr and by Einstein, but probably closer to Einstein's.

Surely, quantum mechanics and its more recent development, quantum field theory, have achieved outstanding successes, which appear to preclude a retrogression to the old classical approaches. But acceptance of the new theory forces us in the long run to examine carefully its epistemological implications. In so doing, we should not assume that the present state of the theory is final either. In quantum electrodynamics and in the field of nuclear physics, we have come face to face with very serious difficulties, and we should be prepared for further revisions of even the fundamentals of the theory. The physicist of today must master the many new and strange aspects of quantum theory in order to be able to make his own contribution to the formation of the still stranger concepts of tomorrow.

Further Reading

A number of general references that will be found useful by the beginner in theoretical physics have been given under this heading in the author's *Basic Theories of Physics, Mechanics and Electrodynamics*, published in 1949 by Prentice-Hall, Inc. We shall give here a partial listing of books dealing with heat or with quantum theory.

A textbook on heat, of superior organization and clarity, is Planck's *Theorie der Wärme* ("Theory of Heat"), S. Hirzel, Leipzig, 1930. It is available in English translation (by H. Brose) as the fifth volume of *Introduction to Theoretical Physics*, Macmillan, New York, 1933. *Thermodynamics and the Free Energy of Chemical Substances*, by G. N. Lewis and M. Randall, McGraw-Hill, New York, 1923, deals exclusively with classical thermodynamics and its application to chemical problems, but within its limited field has become a standard text. There are several excellent texts on statistical mechanics. *Statistical Mechanics* by J. E. Mayer and M. G. Mayer, Wiley, New York, 1940, deals primarily with applications to equations of state and to heat capacities, using, however, both classical and quantum-mechanical techniques. The first hundred pages or so are devoted to a clear and succinct general introduction to the subject. Two very able monographs on the same subject are R. H. Fowler, *Statistical Mechanics*, 2d ed., Cambridge University Press, 1936, and R. C. Tolman, *Principles of Statistical Mechanics*, Oxford University Press, 1938. Fowler was the first to develop new and powerful methods of asymptotic approximation to the integrals that need to be evaluated for the partition functions of various systems. In 1946, E. Schrödinger wrote a beautiful little book *Statistical Thermodynamics*, published by the Cambridge University Press; in eighty-eight pages, this work addresses itself to all the conceptual difficulties of both classical and quantum-mechanical statistics and contributes new and interesting approaches. It is definitely not for the beginner, but will be enjoyed by the intermediate and advanced student of the theory of heat. *Mathematical Foundations of Statistical Mechanics* by the well-known Russian mathematician A. I. Khinchin, translated by George Gamow and published in 1949 by Dover Publications, New York, contains the most lucid account of the mathematical and statistical arguments leading to the Boltzmann factor known to this writer.

In quantum mechanics, in spite of the transcending importance of the subject in contemporary physics, there is no great number of texts to choose from. The classical account by A. Sommerfeld, *Wave Mechanics*, is available in English translation (Dutton, New York, 1929). Probably because it was written over twenty years ago, this book is not too abstract and is very readable, but should not be considered an introduction to all the important applications of quantum mechanics known today. A very excellent text by H. A. Kramers, *Die Grundlagen der Quantentheorie—Quantentheorie des Elektrons und der Strahlung* (Akademische Verlagsgesellschaft, Leipzig, 1938, reprinted by Edwards Bros., Ann Arbor, Mich., 1944), and the famous *Handbuch* article by W. Pauli, "Die Allgemeinen Prinzipien der Wellenmechanik" (reprinted by Edwards Bros. in 1946) have not been translated into English.

Among the elementary introductions to quantum mechanics in English, V. Rojansky's *Introductory Quantum Mechanics* (Prentice-Hall, 1938), provides thorough drill in the mathematical techniques required for the treatment of single-particle problems; L. Pauling and E. B. Wilson have written an *Introduction to Quantum Mechanics* (McGraw-Hill, New York, 1935) that also requires only relatively elementary mathematical knowledge on the part of the reader (it is intended to be comprehensible to graduate students of chemistry as well as of physics), but which carries its discussion forward to the quantum theory of the chemical bond and molecular structure. This book is written with a certain lightness of style that facilitates the study of even the more difficult problems. *Fundamentals of Quantum Mechanics*, by E. Persico (translated by G. M. Temmer, Prentice-Hall, Inc., 1950), is a recent addition to the introductory presentations. Persico devotes considerable effort to the elucidation of the fundamentals of quantum mechanics, discussing thoroughly the experimental evidence suggesting the correctness of new quantum-theoretical concepts.

Among the more advanced texts, there is one by L. Schiff, *Quantum Mechanics* (McGraw-Hill, 1949), and another by D. Bohm, *Quantum Theory*, (Prentice-Hall, 1951). Schiff's book is a very comprehensive treatment and includes the presentation of the theory of continuous spectra, collision problems, Dirac's relativistic theory of the spinning electron, and an introduction to quantized fields. Bohm's book contains less material but deals extensively with the physical significance of the quantum-theoretical methods, including a very thorough discussion of the quantum theory of the process of measurement.

P. A. M. Dirac's *The Principles of Quantum Mechanics* (Oxford, 3d ed., 1947) is a definitive treatment of all the fundamental aspects of the subject, including quantum electrodynamics, on a very high level. For an introduction to the quantization of wave fields, two books are to be mentioned (in addition to Pauli, Kramers, Schiff, and Dirac above): W. Heitler's *Quantum Theory of Radiation* (Oxford, 1944) and G. Wentzel's *Einführung in die Quantentheorie der Wellenfelder* (Deuticke, Vienna, 1943, reprinted in 1946 by Edwards Bros.; translated in 1949 by Houtermans and Jauch for Interscience Publishers, New York). Wentzel is very complete and includes a good deal of material on meson fields.

Index

CATALOG OF DOVER BOOKS

BOOKS EXPLAINING SCIENCE AND MATHEMATICS

THE COMMON SENSE OF THE EXACT SCIENCES, W. K. Clifford. Introduction by James Newman, edited by Karl Pearson. For 70 years this has been a guide to classical scientific and mathematical thought. Explains with unusual clarity basic concepts, such as extension of meaning of symbols, characteristics of surface boundaries, properties of plane figures, vectors, Cartesian method of determining position, etc. Long preface by Bertrand Russell. Bibliography of Clifford. Corrected, 130 diagrams redrawn. 249pp. 5⅜ x 8.
T61 Paperbound $1.60

SCIENCE THEORY AND MAN, Erwin Schrödinger. This is a complete and unabridged reissue of SCIENCE AND THE HUMAN TEMPERAMENT plus an additional essay: "What is an Elementary Particle?" Nobel Laureate Schrödinger discusses such topics as nature of scientific method, the nature of science, chance and determinism, science and society, conceptual models for physical entities, elementary particles and wave mechanics. Presentation is popular and may be followed by most people with little or no scientific training. "Fine practical preparation for a time when laws of nature, human institutions . . . are undergoing a critical examination without parallel," Waldemar Kaempffert, N. Y. TIMES. 192pp. 5⅜ x 8.
T428 Paperbound $1.35

PIONEERS OF SCIENCE, O. Lodge. Eminent scientist-expositor's authoritative, yet elementary survey of great scientific theories. Concentrating on individuals—Copernicus, Brahe, Kepler, Galileo, Descartes, Newton, Laplace, Herschel, Lord Kelvin, and other scientists—the author presents their discoveries in historical order adding biographical material on each man and full, specific explanations of their achievements. The clear and complete treatment of the post-Newtonian astronomers is a feature seldom found in other books on the subject. Index. 120 illustrations. xv + 404pp. 5⅜ x 8.
T716 Paperbound $1.50

THE EVOLUTION OF SCIENTIFIC THOUGHT FROM NEWTON TO EINSTEIN, A. d'Abro. Einstein's special and general theories of relativity, with their historical implications, are analyzed in non-technical terms. Excellent accounts of the contributions of Newton, Riemann, Weyl, Planck, Eddington, Maxwell, Lorentz and others are treated in terms of space and time, equations of electromagnetics, finiteness of the universe, methodology of science. 21 diagrams. 482pp. 5⅜ x 8.
T2 Paperound $2.00

THE RISE OF THE NEW PHYSICS, A. d'Abro. A half-million word exposition, formerly titled THE DECLINE OF MECHANISM, for readers not versed in higher mathematics. The only thorough explanation, in everyday language, of the central core of modern mathematical physical theory, treating both classical and modern theoretical physics, and presenting in terms almost anyone can understand the equivalent of 5 years of study of mathematical physics. Scientifically impeccable coverage of mathematical-physical thought from the Newtonian system up through the electronic theories of Dirac and Heisenberg and Fermi's statistics. Combines both history and exposition; provides a broad yet unified and detailed view, with constant comparison of classical and modern views on phenomena and theories. "A must for anyone doing serious study in the physical sciences," JOURNAL OF THE FRANKLIN INSTITUTE. "Extraordinary faculty . . . to explain ideas and theories of theoretical physics in the language of daily life," ISIS. First part of set covers philosophy of science, drawing upon the practice of Newton, Maxwell, Poincaré, Einstein, others, discussing modes of thought, experiment, interpretations of causality, etc. In the second part, 100 pages explain grammar and vocabulary of mathematics, with discussions of functions, groups, series, Fourier series, etc. The remainder is devoted to concrete, detailed coverage of both classical and quantum physics, explaining such topics as analytic mechanics, Hamilton's principle, wave theory of light, electromagnetic waves, groups of transformations, thermodynamics, phase rule, Brownian movement, kinetics, special relativity, Planck's original quantum theory, Bohr's atom, Zeeman effect, Broglie's wave mechanics, Heisenberg's uncertainty, Eigen-values, matrices, scores of other important topics. Discoveries and theories are covered for such men as Alembert, Born, Cantor, Debye, Euler, Foucault, Galois, Gauss, Hadamard, Kelvin, Kepler, Laplace, Maxwell, Pauli, Rayleigh, Volterra, Weyl, Young, more than 180 others. Indexed. 97 illustrations. ix + 982pp. 5⅜ x 8.
T3 Volume 1, Paperbound $2.00
T4 Volume 2, Paperbound $2.00

CONCERNING THE NATURE OF THINGS, Sir William Bragg. Christmas lectures delivered at the Royal Society by Nobel laureate. Why a spinning ball travels in a curved track; how uranium is transmuted to lead, etc. Partial contents: atoms, gases, liquids, crystals, metals, etc. No scientific background needed; wonderful for intelligent child. 32pp. of photos, 57 figures. xii + 232pp. 5⅜ x 8.
T31 Paperbound $1.35

THE UNIVERSE OF LIGHT, Sir William Bragg. No scientific training needed to read Nobel Prize winner's expansion of his Royal Institute Christmas Lectures. Insight into nature of light, methods and philosophy of science. Explains lenses, reflection, color, resonance, polarization, x-rays, the spectrum, Newton's work with prisms, Huygens' with polarization, Crookes' with cathode ray, etc. Leads into clear statement or 2 major historical theories of light, corpuscle and wave. Dozens of experiments you can do. 199 illus., including 2 full-page color plates. 293pp. 5⅜ x 8.
S538 Paperbound $1.85

PHYSICS, THE PIONEER SCIENCE, L. W. Taylor. First thorough text to place all important physical phenomena in cultural-historical framework; remains best work of its kind. Exposition of physical laws, theories developed chronologically, with great historical, illustrative experiments diagrammed, described, worked out mathematically. Excellent physics text for self-study as well as class work. Vol. 1: Heat, Sound: motion, acceleration, gravitation, conservation of energy, heat engines, rotation, heat, mechanical energy, etc. 211 illus. 407pp. 5⅜ x 8. Vol. 2: Light, Electricity: images, lenses, prisms, magnetism, Ohm's law, dynamos, telegraph, quantum theory, decline of mechanical view of nature, etc. Bibliography. 13 table appendix. Index. 551 illus. 2 color plates. 508pp. 5⅜ x 8.

Vol. 1 S565 Paperbound **$2.00**
Vol. 2 S566 Paperbound **$2.00**
The set **$4.00**

FROM EUCLID TO EDDINGTON: A STUDY OF THE CONCEPTIONS OF THE EXTERNAL WORLD, Sir Edmund Whittaker. A foremost British scientist traces the development of theories of natural philosophy from the western rediscovery of Euclid to Eddington, Einstein, Dirac, etc. The inadequacy of classical physics is contrasted with present day attempts to understand the physical world through relativity, non-Euclidean geometry, space curvature, wave mechanics, etc. 5 major divisions of examination: Space; Time and Movement; the Concepts of Classical Physics; the Concepts of Quantum Mechanics; the Eddington Universe. 212pp. 5⅜ x 8.
T491 Paperbound **$1.35**

THE STORY OF ATOMIC THEORY AND ATOMIC ENERGY, J. G. Feinberg. Wider range of facts on physical theory, cultural implications, than any other similar source. Completely non-technical. Begins with first atomic theory, 600 B.C., goes through A-bomb, developments to 1959. Avogadro, Rutherford, Bohr, Einstein, radioactive decay, binding energy, radiation danger, future benefits of nuclear power, dozens of other topics, told in lively, related, informal manner. Particular stress on European atomic research. "Deserves special mention . . . authoritative," Saturday Review. Formerly "The Atom Story." New chapter to 1959. Index. 34 illustrations. 251pp. 5⅜ x 8.
T625 Paperbound **$1.45**

THE STRANGE STORY OF THE QUANTUM, AN ACCOUNT FOR THE GENERAL READER OF THE GROWTH OF IDEAS UNDERLYING OUR PRESENT ATOMIC KNOWLEDGE, B. Hoffmann. Presents lucidly and expertly, with barest amount of mathematics, the problems and theories which led to modern quantum physics. Dr. Hoffmann begins with the closing years of the 19th century, when certain trifling discrepancies were noticed, and with illuminating analogies and examples takes you through the brilliant concepts of Planck, Einstein, Pauli, de Broglie, Bohr, Schroedinger, Heisenberg, Dirac, Sommerfeld, Feynman, etc. This edition includes a new, long postscript carrying the story through 1958. "Of the books attempting an account of the history and contents of our modern atomic physics which have come to my attention, this is the best," H. Margenau, Yale University, in "American Journal of Physics." 32 tables and line illustrations. Index. 275pp. 5⅜ x 8.
T518 Paperbound **$1.45**

SPACE AND TIME, Emile Borel. An entirely non-technical introduction to relativity, by world-renowned mathematician, Sorbonne Professor. (Notes on basic mathematics are included separately.) This book has never been surpassed for insight, and extraordinary clarity of thought, as it presents scores of examples, analogies, arguments, illustrations, which explain such topics as: difficulties due to motion; gravitation a force of inertia; geodesic lines; wave-length and difference of phase; x-rays and crystal structure; the special theory of relativity; and much more. Indexes. 4 appendixes. 15 figures. xvi + 243pp. 5⅜ x 8.
T592 Paperbound **$1.45**

THE RESTLESS UNIVERSE, Max Born. New enlarged version of this remarkably readable account by a Nobel laureate. Moving from sub-atomic particles to universe, the author explains in very simple terms the latest theories of wave mechanics. Partial contents: air and its relatives, electrons & ions, waves & particles, electronic structure of the atom, nuclear physics. Nearly 1000 illustrations, including 7 animated sequences. 325pp. 6 x 9.
T412 Paperbound **$2.00**

SOAP SUBBLES, THEIR COLOURS AND THE FORCES WHICH MOULD THEM, C. V. Boys. Only complete edition, half again as much material as any other. Includes Boys' hints on performing his experiments, sources of supply. Dozens of lucid experiments show complexities of liquid films, surface tension, etc. Best treatment ever written. Introduction. 83 illustrations. Color plate. 202pp. 5⅜ x 8.
T542 Paperbound **95¢**

SPINNING TOPS AND GYROSCOPIC MOTION, John Perry. Well-known classic of science still unsurpassed for lucid, accurate, delightful exposition. How quasi-rigidity is induced in flexible and fluid bodies by rapid motions; why gyrostat falls, top rises; nature and effect on climatic conditions of earth's precessional movement; effect of internal fluidity on rotating bodies, etc. Appendixes describe practical uses to which gyroscopes have been put in ships, compasses, monorail transportation. 62 figures. 128pp. 5⅜ x 8.
T416 Paperbound **$1.00**

MATTER & LIGHT, THE NEW PHYSICS, L. de Broglie. Non-technical papers by a Nobel laureate explain electromagnetic theory, relativity, matter, light and radiation, wave mechanics, quantum physics, philosophy of science. Einstein, Planck, Bohr, others explained so easily that no mathematical training is needed for all but 2 of the 21 chapters. Unabridged. Index. 300pp. 5⅜ x 8.
T35 Paperbound **$1.60**

A SURVEY OF PHYSICAL THEORY, Max Planck. One of the greatest scientists of all time, creator of the quantum revolution in physics, writes in non-technical terms of his own discoveries and those of other outstanding creators of modern physics. Planck wrote this book when science had just crossed the threshold of the new physics, and he communicates the excitement felt then as he discusses electromagnetic theories, statistical methods, evolution of the concept of light, a step-by-step description of how he developed his own momentous theory, and many more of the basic ideas behind modern physics. Formerly "A Survey of Physics." Bibliography. Index. 128pp. 5⅜ x 8. S650 Paperbound **$1.15**

THE NATURE OF LIGHT AND COLOUR IN THE OPEN AIR, M. Minnaert. Why is falling snow sometimes black? What causes mirages, the fata morgana, multiple suns and moons in the sky? How are shadows formed? Prof. Minnaert of the University of Utrecht answers these and similar questions in optics, light, colour, for non-specialists. Particularly valuable to nature, science students, painters, photographers. Translated by H. M. Kremer-Priest, K. Jay. 202 illustrations, including 42 photos. xvi + 362pp. 5⅜ x 8. T196 Paperbound **$1.95**

THE STORY OF X-RAYS FROM RONTGEN TO ISOTOPES, A. R. Bleich. Non-technical history of x-rays, their scientific explanation, their applications in medicine, industry, research, and art, and their effect on the individual and his descendants. Includes amusing early reactions to Röntgen's discovery, cancer therapy, detections of art and stamp forgeries, potential risks to patient and operator, etc. Illustrations show x-rays of flower structure, the gall bladder, gears with hidden defects, etc. Original Dover publication. Glossary. Bibliography. Index. 55 photos and figures. xiv + 186pp. 5⅜ x 8. T662 Paperbound **$1.35**

TEACH YOURSELF ELECTRICITY, C. W. Wilman. Electrical resistance, inductance, capacitance, magnets, chemical effects of current, alternating currents, generators and motors, transformers, rectifiers, much more. 230 questions, answers, worked examples. List of units. 115 illus. 194pp. 6⅞ x 4¼. Clothbound **$2.00**

TEACH YOURSELF HEAT ENGINES, E. De Ville. Measurement of heat, development of steam and internal combustion engines, efficiency of an engine, compression-ignition engines, production of steam, the ideal engine, much more. 318 exercises, answers, worked examples. Tables. 76 illus. 220pp. 6⅞ x 4¼. Clothbound **$2.00**

TEACH YOURSELF MECHANICS, P. Abbott. The lever, centre of gravity, parallelogram of force, friction, acceleration, Newton's laws of motion, machines, specific gravity, gas, liquid pressure, much more. 280 problems, solutions. Tables. 163 illus. 271pp. 6⅞ x 4¼. Clothbound **$2.00**

GREAT IDEAS OF MODERN MATHEMATICS: THEIR NATURE AND USE, Jagjit Singh. Reader with only high school math will understand main mathematical ideas of modern physics, astronomy, genetics, psychology, evolution, etc., better than many who use them as tools, but comprehend little of their basic structure. Author uses his wide knowledge of non-mathematical fields in brilliant exposition of differential equations, matrices, group theory, logic, statistics, problems of mathematical foundations, imaginary numbers, vectors, etc. Original publication. 2 appendixes. 2 indexes. 65 illustr. 322pp. 5⅜ x 8. S587 Paperbound **$1.55**

MATHEMATICS IN ACTION, O. G. Sutton. Everyone with a command of high school algebra will find this book one of the finest possible introductions to the application of mathematics to physical theory. Ballistics, numerical analysis, waves and wavelike phenomena, Fourier series, group concepts, fluid flow and aerodynamics, statistical measures, and meteorology are discussed with unusual clarity. Some calculus and differential equations theory is developed by the author for the reader's help in the more difficult sections. 88 figures. Index. viii + 236pp. 5⅜ x 8. T440 Clothbound **$3.50**

THE FOURTH DIMENSION SIMPLY EXPLAINED, edited by H. P. Manning. 22 essays, originally Scientific American contest entries, that use a minimum of mathematics to explain aspects of 4-dimensional geometry: analogues to 3-dimensional space, 4-dimensional absurdities and curiosities (such as removing the contents of an egg without puncturing its shell), possible measurements and forms, etc. Introduction by the editor. Only book of its sort on a truly elementary level, excellent introduction to advanced works. 82 figures. 251pp. 5⅜ x 8. T711 Paperbound **$1.35**

FAMOUS BRIDGES OF THE WORLD, D. B. Steinman. An up-to-the-minute revised edition of a book that explains the fascinating drama of how the world's great bridges came to be built. The author, designer of the famed Mackinac bridge, discusses bridges from all periods and all parts of the world, explaining their various types of construction, and describing the problems their builders faced. Although primarily for youngsters, this cannot fail to interest readers of all ages. 48 illustrations in the text. 23 photographs. 99pp. 6⅛ x 9¼. T161 Paperbound **$1.00**

BRIDGES AND THEIR BUILDERS, David Steinman and Sara Ruth Watson. Engineers, historians, everyone who has ever been fascinated by great spans will find this book an endless source of information and interest. Dr. Steinman, recipient of the Louis Levy medal, was one of the great bridge architects and engineers of all time, and his analysis of the great bridges of history is both authoritative and easily followed. Greek and Roman bridges, medieval bridges, Oriental bridges, modern works such as the Brooklyn Bridge and the Golden Gate Bridge, and many others are described in terms of history, constructional principles, artistry, and function. All in all this book is the most comprehensive and accurate semipopular history of bridges in print in English. New, greatly revised, enlarged edition. 23 photographs, 26 line drawings. Index. xvii + 401pp. 5⅜ x 8.   **T431 Paperbound $2.00**

FADS AND FALLACIES IN THE NAME OF SCIENCE, Martin Gardner. Examines various cults, quack systems, frauds, delusions which at various times have masqueraded as science. Accounts of hollow-earth fanatics like Symmes; Velikovsky and wandering planets; Hoerbiger; Bellamy and the theory of multiple moons; Charles Fort; dowsing, pseudoscientific methods for finding water, ores, oil. Sections on naturopathy, iridiagnosis, zone therapy, food fads, etc. Analytical accounts of Wilhelm Reich and orgone sex energy; L. Ron Hubbard and Dianetics; A. Korzybski and General Semantics; many others. Brought up to date to include Bridey Murphy, others. Not just a collection of anecdotes, but a fair, reasoned appraisal of eccentric theory. Formerly titled IN THE NAME OF SCIENCE. Preface. Index. x + 384pp. 5⅜ x 8.   **T394 Paperbound $1.50**

See also: **A PHILOSOPHICAL ESSAY ON PROBABILITIES,** P. de Laplace; **ON MATHEMATICS AND MATHEMATICIANS,** R. E. Moritz; **AN ELEMENTARY SURVEY OF CELESTIAL MECHANICS,** Y. Ryabov; **THE SKY AND ITS MYSTERIES,** E. A. Beet; **THE REALM OF THE NEBULAE,** E. Hubble; **OUT OF THE SKY,** H. H. Nininger; **SATELLITES AND SCIENTIFIC RESEARCH,** D. King-Hele; **HEREDITY AND YOUR LIFE,** A. M. Winchester; **INSECTS AND INSECT LIFE,** S. W. Frost; **PRINCIPLES OF STRATIGRAPHY,** A. W. Grabau; **TEACH YOURSELF SERIES.**

HISTORY OF SCIENCE AND MATHEMATICS

DIALOGUES CONCERNING TWO NEW SCIENCES, Galileo Galilei. This classic of experimental science, mechanics, engineering, is as enjoyable as it is important. A great historical document giving insights into one of the world's most original thinkers, it is based on 30 years' experimentation. It offers a lively exposition of dynamics, elasticity, sound, ballistics, strength of materials, the scientific method. "Superior to everything else of mine," Galileo. Trans. by H. Crew, A. Salvio. 126 diagrams. Index. xxi + 288pp. 5⅜ x 8.
S99 Paperbound $1.65

A DIDEROT PICTORIAL ENCYCLOPEDIA OF TRADES AND INDUSTRY, Manufacturing and the Technical Arts in Plates Selected from "L'Encyclopédie ou Dictionnaire Raisonné des Sciences, des Arts, et des Métiers" of Denis Diderot. Edited with text by C. Gillispie. This first modern selection of plates from the high point of 18th century French engraving is a storehouse of valuable technological information to the historian of arts and science. Over 2000 illustrations on 485 full page plates, most of them original size, show the trades and industries of a fascinating era in such great detail that the processes and shops might very well be reconstructed from them. The plates teem with life, with men, women, and children performing all of the thousands of operations necessary to the trades before and during the early stages of the industrial revolution. Plates are in sequence, and show general operations, closeups of difficult operations, and details of complex machinery. Such important and interesting trades and industries are illustrated as sowing, harvesting, beekeeping, cheesemaking, operating windmills, milling flour, charcoal burning, tobacco processing, indigo, fishing, arts of war, salt extraction, mining, smelting, casting iron, steel, extracting mercury, zinc, sulphur, copper, etc., slating, tinning, silverplating, gilding, making gunpowder, cannons, bells, shoeing horses, tanning, papermaking, printing, dyeing, and more than 40 other categories. Professor Gillispie, of Princeton, supplies a full commentary on all the plates, identifying operations, tools, processes, etc. This material, presented in a lively and lucid fashion, is of great interest to the reader interested in history of science and technology. Heavy library cloth. 920pp. 9 x 12.   **T421 Two volume set $18.50**

DE MAGNETE, William Gilbert. This classic work on magnetism founded a new science. Gilbert was the first to use the word "electricity", to recognize mass as distinct from weight, to discover the effect of heat on magnetic bodies; invent an electroscope, differentiate between static electricity and magnetism, conceive of the earth as a magnet. Written by the first great experimental scientist, this lively work is valuable not only as an historical landmark, but as the delightfully easy to follow record of a perpetually searching, ingenious mind. Translated by P. F. Mottelay. 25 page biographical memoir. 90 figures. lix + 368pp. 5⅜ x 8.   **S470 Paperbound $2.00**

CHARLES BABBAGE AND HIS CALCULATING ENGINES, edited by P. Morrison and E. Morrison. Babbage, leading 19th century pioneer in mathematical machines and herald of modern operational research, was the true father of Harvard's relay computer Mark I. His Difference Engine and Analytical Engine were the first machines in the field. This volume contains a valuable introduction on his life and work; major excerpts from his autobiography, revealing his eccentric and unusual personality; and extensive selections from "Babbage's Calculating Engines," a compilation of hard-to-find journal articles by Babbage, the Countess of Lovelace, L. F. Menabrea, and Dionysius Lardner. 8 illustrations, Appendix of miscellaneous papers. Index. Bibliography. xxxviii + 400pp. 5⅜ x 8.   T12 Paperbound **$2.00**

A HISTORY OF ASTRONOMY FROM THALES TO KEPLER, J. L. E. Dreyer. (Formerly A HISTORY OF PLANETARY SYSTEMS FROM THALES TO KEPLER.) This is the only work in English to give the complete history of man's cosmological views from prehistoric times to Kepler and Newton. Partial contents: Near Eastern astronomical systems, Early Greeks, Homocentric Spheres of Eudoxus, Epicycles, Ptolemaic system, medieval cosmology, Copernicus, Kepler, etc. Revised, foreword by W. H. Stahl. New bibliography. xvii + 430pp. 5⅜ x 8.
S79 Paperbound **$1.98**

A SHORT HISTORY OF ANATOMY AND PHYSIOLOGY FROM THE GREEKS TO HARVEY, Charles Singer. Corrected edition of THE EVOLUTION OF ANATOMY, classic work tracing evolution of anatomy and physiology from prescientific times through Greek & Roman periods, Dark Ages, Renaissance, to age of Harvey and beginning of modern concepts. Centered on individuals, movements, periods that definitely advanced anatomical knowledge: Plato, Diocles, Aristotle, Theophrastus, Herophilus, Erasistratus, the Alexandrians, Galen, Mondino, da Vinci, Linacre, Sylvius, others. Special section on Vesalius; Vesalian atlas of nudes, skeletons, muscle tabulae. Index of names, 20 plates. 270 extremely interesting illustrations of ancient, medieval, Renaissance, Oriental origin. xii + 209pp. 5⅜ x 8.   T389 Paperbound **$1.75**

FROM MAGIC TO SCIENCE, Charles Singer. A great historian examines aspects of medical science from the Roman Empire through the Renaissance. Includes perhaps the best discussion of early herbals, and a penetrating physiological interpretation of "The Visions of Hildegarde of Bingen." Also examined are Arabian and Galenic influences; the Sphere of Pythagoras; Paracelsus; the reawakening of science under Leonardo da Vinci, Vesalius; the Lorica of Gildas the Briton; etc. Frequent quotations with translations. New Introduction by the author. New unabridged, corrected edition. 158 unusual illustrations from classical and medieval sources. Index. xxvii + 365pp. 5⅜ x 8.   T390 Paperbound **$2.00**

HISTORY OF MATHEMATICS, D. E. Smith. Most comprehensive non-technical history of math in English. Discusses lives and works of over a thousand major and minor figures, with footnotes supplying technical information outside the book's scheme, and indicating disputed matters. Vol I: A chronological examination, from primitive concepts through Egypt, Babylonia, Greece, the Orient, Rome, the Middle Ages, the Renaissance, and up to 1900. Vol 2: The development of ideas in specific fields and problems, up through elementary calculus. Two volumes, total of 510 illustrations, 1355pp. 5⅜ x 8. Set boxed in attractive container.   T429, 430 Paperbound, the set **$5.00**

A SHORT ACCOUNT OF THE HISTORY OF MATHEMATICS, W. W. R. Ball. Most readable non-technical history of mathematics treats lives, discoveries of every important figure from Egyptian, Phoenician mathematicians to late 19th century. Discusses schools of Ionia, Pythagoras, Athens, Cyzicus, Alexandria, Byzantium, systems of numeration; primitive arithmetic; Middle Ages, Renaissance, including Arabs, Bacon, Regiomontanus, Tartaglia, Cardan, Stevinus, Galileo, Kepler; modern mathematics of Descartes, Pascal, Wallis, Huygens, Newton, Leibnitz, d'Alembert, Euler, Lambert, Laplace, Legendre, Gauss, Hermite, Weierstrass, scores more. Index. 25 figures. 546pp. 5⅜ x 8.   S630 Paperbound **$2.00**

A SOURCE BOOK IN MATHEMATICS, D. E. Smith. Great discoveries in math, from Renaissance to end of 19th century, in English translation. Read announcements by Dedekind, Gauss, Delamain, Pascal, Fermat, Newton, Abel, Lobachevsky, Bolyai, Riemann, De Moivre, Legendre, Laplace, others of discoveries about imaginary numbers, number congruence, slide rule, equations, symbolism, cubic algebraic equations, non-Euclidean forms of geometry, calculus, function theory, quaternions, etc. Succinct selections from 125 different treatises, articles, most unavailable elsewhere in English. Each article preceded by biographical, historical introduction. Vol. I: Fields of Number, Algebra. Index. 32 illus. 338pp. 5⅜ x 8. Vol. II: Fields of Geometry, Probability, Calculus, Functions, Quaternions. 83 illus. 432pp. 5⅜ x 8.
Vol. 1: S552 Paperbound **$1.85**
Vol. 2: S553 Paperbound **$1.85**
2 vol. set, boxed **$3.50**

A HISTORY OF THE CALCULUS, AND ITS CONCEPTUAL DEVELOPMENT, Carl B. Boyer. Provides laymen and mathematicians a detailed history of the development of the calculus, from early beginning in antiquity to final elaboration as mathematical abstractions. Gives a sense of mathematics not as a technique, but as a habit of mind, in the progression of ideas of Zeno, Plato, Pythagoras, Eudoxus, Arabic and Scholastic mathematicians, Newton, Leibnitz, Taylor, Descartes, Euler, Lagrange, Cantor, Weierstrass, and others. This first comprehensive critical history of the calculus was originally titled "The Concepts of the Calculus." Foreword by R. Courant. Preface. 22 figures. 25-page bibliography. Index. v + 364pp. 5⅜ x 8.   S509 Paperbound **$2.00**

A CONCISE HISTORY OF MATHEMATICS, D. Struik. Lucid study of development of mathematical ideas, techniques from Ancient Near East, Greece, Islamic science, Middle Ages, Renaissance, modern times. Important mathematicians are described in detail. Treatment is not anecdotal, but analytical development of ideas. "Rich in content, thoughtful in interpretation," U.S. QUARTERLY BOOKLIST. Non-technical; no mathematical training needed. Index. 60 illustrations, including Egyptian papyri, Greek mss., portraits of 31 eminent mathematicians. Bibliography. 2nd edition. xix + 299pp. 5⅜ x 8.   T255 Paperbound **$1.75**

See also: **NON-EUCLIDEAN GEOMETRY, R. Bonola; THEORY OF DETERMINANTS IN HISTORICAL ORDER OF DEVELOPMENT, T. Muir; HISTORY OF THE THEORY OF ELASTICITY AND STRENGTH OF MATERIALS, I. Todhunter and K. Pearson; A SHORT HISTORY OF ASTRONOMY, A. Berry; CLASSICS OF SCIENCE.**

PHILOSOPHY OF SCIENCE AND MATHEMATICS

FOUNDATIONS OF SCIENCE: THE PHILOSOPHY OF THEORY AND EXPERIMENT, N. R. Campbell. A critique of the most fundamental concepts of science in general and physics in particular. Examines why certain propositions are accepted without question, demarcates science from philosophy, clarifies the understanding of the tools of science. Part One analyzes the presuppositions of scientific thought: existence of the material world, nature of scientific laws, multiplication of probabilities, etc.; Part Two covers the nature of experiment and the application of mathematics: conditions for measurement, relations between numerical laws and theories, laws of error, etc. An appendix covers problems arising from relativity, force, motion, space, and time. A classic in its field. Index. xiii + 565pp. 5⅝ x 8⅜.
S372 Paperbound **$2.95**

WHAT IS SCIENCE?, Norman Campbell. This excellent introduction explains scientific method, role of mathematics, types of scientific laws. Contents: 2 aspects of science, science & nature, laws of science, discovery of laws, explanation of laws, measurement & numerical laws, applications of science. 192pp. 5⅜ x 8.   S43 Paperbound **$1.25**

THE VALUE OF SCIENCE, Henri Poincaré. Many of the most mature ideas of the "last scientific universalist" covered with charm and vigor for both the beginning student and the advanced worker. Discusses the nature of scientific truth, whether order is innate in the universe or imposed upon it by man, logical thought versus intuition (relating to math, through the works of Weierstrass, Lie, Klein, Riemann), time and space (relativity, psychological time, simultaneity), Hertz's concept of force, interrelationship of mathematical physics to pure math, values within disciplines of Maxwell, Carnot, Mayer, Newton, Lorentz, etc. Index. iii + 147pp. 5⅜ x 8.   S469 Paperbound **$1.35**

SCIENCE AND METHOD, Henri Poincaré. Procedure of scientific discovery, methodology, experiment, idea-germination—the intellectual processes by which discoveries come into being. Most significant and most interesting aspects of development, application of ideas. Chapters cover selection of facts, chance, mathematical reasoning, mathematics, and logic; Whitehead, Russell, Cantor; the new mechanics, etc. 288pp. 5⅜ x 8.   S222 Paperbound **$1.35**

SCIENCE AND HYPOTHESIS, Henri Poincaré. Creative psychology in science. How such concepts as number, magnitude, space, force, classical mechanics were developed, and how the modern scientist uses them in his thought. Hypothesis in physics, theories of modern physics. Introduction by Sir James Larmor. "Few mathematicians have had the breadth of vision of Poincaré, and none is his superior in the gift of clear exposition," E. T. Bell. Index. 272pp. 5⅜ x 8.   S221 Paperbound **$1.35**

PHILOSOPHY AND THE PHYSICISTS, L. S. Stebbing. The philosophical aspects of modern science examined in terms of a lively critical attack on the ideas of Jeans and Eddington. Discusses the task of science, causality, determinism, probability, consciousness, the relation of the world of physics to that of everyday experience. Probes the philosophical significance of the Planck-Bohr concept of discontinuous energy levels, the inferences to be drawn from Heisenberg's Uncertainty Principle, the implications of "becoming" involved in the 2nd law of thermodynamics, and other problems posed by the discarding of Laplacean determinism. 285pp. 5⅜ x 8.   T480 Paperbound **$1.65**

EXPERIMENT AND THEORY IN PHYSICS, Max Born. A Nobel laureate examines the nature and value of the counterclaims of experiment and theory in physics. Synthetic versus analytical scientific advances are analyzed in the work of Einstein, Bohr, Heisenberg, Planck, Eddington, Milne, and others by a fellow participant. 44pp. 5⅜ x 8.   S308 Paperbound **60¢**

THE NATURE OF PHYSICAL THEORY, P. W. Bridgman. Here is how modern physics looks to a highly unorthodox physicist—a Nobel laureate. Pointing out many absurdities of science, and demonstrating the inadequacies of various physical theories, Dr. Bridgman weighs and analyzes the contributions of Einstein, Bohr, Newton, Heisenberg, and many others. This is a non-technical consideration of the correlation of science and reality. Index. xi + 138pp. 5⅜ x 8.   S33 Paperbound **$1.25**

THE PHILOSOPHY OF SPACE AND TIME, H. Reichenbach. An important landmark in the development of the empiricist conception of geometry, covering the problem of the foundations of geometry, the theory of time, the consequences of Einstein's relativity, including: relations between theory and observations; coordinate and metrical properties of space; the psychological problem of visual intuition of non-Euclidean structures; and many other important topics in modern science and philosophy. The majority of ideas require only a knowledge of intermediate math. Introduction by R. Carnap. 49 figures. Index. xviii + 296pp. 5⅜ x 8.
S443 Paperbound **$2.00**

MATTER & MOTION, James Clerk Maxwell, This excellent exposition begins with simple particles and proceeds gradually to physical systems beyond complete analysis: motion, force, properties of centre of mass of material system, work, energy, gravitation, etc. Written with all Maxwell's original insights and clarity. Notes by E. Larmor. 17 diagrams. 178pp. 5⅜ x 8.
S188 Paperbound **$1.35**

THE ANALYSIS OF MATTER, Bertrand Russell. How do our senses concord with the new physics? This volume covers such topics as logical analysis of physics, prerelativity physics, causality, scientific inference, physics and perception, special and general relativity, Weyl's theory, tensors, invariants and their physical interpretation, periodicity and qualitative series. "The most thorough treatment of the subject that has yet been published," THE NATION. Introduction by L. E. Denonn. 422pp. 5⅜ x 8.   T231 Paperbound **$1.95**

SUBSTANCE AND FUNCTION, & EINSTEIN'S THEORY OF RELATIVITY, Ernst Cassirer. Two books bound as one. Cassirer establishes a philosophy of the exact sciences that takes into consideration newer developments in mathematics, and also shows historical connections. Partial contents: Aristotelian logic, Mill's analysis, Helmholtz & Kronecker, Russell & cardinal numbers, Euclidean vs. non-Euclidean geometry, Einstein's relativity. Bibliography. Index. xxi + 465pp. 5⅜ x 8.   T50 Paperbound **$2.00**

PRINCIPLES OF MECHANICS, Heinrich Hertz. This last work by the great 19th century physicist is not only a classic, but of great interest in the logic of science. Creating a new system of mechanics based upon space, time, and mass, it returns to axiomatic analysis, to understanding of the formal or structural aspects of science, taking into account logic, observation, and a priori elements. Of great historical importance to Poincaré, Carnap, Einstein, Milne. A 20-page introduction by R. S. Cohen, Wesleyan University, analyzes the implications of Hertz's thought and the logic of science. Bibliography. 13-page introduction by Helmholtz. xlii + 274pp. 5⅜ x 8.   S316 Clothbound **$3.50**
S317 Paperbound **$1.85**

THE PHILOSOPHICAL WRITINGS OF PEIRCE, edited by Justus Buchler. (Formerly published as THE PHILOSOPHY OF PEIRCE.) This is a carefully balanced exposition of Peirce's complete system, written by Peirce himself. It covers such matters as scientific method, pure chance vs. law, symbolic logic, theory of signs, pragmatism, experiment, and other topics. Introduction by Justus Buchler, Columbia University. xvi + 368pp. 5⅜ x 8.
T217 Paperbound **$1.95**

ESSAYS IN EXPERIMENTAL LOGIC, John Dewey. This stimulating series of essays touches upon the relationship between inquiry and experience, dependence of knowledge upon thought, character of logic; judgments of practice, data and meanings, stimuli of thought, etc. Index. viii + 444pp. 5⅜ x 8.   T73 Paperbound **$1.95**

LANGUAGE, TRUTH AND LOGIC, A. Ayer. A clear introduction to the Vienna and Cambridge schools of Logical Positivism. It sets up specific tests by which you can evaluate validity of ideas, etc. Contents: Function of philosophy, elimination of metaphysics, nature of analysis, a priori, truth and probability, etc. 10th printing. "I should like to have written it myself," Bertrand Russell. Index. 160pp. 5⅜ x 8.   T10 Paperbound **$1.25**

THE PSYCHOLOGY OF INVENTION IN THE MATHEMATICAL FIELD, J. Hadamard. Where do ideas come from? What role does the unconscious play? Are ideas best developed by mathematical reasoning, word reasoning, visualization? What are the methods used by Einstein, Poincaré, Galton, Riemann? How can these techniques be applied by others? Hadamard, one of the world's leading mathematicians, discusses these and other questions. xiii + 145pp. 5⅜ x 8.
T107 Paperbound **$1.25**

FOUNDATIONS OF GEOMETRY, Bertrand Russell. Analyzing basic problems in the overlap area between mathematics and philosophy, Nobel laureate Russell examines the nature of geometrical knowledge, the nature of geometry, and the application of geometry to space. It covers the history of non-Euclidean geometry, philosophic interpretations of geometry—especially Kant—projective and metrical geometry. This is most interesting as the solution offered in 1897 by a great mind to a problem still current. New introduction by Prof. Morris Kline of N. Y. University. xii + 201pp. 5⅜ x 8.   S232 Clothbound **$3.25**
S233 Paperbound **$1.60**

BIBLIOGRAPHIES

GUIDE TO THE LITERATURE OF MATHEMATICS AND PHYSICS, N. G. Parke III. Over 5000 entries included under approximately 120 major subject headings, of selected most important books, monographs, periodicals, articles in English, plus important works in German, French, Italian, Spanish, Russian (many recently available works). Covers every branch of physics, math, related engineering. Includes author, title, edition, publisher, place, date, number of volumes, number of pages. A 40-page introduction on the basic problems of research and study provides useful information on the organization and use of libraries, the psychology of learning, etc. This reference work will save you hours of time. 2nd revised edition. Indices of authors, subjects. 464pp. 5⅜ x 8. S447 Paperbound **$2.49**

THE STUDY OF THE HISTORY OF MATHEMATICS & THE STUDY OF THE HISTORY OF SCIENCE, George Sarton. Scientific method & philosophy in 2 scholarly fields. Defines duty of historian of math., provides especially useful bibliography with best available biographies of modern mathematicians, editions of their collected works, correspondence. Observes combination of history & science, will aid scholar in understanding science today. Bibliography includes best known treatises on historical methods. 200-item critically evaluated bibliography. Index. 10 illustrations. 2 volumes bound as one. 113pp. + 75pp. 5⅜ x 8. T240 Paperbound **$1.25**

MATHEMATICAL PUZZLES

AMUSEMENTS IN MATHEMATICS, Henry Ernest Dudeney. The foremost British originator of mathematical puzzles is always intriguing, witty, and paradoxical in this classic, one of the largest collections of mathematical amusements. More than 430 puzzles, problems, and paradoxes. Mazes and games, problems on number manipulation, unicursal and other route problems, puzzles on measuring, weighing, packing, age, kinship, chessboards, joiners', crossing river, plane figure dissection, and many others. Solutions. More than 450 illustrations. vii + 258pp. 5⅜ x 8. T473 Paperbound **$1.25**

THE CANTERBURY PUZZLES, Henry Ernest Dudeney. Chaucer's pilgrims set one another problems in story form. Also Adventures of the Puzzle Club, the Strange Escape of the King's Jester, the Monks of Riddlewell, the Squire's Christmas Puzzle Party, and others. All puzzles are original, based on dissecting plane figures, arithmetic, algebra, elementary calculus, and other branches of mathematics, and purely logical ingenuity. "The limit of ingenuity and intricacy . . ." The Observer Over 110 puzzles. Full solutions. 150 illustrations. viii + 225pp. 5⅜ x 8. T474 Paperbound **$1.25**

SYMBOLIC LOGIC and THE GAME OF LOGIC, Lewis Carroll. "Symbolic Logic" is not concerned with modern symbolic logic, but is instead a collection of over 380 problems posed with charm and imagination, using the syllogism, and a fascinating diagrammatic method of drawing conclusions. In "The Game of Logic," Carroll's whimsical imagination devises a logical game played with 2 diagrams and counters (included) to manipulate hundreds of tricky syllogisms. The final section, "Hit or Miss" is a lagniappe of 101 additional puzzles in the delightful Carroll manner. Until this reprint edition, both of these books were rarities costing up to $15 each. Symbolic Logic: Index, xxxi + 199pp. The Game of Logic: 96pp. Two vols. bound as one. 5⅜ x 8. T492 Paperbound **$1.50**

PILLOW PROBLEMS and A TANGLED TALE, Lewis Carroll. One of the rarest of all Carroll's works, "Pillow Problems" contains 72 original math puzzles, all typically ingenious. Particularly fascinating are Carroll's answers which remain exactly as he thought them out, reflecting his actual mental processes. The problems in "A Tangled Tale" are in story form, originally appearing as a monthly magazine serial. Carroll not only gives the solutions, but uses answers sent in by readers to discuss wrong approaches and misleading paths, and grades them for insight. Both of these books were rarities until this edition, "Pillow Problems" costing up to $25, and "A Tangled Tale" $15. Pillow Problems: Preface and introduction by Lewis Carroll. xx + 109pp. A Tangled Tale: 6 illustrations. 152pp. Two vols. bound as one. 5⅜ x 8. T493 Paperbound **$1.50**

DIVERSIONS AND DIGRESSIONS OF LEWIS CARROLL. A major new treasure for Carroll fans! Rare privately published puzzles, mathematical amusements and recreations, games. Includes the fragmentary Part III of "Curiosa Mathematica." Also contains humorous and satirical pieces: "The New Belfry," "The Vision of the Three T's," and much more. New 32-page supplement of rare photographs taken by Carroll. Formerly titled "The Lewis Carroll Picture Book." Edited by S. Collingwood. x + 375pp. 5⅜ x 8. T732 Paperbound **$1.50**